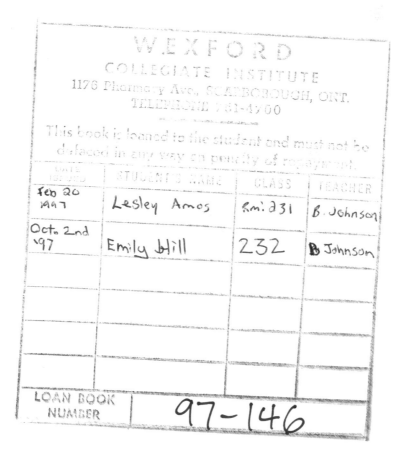

WEXFORD
COLLEGIATE INSTITUTE
1176 Pharmacy Ave., SCARBOROUGH, ONT.
TELEPHONE 751-4700

This book is loaned to the student and must not be
defaced in any way on penalty of repayment.

DATE ISSUED	STUDENT'S NAME	CLASS	TEACHER
Feb 20 1997	Lesley Amos	Rm: 231	B. Johnson
Oct. 2nd '97	Emily Hill	232	B Johnson

LOAN BOOK NUMBER	97-146

CONTACT CANADA

SECOND EDITION

FRASER CARTWRIGHT
GARY BIRCHALL / GERRY PIERCE

Toronto
OXFORD UNIVERSITY PRESS
1996

Oxford University Press Canada, 70 Wynford Drive, Don Mills, Ontario, Canada M3C 1J9

Oxford New York Athens Auckland Bangkok Bombay Calcutta Cape Town Dar es Salaam Delhi Florence Hong Kong Istanbul Karachi Kuala Lumpur Madras Madrid Melbourne Mexico City Nairobi Paris Singapore Taipei Tokyo Toronto

and associated companies in
Berlin Ibadan

OXFORD is a trademark of Oxford University Press.

Canadian Cataloguing in Publication Data
Cartwright, Fraser, 1947-
    Contact Canada

2nd ed.
Includes index.
ISBN 0-19-541148-X

1. Canada - Description and travel. I. Birchall, Gary, 1942 - .
II. Title.

FC75.C38 1996   917.1   C95-931830-5
F1017.C38 1996

Editor: Loralee Case
Design: Brett Miller
Illustrations and layout: VISU*TronX*
Photo research: Patricia Buckley Editorial Services
Cover illustration: Anson Liaw
Film Separations: Gandalf Graphics Limited
Printed in Canada by Friesens

1 2 3 4 5 6   01 00 99 98 97 96

Acknowledgments

A book is not the work of the authors alone. It is the result of the contributions of many people. We would like to extend our appreciation to all those who responded to our many requests for information. We would also like to thank our students who worked with the first edition of *Contact Canada* and who provided valuable insights for the second edition. We are also grateful to the reviewers listed below, whose advice and recommendations were carefully heeded. We would also like to thank the publishing staff at Oxford University Press, who so professionally transformed our ideas, information, and sketches into the final product. Finally, we would like to express special thanks to our families and friends for their patience, support, and encouragement.

Fraser Cartwright   Gary Birchall   Gerry Pierce

The publisher wishes to thank the following people for reviewing the manuscript of this text.

Paul Dwyer
O'Donel High School
Mount Pearl, Newfoundland

Don Farquharson
Port Perry High School
Port Perry, Ontario

Jacob Hunt
William Mercer Academy
Dover, Newfoundland

Edward Lanktree
Windsor Board of Education
Windsor, Ontario

The publisher also wishes to thank Karen Coombs and Suzanne Taylor of the Department of Fisheries and Aquaculture in New Brunswick and Jacqueline Moore Daigle, First Nation Education Consultant, University of Toronto, for their assistance.

Data from Statistics Canada reproduced by authority of the Minister of Industry, 1996.

The publisher wishes to acknowledge the Metropolitan Toronto Police Service.

Contents

Picture Credits

t=top; c=centre; b=bottom; l=left; r=right

INTRODUCTION

The diversity of spectacular landforms, climate, resources, traditions, and people makes Canada one of the best countries in the world to study geography. It provides a uniquely inviting challenge!

In writing this book, we extend this challenge to you, our students. We invite you to experience close contact with Canadian geography through activities in which you will discover knowledge and concepts for yourself. The material in this text has been presented in clear, self-contained units in which concepts are developed starting with situations that you, as students, may experience. These are then applied to broader situations in Canada and the world.

As you use this text, you will actively participate in step-by-step exercises that will teach you new concepts as you develop new skills. Interesting simulation exercises allow you to apply what you have learned to new and challenging situations. You will also learn to manage tasks, solve problems, use organizers, and co-operate with your classmates as you develop your interpersonal skills. Enrichment activities that challenge you to extend your abilities are indicated with a box ▮. Key terms are highlighted in bold and are defined in the Glossary.

Geography influences our lives in a variety of ways. This is an ideal time in your school career to learn what role it plays. Working through *Contact Canada*, you, as active learners, will gain a better understanding of and have a positive influence on our unique country.

Unit 1

YOU AND CANADA

One suspects that the simple reason for the growing interest in Canada is a deepening longing to go to those parts of the world where history and culture have to do with great forests, with birds in clear skies, with shining mountains, with untouched prairies. More and more people would like to go where humans have not yet destroyed the earth, and Canada is imagined to be one of those places.

David Plante, American novelist of French-Canadian background, in *The Times Literary Supplement*, 15 April 1988.

Les Laurentides by Madeleine Des Rosiers/Musée du Quebec

Space! Every person occupies it. Each of us shares our planet with over 6 billion other people. Can you imagine that? And there are more people sharing our space every day. The world's population increases by nearly 100 million people each year. That's more than three times the population of Canada!

Our planet contains vast amounts of surface space—511 000 000 km², in fact. But 70 per cent of this space is taken up by water. Only 30 per cent is land. This is where all 6 billion of us live. It includes the many things created by nature, such as forests, deserts, and mountains, as well as all those things created by people, such as highways, cities, and farms.

Space is valuable. It provides us with the things we need in order to survive: food, water, shelter, and air. Geography is concerned with the study of space. It looks at how people have used space in the past, how they are using space today, and how they may use space in the future. Geographers study the distribution of things in space so that we can all learn to use our space more wisely and efficiently.

Using your own space

The space that is of the greatest concern to each of us is the small space in which we spend our daily lives. We would like our living space to be designed so that we can move around it easily and efficiently. Our living space includes our community, our school, and our home. Let's consider the most personal of our living spaces—our own bedrooms.

Figure 1.1 is a plan of one teenager's bedroom. A plan is a kind of map. It shows where objects are located within a particular space. Like all good plans, Figure 1.1 provides specific information that allows us to read it accurately. It also contains a title that identifies it, a **linear scale**, and a **directional symbol**. The linear scale is a line that gives the equivalent actual distance. In this plan it enables us to determine the actual sizes of the objects in the room. We simply mark off the length of the object on a piece of paper. We then align the paper on the scale to determine the length. The directional symbol usually indicates north. It enables us to say which direction we are facing. In a room plan, it may also help us to decide where to locate the furniture.

1 a) What is the length and width of each of the following: the computer desk; the bookcase; the TV stand; the bed?
   b) What is the area of the bedroom?
   c) How many square metres is the surface area of the bed?
   d) Other than the bed, which piece of furniture uses the most space?
   e) If you like a challenge, try to calculate the total area occupied by all of the furniture in the room. To do this, add together the size of the bed, the night table, the stereo and speakers, the TV stand, the chest of drawers, the desk, the chair, and the bookcase.

2 a) Against which wall is each of the following: the desk; the TV stand; the night table?
  b) In which direction would you walk to leave the bedroom?
  c) The sun rises in the east and sets in the west. Does the bedroom receive any direct sunlight? Explain your answer.

We move around our bedroom for many purposes—to work at our desk, to collect a book, to adjust the stereo, or to change our clothes. When deciding where to locate the furniture in our bedroom, one of the things we should consider is how we can make our movements more efficient.

3 Suppose you are completing your math homework at your desk. You're stuck on a particular problem, but you know that another book has the magic formula. Using the linear scale, estimate how far you would have to go from the chair to get the book from the bookcase and return to your desk. Be sure you walk *around* the bed!

Home decorating magazines present a variety of "ideal" bedrooms. They often illustrate ways in which we can use our personal space more efficiently and effectively. They consider such factors as ease of movement and natural lighting as well as ways of making a small space seem larger. How can we apply geography skills to create our own ideal bedroom?

4 a) On a piece of graph paper, draw an outline of the bedroom in Figure 1.1. Using the same scale and furniture, redesign the room in the way you think makes the best use of space. Consider such factors as movement, convenience, natural light, and noise that may carry outside your room. Create as much open space as possible to make the room seem larger.
  b) Now that you have had a practice run, try this exercise with your own bedroom. See if you can give your room a brand new look while using your space more efficiently.

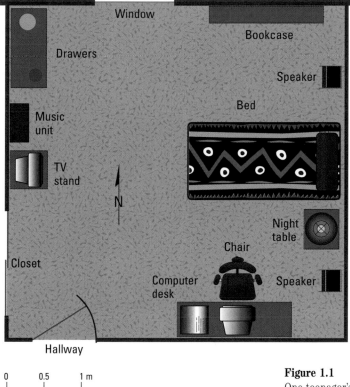

0   0.5   1 m
Scale

Figure 1.1
One teenager's bedroom

Now that we have looked at a small space, let's consider how we might use a larger space with several rooms. Figure 1.2 shows the movements made by one person in a two-bedroom apartment during a one-hour period. By measuring the length of the **flow lines** showing the direction of movement in the apartment, we can calculate the total distance the person travelled. Notice that the scale on this plan is different from the scale on the bedroom plan. This plan contains a **statement scale** of 1 cm to 1 m. This means that 1 cm on the plan represents 1 m in the actual apartment. Be careful not to write the scale as 1 cm = 1 m. This is wrong because 1 cm does not *equal* 1 m, it only *represents* it!

Figure 1.3
The number of times each room in Figure 1.2 was visited

ROOM/AREA	NUMBER OF VISITS
Bedroom A	2
Bedroom B	
Bathroom	
Closet	
Kitchen	
Dining room	
Walk-in closet	
Living room	
Balcony	

Figure 1.2
Plan of a two-bedroom apartment

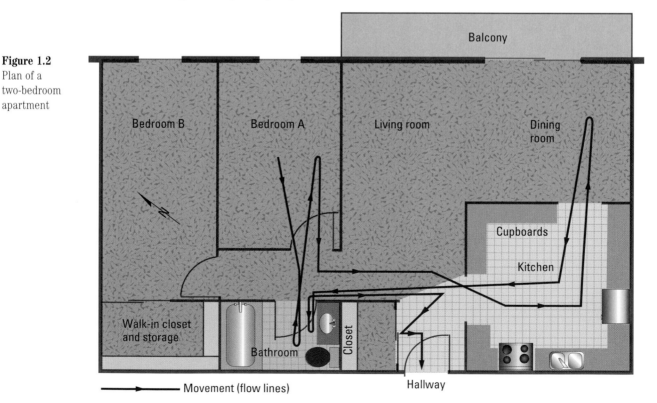

Scale: 1 cm to 1 m

5 Figure 1.3 shows the number of times the person visited Bedroom A. Make a copy of this chart in your notebook. Determine the number of times the person visited each room or area using the information in Figure 1.2.

6 Using the statement scale:
   a) measure the length of Bedroom A from the window to the opposite wall;
   b) measure all of the flow lines to calculate the total distance the person travelled.

Drawing and using street maps

When walking back and forth to school, how much attention do you pay to the route you take? You may be too busy talking with your friends to notice street names or the direction in which you are walking. But what if you were having a party after school and you had to give directions to your house? What information would you need to include on your map to ensure that everyone arrived at the party?

7 a) Figure 1.4 is a sketch map showing one student's route home from school. What features make this map useful?
   b) Draw a map that shows *your* route home from school.
   c) Trade maps with someone in your class. See if you can answer the following questions based on your classmate's map:
      i) In what general direction does your classmate travel from school to home?
      ii) How far does your classmate travel from school to home?
      iii) Through what type of physical environment does your classmate travel?
      iv) Does your classmate pass by any identifiable landmark?
      v) In what type of building does your classmate live?

If you were able to answer all of these questions, your classmate has drawn a useful map!

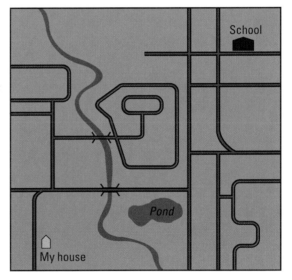

Figure 1.4 The route from school

It is likely that two or more students following the same route home from school will produce quite different maps. This is because most people remember different details about their surroundings. A map produced from memory is called a mental map. These maps are usually not too accurate, especially when we try to indicate distance or pinpoint exact locations. A better way to locate places and find out how to reach them is to use a street map. Figure

Figure 1.5
Street map of
St. John's,
Newfoundland
*What types of
information
does this map
provide?*

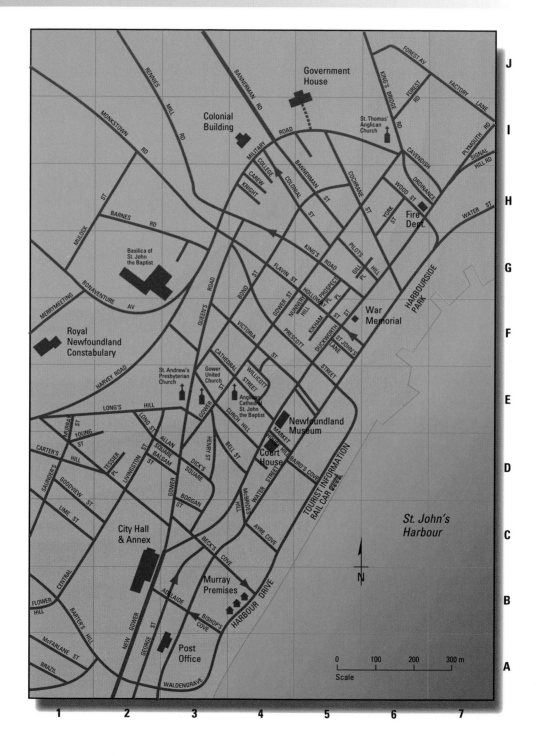

Figure 1.6
Aerial photograph of St. John's

1.5 is a street map of the downtown area of St. John's, Newfoundland.

The borders of the street map are labelled from south to north with letters and from west to east with numbers. Vertical and horizontal lines connect the letters and numbers to create a **grid**. These squares are used to provide grid references which identify specific locations. In grid references, the number is always given first, followed by the letter. For example, the Court House on the map of St. John's is found at 4D.

When a place is located at the corner of two streets, we often refer to the intersection where the two streets meet when giving its location. For example, Murray Premises, which is a restored warehouse now filled with shops and restaurants, is located at the intersection of Harbour Drive and Beck's Cove.

Another method of describing location is to draw a sketch of the street on which a place is located, with all of the intersections labelled. The area between streets represents a block. This type of map enables us to follow the blocks until we reach our destination.

8 a) Give the grid reference for each of the following places: Newfoundland Museum; Royal Newfoundland Constabulary; Colonial Building; Fire Department.
  b) On what streets would you find each of these places?

9 Name the intersections where we would find each of the following places in St.

John's: the Colonial Building; the War Memorial; the Court House.

10 a) Draw a straight line to represent Gower Street between Church Hill and Cochrane Street.
   b) Draw and label short lines at right angles to represent the streets that intersect with Gower.
   c) How many blocks are there on the northwest side of Gower between Church Hill and Cochrane Street?

Directions

When we give information to someone who has asked us where a place is located, we are giving directions. We tell the person to walk or drive north or south, east or west. Of course, we must know the direction of the place in relation to where we are. If we have a street map, we can use the directional symbol to establish north. We can then determine direction.

When giving directions, it is helpful to indicate how far it is to a location. A straight line between two points on a map is the direct distance. This is also called the straight-line distance, or the distance "as the crow flies"! This is easily calculated using the linear or statement scale on the map.

11 Using the directional symbol on the St. John's street map, write out directions for someone travelling from: i) City Hall to Murray Premises; ii) the War Memorial to the Colonial Building; iii) the Tourist Information Rail Car to Government House.

12 Using the linear scale for the street map of St. John's, measure the distance between: i) City Hall and Murray Premises; ii) the War Memorial and the Colonial Building; iii) the Tourist Information Rail Car and Government House.

In real-life situations, it is often impossible to travel a direct distance. We usually have to turn corners and change directions in order to reach our destination. This is called the actual distance. (See Figure 1.7.)

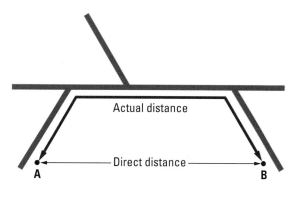

Figure 1.7
Direct and actual distance

Usually, the distance we travel to reach a place is the shortest route. We use what geographers call the **principle of least effort**. It wouldn't make sense to drive 5 km when, with planning, we could reach our destination in 3 km.

Without knowing it, you have already used the principle of least effort on page 7. Check the directions you gave then to see if they were the shortest actual distances.

To measure the actual distance between places when the route is not a straight line, we have to break down the trip into measurable units. We then add up all the units to obtain the actual distance. To do this we can use the edge of a strip of paper. The paper is placed along each straight-line distance. The distance is then marked on the paper. The paper is then turned to follow the next leg of the route. (See Figure 1.8.)

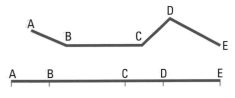

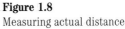

Figure 1.8
Measuring actual distance

13 Using Figure 1.8 as a guide along with the principle of least effort, calculate the distances to be travelled between: i) City Hall and Murray Premises; ii) the War Memorial and the Colonial Building; iii) the Tourist Information Rail Car and Government House.

When determining the easiest route between two places, we usually want to know how long the trip will take. We have to consider two things: the method and speed of travel (for example, walking at 3 km/h or driving at 30 km/h) and the distance to be travelled. We can work out how long a trip will take by dividing the distance by the speed. For example, if the distance to be travelled is 2 km and we are travelling at a speed of 4 km/h, our calculation would be:

2 km (distance) ÷ 4 km/h (speed)
= 0.5 h (travel time)

14 Calculate how long it would take a tourist walking at a speed of 3 km/h to get from the intersection of Adelaide and Water streets to the intersection of Cochrane and Water streets.

15 a) A tourist plans to take a walking tour of central St. John's. Using Figure 1.5, plan a route based on the principle of least effort. The tour should include the Newfoundland Museum, Harbourside Park, Government House, the Colonial Building, and the Court House.
 b) Using the scale on the map, estimate the length of the tour you have outlined.
 c) Based on a walking speed of 3 km/h, estimate the time needed to complete the tour.

16 Obtain a street map of your community.
 a) Draw a map of the route you take to school. Be sure to include a scale.
 b) Count the number of intersections you pass on your trip.
 c) Calculate both the actual and the direct distance between your home and your school. (If you have a bicycle with an odometer, you can use this to obtain the actual distance.)

17 a) A visitor to your community would like to take a walking tour of the area. Using the principle of least effort, plan a tour that includes four of your community's most interesting sights.
 b) Provide written directions for the walking tour. Refer to specific streets, intersections, buildings, and other places of interest.
 c) Based on a walking speed of 3 km/h, estimate how long the tour will take.

Canadians are fortunate. We have vast amounts of space, with relatively few people occupying it. In fact, Canada has 9 970 600 km² of space! This makes it the second largest country in the world. (See Figure 2.1.)

Of course, Canada's size means there are great distances within the country itself. There are 5514 km between the easternmost and westernmost points in Canada. The greatest distance north to south is 4634 km. To give you another perspective, consider this: the distance between Halifax on the east coast and Vancouver on the west coast is about the same direct distance as it is from Halifax to Paris, France! The distance from north to south between Alert in the Northwest Territories and Point Pelee in Ontario is equal to the distance between Canada's southern boundary and Quito, the capital of Ecuador in South America!

1 a) On a piece of graph paper, outline an area of 30 squares by 30 squares. This represents all the land surface in the world—a total of 148 429 000 km². Each square therefore represents 164 921 km² (148 429 000 ÷ 900).

b) Using the information in Figure 2.1, calculate how many squares would be needed to represent each country. For example, Algeria would need 14.4 squares (2 381 700 ÷ 164 921).

c) On your graph paper, outline the number of squares for each of the ten countries. Be sure to place each country in the approximate position it would occupy on a world map. An atlas will help you.

d) Using a different colour to represent each continent, shade in each country.

e) By area, which continent has the greatest share of the world's ten largest countries?

2 a) The area of the United Kingdom is 245 000 km². How many times would the United Kingdom fit into the area of Canada?

b) The population of Canada is 29 million. The population of the United Kingdom is 58 million. Write two statements expressing the relationship between each country's physical size and its population.

Figure 2.1
The world's ten largest countries

COUNTRY	AREA (km²)
Russia	17 075 000
Canada	9 970 600
China	9 597 000
United States	9 372 600
Brazil	8 511 000
Australia	7 686 900
India	3 287 600
Argentina	2 766 900
Sudan	2 505 800
Algeria	2 238 700

What is the combined size of Canada and the United States? How does this compare with the size of Russia?

We can also discover just how large Canada really is by locating its **geographic centre**. This is the centre point of the country measured from north to south and from east to west. Where would you guess the geographic centre of Canada is located?

3 Refer to Figure 2.2.

a) Label the following places on an outline map of Canada. Draw a line between each pair: i) St. John's, NF, and Mt. Logan, YK; ii) Alert, NT, and Point Pelee, ON; iii) Iqaluit, NT, and Victoria, BC.

b) The lines you drew in part a) created a shape on your map. Place an X in the centre of this shape. This represents Canada's approximate geographic centre. Describe this location. How close is it to the guess you made?

c) Using the linear scale, measure the approximate direct distance from the geographic centre to: i) Toronto; ii) St. John's; iii) Vancouver; iv) Alert.

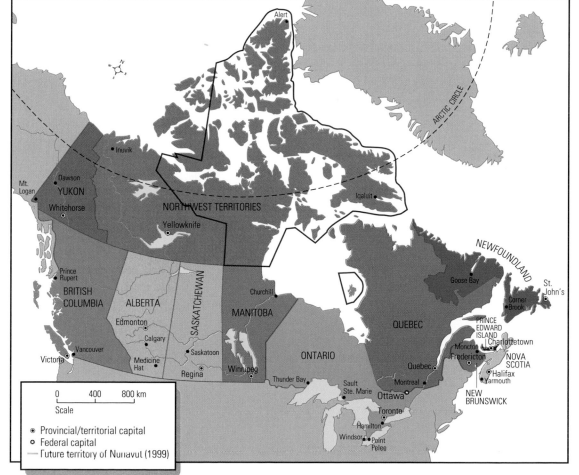

Figure 2.2
Political map of Canada

The effects of Canada's size

The size of a country like Canada has a great impact on our lifestyle. Businesses are affected because of the cost of transporting products across great distances. Consumers are affected because the cost of transportation is reflected in higher prices for the products we buy. Politicians are affected because of the challenges such a huge and diverse country presents. Even students are affected because there is just so much to learn about the geography of Canada!

On the other hand, Canada's size has provided us with one of the world's most diverse and beautiful landscapes. It has also enriched us with an abundant variety of natural resources. Let's consider some of the positive and negative effects of Canada's size.

4 a) In groups of four or five students, **brainstorm**, or think out loud, about the effects of Canada's size. Have one member of the group record all of the responses. (The responses should not be discussed at this stage.) Your brainstorming session should be limited to five minutes.
  b) Following your brainstorming session, discuss as a group what you believe are the three most positive effects and the three most negative effects of Canada's size. Be prepared to explain your choices.
  c) As a class, discuss each group's responses to part b). Try to reach a class **consensus** of the three most positive and the three most negative effects.

Dividing Canada

Canada is a vast country. We have a federal government which is responsible for the needs of all Canadians. Yet because of our size we also need regional governments. In Canada, there are ten provinces and two territories. Each province has its own legislature with responsibility for specific aspects of Canadian life. The two territories are under the control of the federal government in Ottawa.

A political map shows boundary lines between areas with different governments. These include boundaries within countries as well as international boundaries. You can see these boundaries on any political map of Canada.

5 Refer to Figure 2.2.
  a) Follow Canada's southern border with the United States from west to east. List the provinces in order from west to east. Which provinces do not share a land border with the United States?
  b) Identify the capital city of each province and territory. Mark these on an outline map of Canada.

Boundaries

Political boundaries can be either natural or artificial. **Natural boundaries** may take the form of mountains, rivers, lakes, seas, or deserts. **Artificial boundaries** are those that are not established by any physical features. Many of these boundaries follow lines of **longitude** or **latitude**.

6 a) Using Figure 2.2 and a physical map of Canada, identify i) the natural political boundaries and ii) the artificial political boundaries in Canada.

b) On an outline map of Canada, highlight the natural and artificial boundaries using different colours for each type. Be sure to identify the colours in the legend.

Regions

Most of us have more contacts with places that are near than with places that are far away. We may make hundreds of contacts with places within our community, dozens of trips to places within 50 km of our community, a few visits to places in the same province, and perhaps only a rare journey to places outside our province. The reason most of our contacts are within our own community is simple: local events have a greater impact on our daily lives.

A **region** is an area that shares certain features or characteristics. Canada is made up of many regions. Of course, these regions are much larger than the communities in which we have most of our personal contacts. Regions are created through the physical landscape. It can either separate people, as mountains and rivers do, or unite them through common characteristics, such as the sea.

7 Look at an atlas map of Canada's physical features. Which provinces would you group together as a region? Why? List these groups in your notebook. Give each a title and write a few sentences explaining why you think each group forms a region.

You have just completed one task of geographers: dividing a country into regions based on shared characteristics. Sometimes geographers create regions based on a single characteristic, such as climate. These are called **single-factor regions**. Most regions have more than one thing in common, however. While climate is a single factor, it influences a region's soil type, agriculture, population patterns, and so on. Regions that have many shared characteristics are called **multi-factor regions**.

Figure 2.3 shows some of the things that interest a geographer. Arrows have been drawn between some of the headings to show that they have a relationship. For example, types of rock influence **relief**; harder, more resistant rocks do not wear away as quickly as softer rocks. Water affects plants, since certain types of vegetation need different amounts of water. Notice that some arrows (for example, the one between climate and relief) are two-way. While mountains create certain climatic conditions,

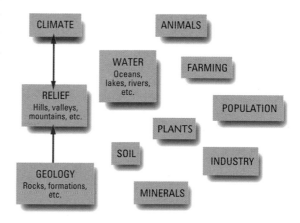

Figure 2.3
Relationships in geography

heavy amounts of precipitation also wear away the rock and change the relief.

8 a) Figure 2.3 is incomplete. Draw a similar diagram in your notebook. Add arrows between those features that you believe have relationships.
   b) Choose three features from Figure 2.3. Describe each one as it applies to the region in which you live.

A regional perspective

The regional differences across Canada seldom affect us personally. Only when we have contact with another region do we become aware of some of our regional differences. When placing a phone call from one region to another, for example, we have to consider **time zones**. Are we calling a person too early—or too late? If we are planning a trip to another region, we might want to check the weather so we will know what to pack.

It is not unusual for people to be unaware of our regional differences. This is because we spend so much time in our own communities that we naturally tend to focus on local conditions and events. Much of our knowledge about other regions usually comes from sources other than our own personal experiences.

Using our own community as the **focal point** from where we view the rest of the country creates a certain perspective, or way of viewing other regions. Our perspectives are influenced by our **geographic location**. To some of us, the rest of Canada is "down south;" for others, it is "out west." Figure 2.4 on page 17 shows Canada as it might be viewed by someone in St. John's, Newfoundland.

9 a) Describe how someone in St. John's might view the following regions: i) the Great Lakes; ii) British Columbia; iii) the Arctic; iv) Nova Scotia.
   b) Describe how someone in Winnipeg might view the same locations.
   c) Describe how someone in the following cities might view Canada's location: i) London, England; ii) Brisbane, Australia; iii) Dhaka, Bangladesh.

10 As the political journalist for your local newspaper, you have to visit each capital in Canada (federal, provincial, and territorial) in preparation for the prime minister's upcoming cross-country tour. To keep your travel expenses down, you must travel the shortest distance possible, visiting each capital only once.
   a) On an outline map of Canada, locate the cities you will be visiting.
   b) Using Figure 2.2, calculate the distance from your home base to the closest city you will visit. Then calculate the distance to the farthest city. Decide at which city you should begin your journey.
   c) Plan what you believe will be the most efficient route. Use arrows to chart your route on your map. Above each arrow indicate the direct distance between each destination.
   d) Calculate the total distance travelled in the route you have created. Compare your answer with those of your classmates. Of all the possible routes, which one covers all of the capitals in the fewest number of kilometres?

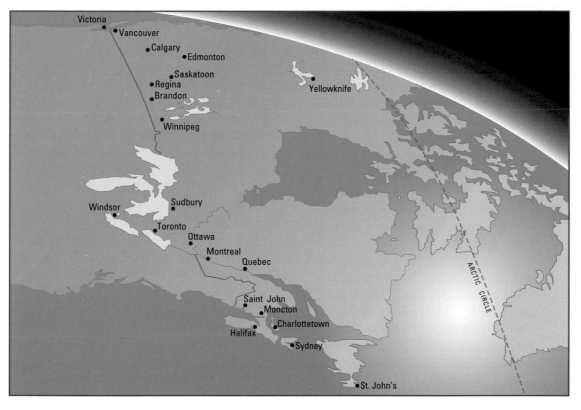

Figure 2.4
Canada viewed from an eastern perspective

Figure 2.5
Travel schedule

FLIGHTS BETWEEN WINNIPEG AND TORONTO		
	DEPARTURES	ARRIVALS
Air Canada	7:00	10:15
Canadian Airlines	7:30	12:35
Air Canada	10:10	13:25
Air Canada	12:40	18:40
Canadian Airlines	13:00	16:14
Canadian Airlines	14:30	17:45
Air Canada	15:30	18:38
Canadian Airlines	16:30	21:00
Air Canada	17:30	20:45
Canadian Airlines	19:00	22:12
Air Canada	20:00	23:14

Buses run from the airport to downtown Toronto every 30 min. The trip itself takes 30 min.

VIA RAIL BETWEEN TORONTO AND OTTAWA	
DEPARTURES	ARRIVALS
7:30	11:30
10:00	15:00
17:30	21:30
01:35	06:25

11 On your cross-country tour, assume you will be making a stop in Winnipeg. The following morning you must fly to Toronto for a meeting at 15:00 h in a downtown location. After an overnight stay in Toronto, you are to travel by Via Rail to the nation's capital. There you have a meeting on Parliament Hill at 14:30 h.

a) Using the schedules shown in Figure 2.5, plan your travel itinerary to ensure that you are on time for the meetings in Toronto and Ottawa. Your itinerary should include departure and arrival times, method of transportation, and the actual time spent travelling on each journey. Why might the flight times differ?

b) What perspective would you have when you are in Winnipeg thinking about your trip to Toronto and Ottawa?

c) What effects will you experience that will remind you of just how big Canada really is?

World space

We have seen how Canadians in different regions have different perspectives of our own country. In the same way, people in different regions of the world have their own perspectives about other regions. Often these perspectives are based on simple geographic location. For example, Canadians often say we are going "down south" when we refer to a trip we are taking to the southern United States.

Latitude and longitude

Just as Canada is divided into regions, the world is divided into four **hemispheres**— Northern, Southern, Eastern, and Western. Each hemisphere is divided by imaginary parallels of **latitude** and meridians of **longitude**. Lines of latitude run horizontally around the earth. They are measured in degrees from north to south from the Equator. These parallels of latitude indicate the angle created by the Equator and the earth's axis. (See Figure 2.6 on page 19.) They are called parallels because they are always the same distance apart; they never meet. The **Equator** is labelled 0° since it does not make an angle with itself. Places north of the Equator are in the Northern Hemisphere; places south of the Equator are in the Southern Hemisphere.

The highest measurement of latitude is either 90°N or 90°S, where a right angle is formed between the Equator, the centre of the earth, and the North or South poles. Each parallel is 1° apart. This represents 111 km on the earth's surface. Knowing this, we can calculate how far north or south two places are from one another.

Lines of longitude are drawn from north to south. Unlike parallels, the lines of longitude all meet at the poles. They are measured in degrees from east to west from a line at 0° called the **Prime Meridian**. Places to the west of the Prime Meridian are in the Western Hemisphere; places to the east of the Prime Meridian are in the Eastern Hemisphere. Each hemisphere contains 180°.

12 Refer to Figure 2.6.
   a) Give the latitude for the locations labelled A to E.
   b) Calculate the number of kilometres between A and B and between A and C.
   c) Using an atlas, identify Canada's northernmost and southernmost communities and give the lines of latitude for each.
   d) In your notebook, write a statement explaining Canada's general position in the world.

13 Refer to Figure 2.6.
   a) Give the longitude for the locations labelled A to E.
   b) Using an atlas, identify the major European capital through which the Prime Meridian passes.
   c) Using an atlas, identify Canada's easternmost and westernmost communities and give the lines of longitude for each.

Latitude and longitude make it possible to locate any place in the world. When giving a position, the degree of latitude is given first, followed by the degree of longitude. For example, Ottawa is located at 45°N 75°W.

14 Using an atlas map of Canada, give the lines of latitude and longitude for each of the following locations: i) your community; ii) Vancouver; iii) St. John's; iv) Alert; v) Toronto.

15 How many degrees of longitude is your community from each of the following locations: i) Helsinki, Finland; ii) Moscow, Russia; iii) London, England; iv) Tokyo, Japan?

Lines of latitude and longitude are called **co-ordinates**. Knowing how to use

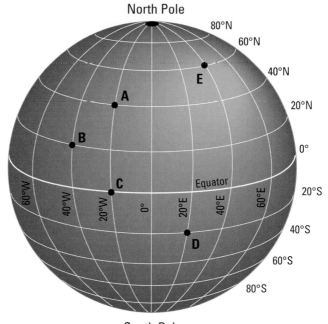

co-ordinates can help you to locate places using a **gazetteer**. A gazetteer is an index found in an atlas. It lists countries, cities, and physical features alphabetically. Beside each entry, the page number of the best map in the atlas for that feature is given, along with its co-ordinates. All you have to do is turn to the given page number, locate the lines of longitude and latitude as indicated, and pinpoint the spot.

The exact location of a place or feature is called its **absolute location**. Co-ordinates enable us to give absolute location. We must remember, however, that degrees of latitude are 111 km apart. This means that different places between degrees of latitude can be far apart yet still have the same co-ordinates. To be more specific in pinpointing locations, each

Figure 2.6
Latitude and longitude *Compare the distance between lines of longitude at 60° latitude and at the Equator. Why does the distance between meridians vary?*

degree of latitude and longitude is further divided into sixty **minutes**. For example, Ottawa is listed as 45°24N 75°38W.

We can also describe a place in terms of its **relative location**. This describes the general location of a place in relation to another physical feature or place. For example, we might describe a community as being in the foothills of Alberta's Rocky Mountains.

16 a) Using an atlas gazetteer, give the co-ordinates for: i) your own community; ii) Markham, ON; iii) Portage la Prairie, MB; iv) London, England; v) Jakarta, Indonesia.
   b) Describe the relative location for each of these places.

Canada's global position

Once you know how to locate and identify different places in the world, it is easier to appreciate Canada's global position. However, don't make the mistake of viewing places simply as they appear on a map. Remember, the world is round! If you had to fly from Toronto to Moscow, which direction would provide the shortest route?

Direction can be defined as movement in relation to the North Pole. If you move towards the North Pole anywhere in the world, you are travelling in a northerly direction. Similarly, if you move towards the South Pole, you are travelling in a southerly direction. On maps that show latitude and longitude, arrows indicating direction are unnecessary. This is because lines of longitude run between the North and South poles and lines of latitude represent easterly and westerly directions.

The four main directions – North, South, East, and West – are called the **cardinal points**. Once you have established north, it is easy to determine other directions.

17 a) Using an atlas map of Canada, indicate the direction you would travel between each of the following co-ordinates:
   i) 50°N 97°W to 50°N 111°W;
   ii) 56°N 117°W to 56°N 98°W;
   iii) 47°N 52°W to 47°N 65°W;
   iv) 47°N 71°W to 44°N 66°W;
   v) 61°N 135°W to 65°N 126°W.
   b) Identify the locations of each of these co-ordinates.

We can use a piece of string to link places on a globe. This provides us with the shortest distance between two points. Try stretching a string across a globe between London, England, and Ottawa, Canada. On the globe, the string appears to be straight. But if you were to "flatten" the earth's surface to create a map, the lines would actually curve in a northward arc. These lines are called **great circle routes**.

18 a) Using a globe and a piece of string, find the great circle route for each of the following. Record the direction you would travel and the countries you would fly over. For example, travelling from Toronto to Moscow you would fly in a northeast direction, across Canada, over the North Atlantic Ocean, and across the southern tip of Greenland and Iceland. You would cross Europe through Norway, Sweden, and Finland. Finally, you would enter Russia and land at its capital, Moscow.

b) Describe the great circle route for i) Vancouver to Paris, and ii) Vancouver to New Delhi.

19 a) Who would use great circle routes?
b) What do great circle routes have in common with direct distance and the principle of least effort?

Time and space

The world is divided into **time zones**. It was a Canadian, Sir Sandford Fleming, who first established the international time zone system. It is based on the earth's rotation from west to east every 24 h. The earth passes through 360° of longitude. This equals 15° for each hour. So the earth was divided into twenty-four time zones. When the system was first established, each zone was 15° across. Since then, boundaries have been changed to make divisions more convenient.

The 0° line of longitude is **Greenwich Mean Time**. Time zones west of 0° are successively one hour earlier; time zones east of 0° are successively one hour later. The two sides meet at 180°, which forms the **International Date Line**. This is a

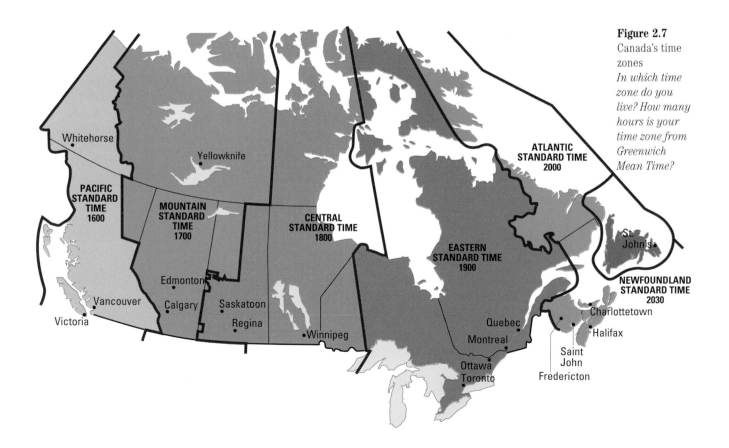

Figure 2.7
Canada's time zones
In which time zone do you live? How many hours is your time zone from Greenwich Mean Time?

PACIFIC STANDARD TIME 1600

MOUNTAIN STANDARD TIME 1700

CENTRAL STANDARD TIME 1800

EASTERN STANDARD TIME 1900

ATLANTIC STANDARD TIME 2000

NEWFOUNDLAND STANDARD TIME 2030

Whitehorse

Yellowknife

Edmonton

Calgary

Saskatoon

Regina

Winnipeg

Vancouver

Victoria

Quebec

Montreal

Ottawa

Toronto

Saint John

Fredericton

Charlottetown

Halifax

St. John's

Figure 2.8
International
flight times

FLIGHT	TIME ZONE DIFFERENCE	DEPARTURE TIME	DURATION OF FLIGHT	ARRIVAL LOCAL TIME
Montreal to Los Angeles	-3 h	12:00 noon	4 h	
Vancouver to Miami	+3 h	11:00 a.m.	4 h	
Halifax to London, England	+4 h	8:00 p.m.	6 h	

Figure 2.9
Distance chart:
official highway
distances
between major
Canadian
centres (km)

	Calgary	Charlottetown	Edmonton	Fredericton	Halifax	Montreal	Ottawa	Quebec City	Regina	St. John's	Saskatoon	Thunder Bay	Toronto	Vancouver	Victoria	Whitehorse	Winnipeg	Yellowknife	
	•	4917	299	4558	5042	3743	3553	4014	764	6183	620	2050	3434	1057	1123	2385	1336	1811	Calgary
		•	4949	359	232	1184	1374	945	4163	1294	4421	2878	1724	5985	6051	7034	3592	6460	Charlottetown
			•	4598	5082	3764	3574	4035	785	6212	528	2071	3455	1244	1310	2086	1357	1511	Edmonton
				•	346	834	1024	586	3813	1622	4070	2527	1373	5634	5700	6684	3241	6109	Fredericton
					•	1318	1508	912	4297	1349	4554	3011	1857	6119	6185	7168	3726	6593	Halifax
						•	190	270	2979	2448	3236	1693	539	4801	4867	5850	2408	5275	Montreal
							•	460	2789	2638	3046	1503	399	4611	4677	5660	2218	5086	Ottawa
								•	3249	2208	3507	1963	810	5071	5137	6120	2678	5546	Quebec City
									•	5427	257	1286	2670	1822	1888	2871	571	2297	Regina
										•	5684	4141	2987	7248	7314	8298	4855	7723	St. John's
											•	1543	2927	1677	1743	2614	829	2039	Saskatoon
												•	1384	3108	3174	4157	715	3582	Thunder Bay
													•	4492	4558	5528	2099	4966	Toronto
														•	66	2697	2232	2411	Vancouver
															•	2763	2298	2477	Victoria
																•	3524	2704	Whitehorse
																	•	2868	Winnipeg
																		•	Yellowknife

line in the Pacific Ocean where the date changes either one day ahead or one day back, depending on your direction.

Some locations lie in the middle of a time zone. In such cases time is adjusted by 30 min. That is why time in St. John's, Newfoundland, which is located 52.5° west of 0°, is 3.5 h behind Greenwich Time.

20 A Calgary Flames home game is being televised live across the country. If the hockey game starts at 8:00 p.m., what time should viewers turn on their television sets in: i) Ottawa; ii) Saskatoon; iii) St. John's? Refer to Figure 2.7 to determine your answers.

21 Copy Figure 2.8 into your notebook. Complete the column "Arrival local time" for each flight from Canada. Remember: Local time refers to the time at the place in which you arrive.

22 A swim meet is being held next summer in your provincial capital. Swimmers will be attending from Vancouver, Edmonton, Whitehorse, Yellowknife, Saskatoon, Winnipeg, Toronto, Quebec City, Halifax, Fredericton, Charlottetown, and St. John's. You have been asked to provide each team with the following information: i) the distance they will have to travel to reach the swim meet and ii) the time difference between your provincial capital and their community.
a) Compile this information using the time zone map and the distance chart.
b) Each team is expecting to receive this information by telephone at 9:00 a.m. local time. If you are calling from your community, at what time will you have to place each of these calls?

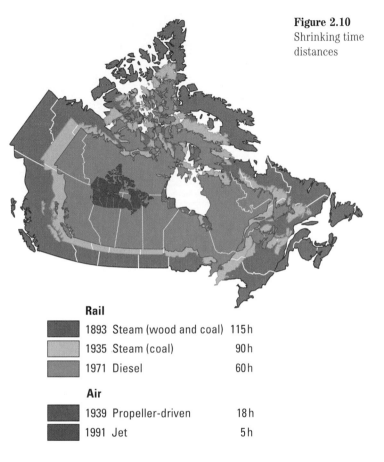

Figure 2.10
Shrinking time distances

Rail

	1893 Steam (wood and coal)	115 h
	1935 Steam (coal)	90 h
	1971 Diesel	60 h

Air

	1939 Propeller-driven	18 h
	1991 Jet	5 h

The time it takes to travel between two places is called the **time distance**. To calculate the time distance you must add the total travel time for each method of transportation used to reach your destination. Figure 2.10 indicates how time distance has been reduced as the methods of transportation have changed.

23 Refer to Figure 2.10. Describe how technology has decreased the time distances between Canadian cities.

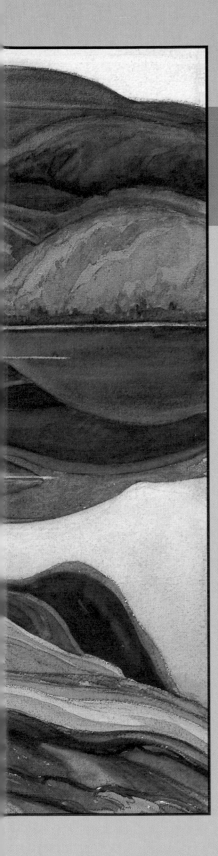

Unit 2

PHYSICAL DIVERSITY

One afternoon, by driving a few miles out to Cape Spear, I made myself for a moment the easternmost person in North America, and was chilled to think, as I stood there in the wind, that while at my back there was nothing but the ocean, before me there extended, almost as far as the imagination could conceive, the awful immensity of Canadian rock, forest, prairie, and mountain.

Jan Morris, travel writer, in *Saturday Night*, March 1989.

Franklin Carmichael, 1890-1945
Mirror Lake 1929
Watercolour on paper
44.0 x 54.5 cm
McMichael Canadian Art Collection
Gift of Mrs. R. G. Mastin
1976.8

If you had to choose one country in the world to show a great variety of landforms, Canada would be a good choice! It makes sense that countries with a large land area often have a variety of physical characteristics. Canada contains both spectacular rugged mountains and vast lowland plains. It has the largest coastline of any country in the world. Yet many parts of the country are hundreds of kilometres away from the nearest ocean.

1 **Look at the series of photographs showing different regions in Canada. Copy Figure 3.1 into your notebook. Use it to complete a description of each photograph.**

Figure 3.1
The diverse regions of Canada

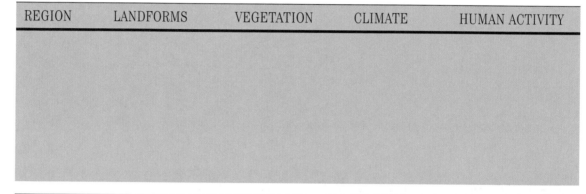

REGION	LANDFORMS	VEGETATION	CLIMATE	HUMAN ACTIVITY

Figure 3.2
The Canadian Shield in northern Ontario

Figure 3.3
The Interior Plains in Saskatchewan

Figure 3.4
The St. Lawrence Lowlands in Quebec

Figure 3.5
The Hudson
Bay Lowlands
in northern
Manitoba

Figure 3.6
The Arctic
Lowlands at
Ellesmere
Island,
Northwest
Territories

Figure 3.7
The Rocky
Mountains
in British
Columbia

Figure 3.8
Fiords in
Gros Morne
National Park
in Newfoundland

Figure 3.9
The Innuitian
Mountains near
Cape Dorset,
Northwest
Territories

Canada has four basic types of landforms: the Canadian Shield, the interior plains, the lowlands, and the mountain rim. (See Figure 3.10.) Although these are distinctly different types of landforms, they are interconnected by the enormous forces of nature that have been at work over millions of years.

2   Refer to Figure 3.10. Identify the provinces and territory that contain part of the Canadian Shield.

3   Using a physical map, draw a profile of Canada along the 50°N line of latitude.
   a) Draw a base line to represent the 50°N line of latitude between the 130°W and 55°W lines of longitude. This line of latitude is curved on your map. To draw it as a straight line, measure the distance between each line of longitude. Then plot these to scale along a straight line. Identify each line of longitude on your base line.

Figure 3.10
Canada's landform regions

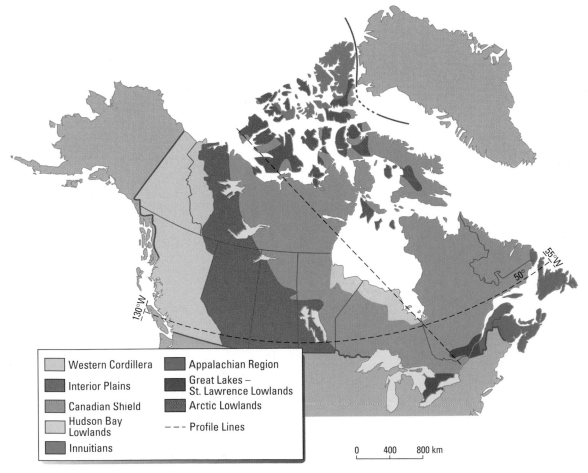

	Western Cordillera		Appalachian Region
	Interior Plains		Great Lakes – St. Lawrence Lowlands
	Canadian Shield		Arctic Lowlands
	Hudson Bay Lowlands	– – –	Profile Lines
	Innuitians		

0   400   800 km

b) At each end of the base line draw a vertical line 4 cm high. Each centimetre represents 1000 m. Mark a scale on the vertical lines at 1000 m intervals.

c) Place the edge of a piece of paper along the 50°N line of latitude on your map. On the paper, note the location and height each time the relief, or colour, changes.

d) Transfer the information you have obtained from the map onto your profile. (See Figure 3.11.) Using your vertical scale as a guide, mark points representing the different heights. Join the height points with a continuous smooth line.

e) Colour your profile, using the same colours for relief as the atlas map. Complete your profile by labelling the physical features, the oceans, and the line of latitude.

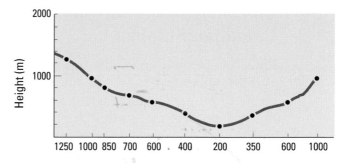

The Canadian Shield

The foundation of the Canadian land mass is a massive bedrock called the **Canadian Shield**. If you were to dig deep enough anywhere in Canada, you would eventually strike the Shield! This bedrock contains some of the oldest rocks in the world.

Rocks are classified by their geological age. Our geological past stretches back 4800 million years. This is when it is believed that the earth first began. This vast history is divided into smaller units called eras. Figure 3.12 shows our geological past.

4 Refer to Figure 3.12.
   a) Which era lasted the longest?
   b) Which era are we in now?
   c) Some parts of the Canadian Shield are over 4800 million years old. During which era were they formed?

Figure 3.11
Creating a profile

Figure 3.12
Our geological past

ERA	BEGAN (millions of years ago)	ENDED (millions of years ago)
Cenozoic	70	—
Mesozoic	225	70
Palaeozoic	600	225
Precambrian	4800	600

The composition of the Canadian Shield

Rocks can be transformed through the **rock cycle**, as shown in Figure 3.13. Rock can be created from hot, melted magma that rises from deep within the earth's crust. It then cools and hardens to form **igneous rock**. This rock may be broken down into particles, or **sediment**. Eventually the sediment hardens to form **sedimentary rock**. Pressure and heat can cause this rock to melt once again, forming **metamorphic rock**. This rock may contain valuable mineral resources. Much of the Canadian Shield is formed from extremely hard igneous rock. The most common type is granite. This is an **impervious** rock, which means that water cannot pass through it.

5 a) **Draw your own copy of the rock cycle. In your own words, describe each rock type and what happens to it during the cycle.**

   b) **Describe what might happen to the igneous rock that forms part of the Canadian Shield.**

6 **Refer to a minerals map in your atlas. What minerals are found within the Shield? Where are most of these minerals located?**

Figure 3.13
The rock cycle

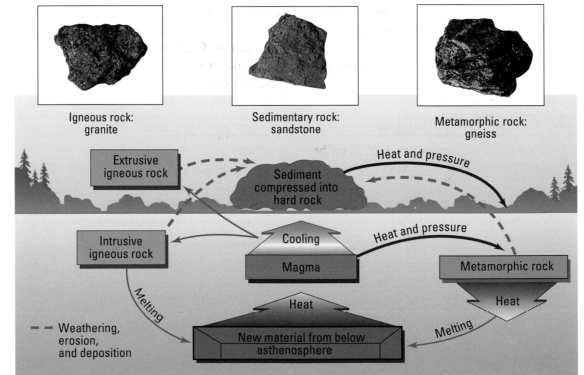

Igneous rock: granite

Sedimentary rock: sandstone

Metamorphic rock: gneiss

Extrusive igneous rock

Sediment compressed into hard rock

Heat and pressure

Intrusive igneous rock

Cooling

Magma

Heat and pressure

Metamorphic rock

Heat

– – Weathering, erosion, and deposition

Melting

Heat

New material from below asthenosphere

Melting

Topographic maps: reading the landscape

The landscape of the Shield is rugged. Forests emerge from the rocky hills that cover the region. Hundreds of lakes and streams dot the landscape. Figure 3.2 on page 26 shows a typical scene in the Canadian Shield.

Figure 3.14 is a **topographic map**. It shows the area surrounding Limerick Lake on the southern edge of the Canadian Shield. Topographic maps use symbols to provide detailed information about physical features and human activities. **Area symbols** are coloured patterns that represent physical features like lakes and woods. **Line symbols** represent linear features like roads and railways. **Point symbols** represent specific features like bridges and buildings. A legend explains what each symbol means. Some of the conventional signs for topographic maps are indicated in Figure 3.15 on page 35.

7 Refer to Figure 3.14 on page 34.
   a) Locate the village of Gilmour. Describe its location so that someone else could find it.
   b) What large features appear within grid squares 9669 and 9771?
   c) Give three examples of line symbols on this map.
   d) The green map symbols represent forest cover; the blue symbols represent water. What do the white areas represent?

Gilmour is situated along a main road, so identifying its location is fairly easy. Sometimes, however, we may have to use a map to describe the location of something far away from an easily identified point.

In Unit 1, you identified places in St. John's using a simple grid system. Topographic maps also have a grid system, but it is more sophisticated. We can use this grid system to locate places like Gilmour.

Notice the numbers along the sides of the map. The numbers across the bottom have lines that run north and south. These are called **eastings**. Imagine travelling in an easterly direction across the map. The last line you would cross before reaching Gilmour is 93. Now look at the numbered lines along the side of the map. These are called **northings**. Moving from the bottom of the map (south) to the top of the map (north), the last northing you would cross before you reach Gilmour is 66. Therefore Gilmour is located in grid square 9366. This is called a **four-figure grid reference**. This type of grid is especially useful when describing the location of a large feature. When giving a grid reference, remember that the easting always comes first.

A four-figure grid reference is useful in locating large features. But what if we want to locate a small feature? Look at Figure 3.16. Notice that the distance between eastings 93 and 94 has been divided into tenths. The cemetary is three-tenths along from 93 to 94. So the eastings reference for the cemetery is 933. The distance between northings is also divided by tenths. The cemetery is four-tenths along from 66. Therefore it is located at 664. Combined, this creates a **six-figure grid reference** of 933664.

8 What point symbols are found at the following grid references: i) 992731;

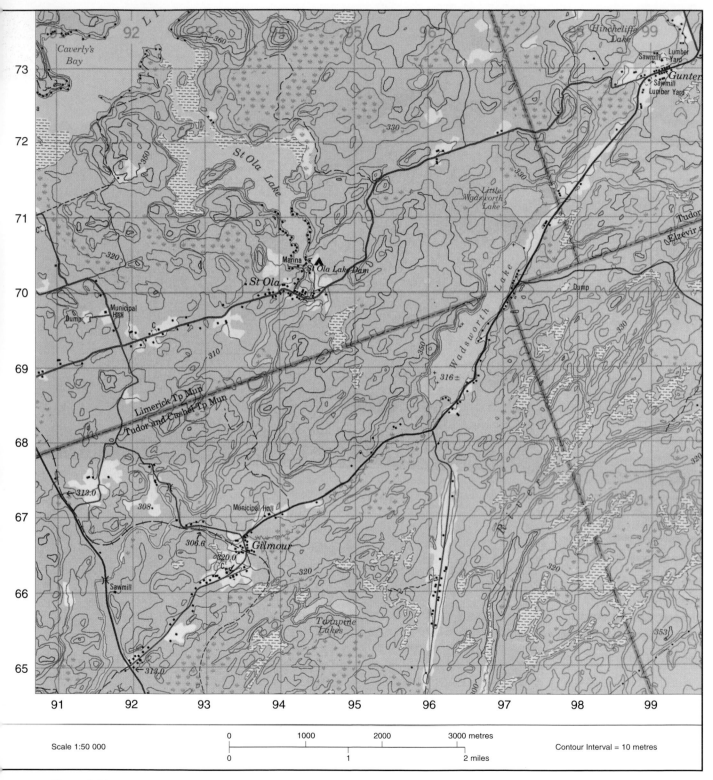

Figure 3.14
Topographic map of Limerick Lake, Ontario

Scale 1:50 000

Contour Interval = 10 metres

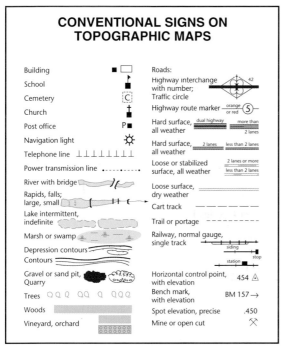

CONVENTIONAL SIGNS ON TOPOGRAPHIC MAPS

Figure 3.15
Conventional signs on topographic maps

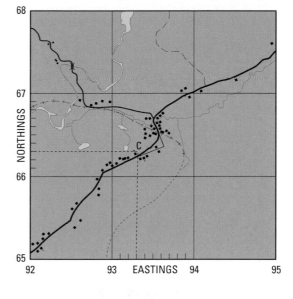

Figure 3.16
Grid references

been used extensively for both recreation and industry?

The forces of erosion

In the geological past, the **elevation** of the Canadian Shield was much higher than it is today. In fact, it was once over 6000 m! Yet today the elevation of the Shield is between 300 and 500 m. How were the mountains of the Shield worn away?

Elevation is affected by **erosion**. This is the gradual wearing down of land or rock by a variety of natural forces. These include temperature, running water, ice, wind, and vegetation. Figure 3.17 on page 36 describes how the forces of erosion work.

In the Canadian Shield, the forces of erosion have been at work over millions of years. As the rock eroded, the Shield became lighter and mountains emerged

ii) 945704; iii) 933663; iv) 916698; v) 918660; vi) 921651?

9 Referring to Figure 3.14, describe the directions and distances on the roads you would use to travel from a cottage on Wadsworth Lake at 967689 to the marina on St. Ola Lake at 943704. Use phrases such as "turn east and travel north." Remember that the top of the map is north and the scale of the map is 1 cm to 50 000 cm (100 000 cm = 1 km).

10 Refer to Figure 3.14.
   a) What evidence is there to suggest that the area contains impervious rock?
   b) What evidence is there that the southern edges of the Canadian Shield have

Figure 3.17
The forces of
erosion

Temperature: Rock expands with hot temperatures and contracts with cold ones. Constant changes in temperature eventually weaken the rock, causing parts of it to break away in small pieces.

Running water: Rainfall, running water, and wave action eventually wear down the surface of the rock. As the rock weakens, it begins to break away.

Ice: When water freezes in the cracks of rocks it expands, causing small pieces to break off. Glacial movement also wears away rock surfaces.

Wind: Wind action carries away small particles of the rock surface. Small rock particles carried in the wind also cause other rock to break away on impact.

Vegetation: When vegetation takes root in small cracks, rocks are weakened. Small pieces of rock gradually break away.

once again. But again, the forces of erosion began to wear down the mountains. This cycle continued until the Shield eventually became a stable land mass. It has been at its present height for millions of years.

The most spectacular environmental force in geologic history started about 1 million years ago and lasted until just 10 000 years ago. Massive ice sheets called **glaciers** swept southward from Hudson Bay and out of the western mountains. A thick sheet of ice up to 3 km thick covered most of Canada and the northern part of the United States. The force of the moving ice eroded parts of the landscape. This created a variety of unique landforms, including **drumlins**, **eskers**, and **moraines**. The **Ice Age** gradually came to an end as a warming trend began to develop around 14 000 years ago. Figure 3.18 shows the extent of the glacial movement in North America.

11 Refer to Figure 3.18.
   a) How much of Canada was covered with ice?
   b) If an ice sheet were to move across Canada today, as it did during the Ice Age, in what ways would it erode the landscape? In what ways would it build up the landscape?

The Interior Plains

As erosion wore away the rocks of the Canadian Shield, the rock particles were carried westward by the movement of rivers, streams, and ice. Eventually they were deposited in the Interior Plains. As the Shield continued to erode, more and more layers of sediment were transported. Each layer was deposited on top of the previous layer. Over millions of years, these sediments were transformed into sedimentary rock.

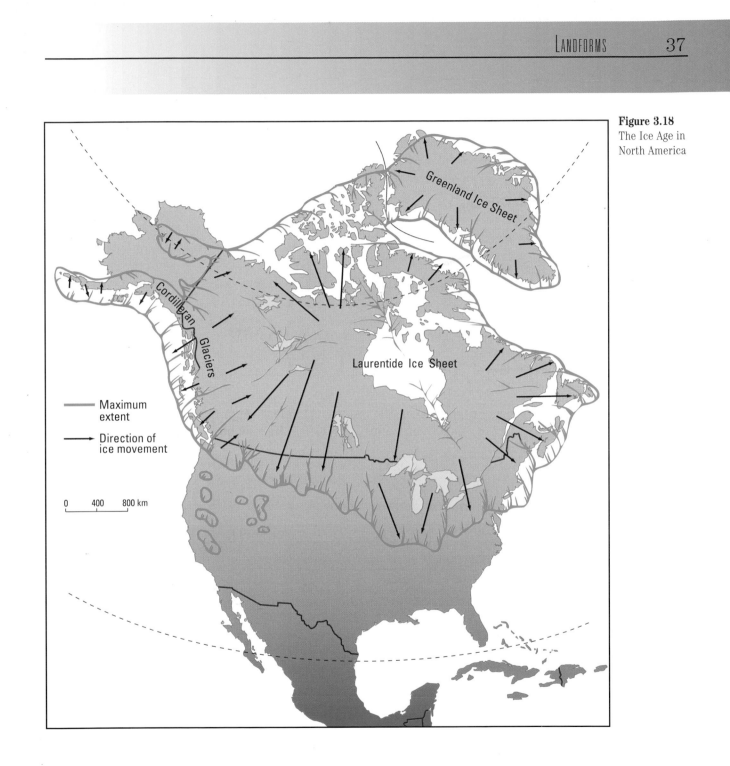

Figure 3.18
The Ice Age in
North America

Greenland Ice Sheet

Cordilleran Glaciers

Laurentide Ice Sheet

— Maximum extent

→ Direction of ice movement

0   400   800 km

12 Figure 3.19 shows the layers of sedimentary rock near the Shield. What evidence is there that i) the Shield eroded at different times, and ii) the Shield rose after it became lighter?

13 If you dug deep into layers of sedimentary rock, where would the newest and oldest rocks be found? Explain your answer.

As the layers of sedimentary rock were deposited over the Interior Plains, they buried evidence of life that existed there millions of years ago. Today rivers have cut deep into these rock layers. Often they reveal fossils of plant and animal life from those ancient times. These enable us to learn a great deal about life on the planet millions of years ago.

The rock layers of the Interior Plains contain valuable mineral resources in addition to fossils. The climate over Canada was once quite different from what it is today. During the Palaeozoic and Mesozoic eras, warm, shallow seas covered Canada's interior. These stretched as far north as the Arctic Ocean. Billions of microscopic sea creatures and plants were deposited on the seabed. Eventually they were buried by sedimentary rock from the Shield. Their decayed remains left a valuable legacy—large amounts of oil and natural gas hidden deep beneath the earth's surface. (For more on these deposits, see pages 214–217.)

Figure 3.19
The Canadian Shield

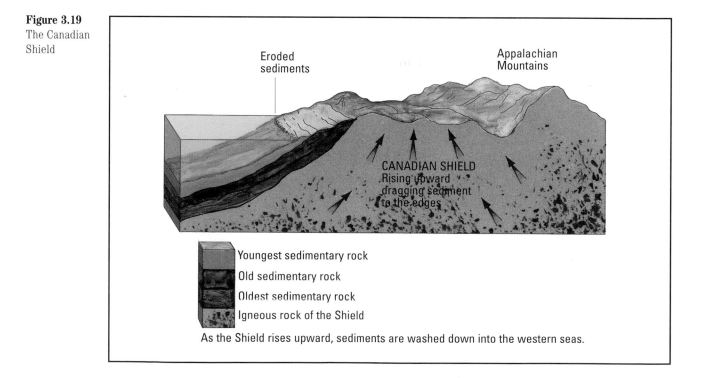

As the Shield rises upward, sediments are washed down into the western seas.

14 Refer to a minerals map in an atlas.
  a) Where are most of Canada's oil and gas deposits located?
  b) What other important minerals are mined in the Interior Plains?

Relief

From east to west, the elevation, or **relief**, of the Interior Plains gradually rises. At Winnipeg it is 239 m. On the western edge of the plains at Calgary it has risen to 1084 m. While the increase in elevation is gradual, there are three distinct plateaus from Manitoba to Alberta.

Relief on topographic maps is shown by **contour lines**. These are lines that connect places of the same elevation. Figure 3.20, for example, shows the elevation of a hill. The closed circles of the contour lines represent areas of the same elevation. The height above sea level in metres is indicated on the line.

Contour lines reveal the shape of a landscape. If the lines are close together, the land is steep. If the lines are far apart, the land has a gentle slope. The difference in elevation between one contour line and another is called the **contour interval**. This is usually indicated at the bottom of the map. In Figure 3.20, the contour interval is 25 m.

15 Refer to the topographic map in Figure 3.22 on page 40.
  a) What is the contour interval?
  b) Using the bench marks described in Figure 3.21 and contour lines, determine the highest point on this map.

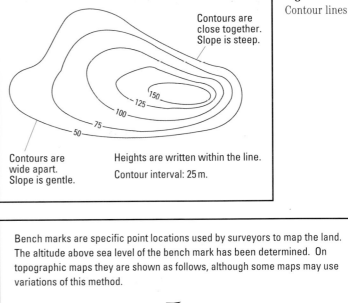

Figure 3.20
Contour lines

Contours are close together. Slope is steep.

150
125
100
75
50

Contours are wide apart. Slope is gentle.

Heights are written within the line.
Contour interval: 25 m.

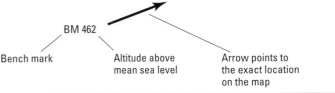

Bench marks are specific point locations used by surveyors to map the land. The altitude above sea level of the bench mark has been determined. On topographic maps they are shown as follows, although some maps may use variations of this method.

BM 462

Bench mark

Altitude above mean sea level

Arrow points to the exact location on the map

Figure 3.21
Bench mark for surveying landscapes

c) Describe the landscape of this area. How does it compare with that of the Shield on page 38?
d) Most of this map is white. What does this indicate?
e) Streams or lakes that are occasionally dry are called **intermittent**. They are shown on topographic maps as broken blue lines. Give the grid references for the two largest intermittent lakes on this map. What do these features indicate about the climate of this area? When would you expect these lakes to be full of water?

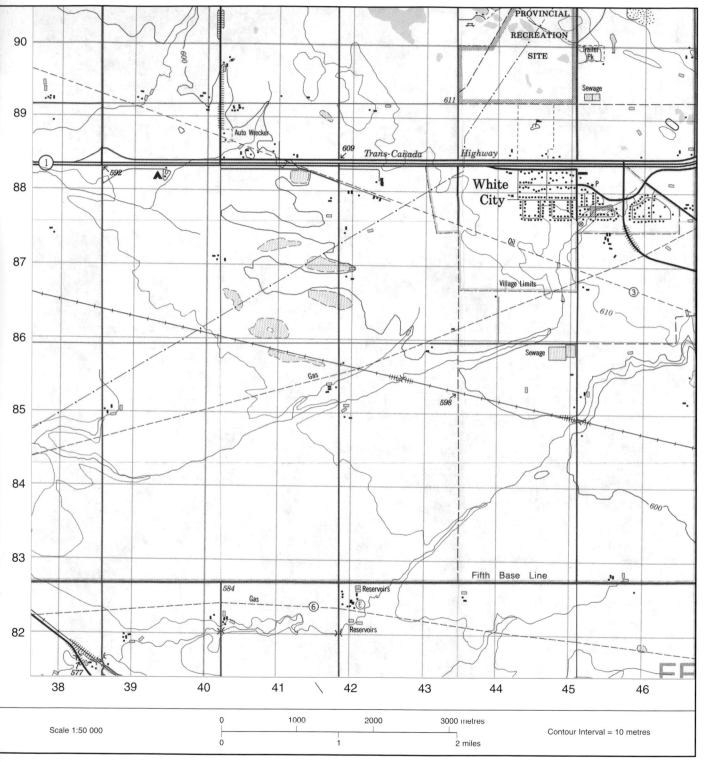

Figure 3.22
Topographic map of White City, Saskatchewan
List all of the line symbols you see on this map. What do they tell you about the prairie economy?

16 Describe the relief of the Interior Plains using Figure 3.3 on page 27.

17 Refer to the profile you drew at the beginning of this chapter.
   a) Describe what happens to the height of the land between longitude 100°W and 112°W.
   b) A sudden rise in elevation is called an escarpment. Identify the escarpments in your profile.

Scales on topographic maps

In Unit 1 we were introduced to linear scales and statement scales. Topographic maps like Figure 3.22 use another type of scale, called a **ratio scale**. On this map the ratio scale is 1:50 000. This means that the distance on the ground is 50 000 times greater than the same distance on the map. For example, 1 cm on the map represents 50 000 cm in actual distance. This is an easy scale to understand. It doesn't matter what the unit of measurement is as long as it is applied to both sides of the ratio.

18 a) Calculate the direct distance between the following:
   i) the bench mark on the Trans-Canada Highway at 386883 and the intersection with the Fifth Base Line at 386827;
   ii) the White City school at 442879 and a farm at 420849.

   b) Estimate the shortest actual distance you would travel by road between:
   i) the farm at 417854 and the auto wreckers at 402888;
   ii) the White City school at 442879 and a farm at 420849;
   iii) the camp site office at 394882 and the nearest post office;
   iv) the trailer park office at 454898 and the post office at 453881.
   (Remember: You have to cross the Trans-Canada Highway safely!).

Map scales vary depending on the amount of detail the map shows. **Large-scale maps** show small areas. They have scales of 1:10 000 to 1:1 000 000. Topographic maps like Figure 3.22 and local road maps are usually large-scale maps. **Small-scale maps** show less detail. They illustrate large areas like countries or oceans. Small-scale maps have scales of 1:1 000 000 to 1:10 000 000. A map of Canada in an atlas is a small-scale map.

19 Compare the area shown in Figure 3.22 with an atlas map of Saskatchewan.
   a) Which map shows more surface area?
   b) Which map shows more detail?
   c) In what situations would each map be useful?
   d) Find the scale on the atlas map. Is this a large-scale map or a small-scale map?

20 Compare Figure 3.22 and the atlas map of Saskatchewan with a wall map of Canada. Describe the differences in the three maps.

The Lowlands

There are three large lowland areas in Canada: the Great Lakes-St. Lawrence Lowlands, the Hudson Bay Lowlands, and the Arctic Lowlands. The **Great Lakes-St. Lawrence Lowlands** is the smallest of the three regions in the physical sense. Yet it is often described as the country's heartland. It is the most densely populated region in Canada. Three out of every five Canadians live here. It contains the country's two largest cities, Toronto and Montreal. It is the destination of the majority of new Canadians. And it contains over 65 per cent of all Canadian manufacturing industries.

The Great Lakes-St. Lawrence Lowlands are divided into two parts. The Great Lakes Lowlands stretch from southwestern Ontario along the shores of Lakes Erie and Ontario to the St. Lawrence River northeast of Kingston. The St. Lawrence Lowlands then follow the river towards Quebec City and the Gulf of St. Lawrence.

Like the Interior Plains, sediments were deposited in the Great Lakes-St. Lawrence Lowlands from the Canadian Shield as well as from the Appalachians to the east. Layers of limestone, sandstone, and shale lie beneath the surface. Figure 3.23 shows the cross-section of bedrock beneath Toronto.

During the last Ice Age, the mass and movement of the ice sheets carved out the low-lying areas that are now the Great Lakes. When the ice melted, the Great Lakes were formed. Originally they were much larger than they are today. In fact, what is now Lake Ontario was once part of a much larger body of water called Lake Iroquois. This lake would have completely submerged what is now the downtown Toronto skyline! Over time, the Great Lakes drained to form their present shape.

Figure 3.23
A cross-section of the bedrock beneath Toronto

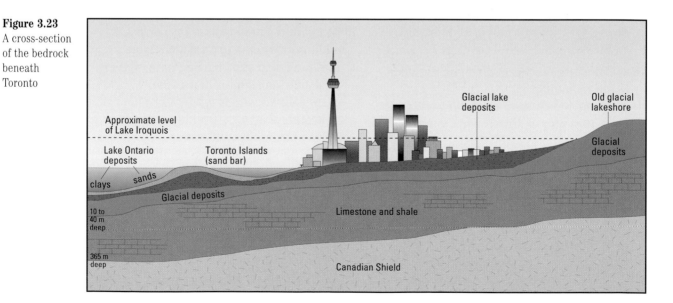

Today these form the world's largest concentration of inland freshwater and provide a major transportation route in North America.

The Ice Age also resulted in millions of tonnes of glacial sediment, or **till**, being dumped around the Great Lakes Lowlands. This till and the rolling landscape combined to create excellent conditions for farming. The St. Lawrence Lowlands also received an abundance of sediment from the ancient Champlain Sea, which once lay to the south of the region. When the area was under the tremendous pressure of the ice sheet, the land sank. This allowed water from the Champlain Sea to flood northward. As it did, it deposited a layer of rich marine sediment. This created a fertile agricultural region.

21 Refer to a relief map of Canada. What is the lowest elevation on the map? What colour represents this elevation?

22 Draw a sketch map of the Great Lakes-St. Lawrence Lowlands using an atlas as a resource. Include main rivers and lakes, cities with populations over 100 000, and main roads and rail lines. Label each of these features.

The **Hudson Bay Lowlands** are found to the south of Hudson Bay. The flat layers of sedimentary rock rest atop the ancient rock of the Shield. At one time Hudson Bay covered much of this region.

The **Arctic Lowlands** are scattered among the islands of the far north. Like the Hudson Bay Lowlands, this region consists of sedimentary rock lying atop older rock from the Shield. Like the Interior Plains, the Arctic Lowlands contain valuable mineral deposits. In both the Hudson Bay Lowlands and the Arctic Lowlands, the ground remains frozen for much of the year due to the cold northern climate.

23 Look at the photographs of the Hudson Bay Lowlands (Figure 3.5 on page 27) and the Arctic Lowlands (Figure 3.6 on page 28). Describe the differences you see between these two lowlands.

24 a) Where are the three lowland areas located in relation to the Canadian Shield?

b) Each lowland area is composed of sedimentary rock. Where do you think this rock came from?

25 Using a relief map in an atlas, identify some of the islands in the Arctic that are lowland areas. Many of these islands have names associated with early explorers. Research how some of these places received their names.

26 a) Draw a profile along a line from the point where the Ottawa River meets the St. Lawrence River to the southernmost point of Banks Island in the Arctic Ocean. Use the method you followed on page 30.

b) Label the bodies of water, physical features, and islands.

c) Your profile passes through the Great Lakes-St. Lawrence Lowlands, the Hudson Bay Lowlands, and the Arctic Lowlands. Label these on your profile.

The Mountain Rim

Around much of the coastal rim of Canada the landscape is anything but flat. Canada has some of the most magnificent mountain scenery in the world. To discover how these mountains were formed, we have to look deep into the earth's crust.

As much as 2900 km beneath the earth's surface lies a very hot form of semi-liquid rock. This mass of rock actually moves around. Think of a pan on the stove. As it is heated, its contents circulate upward in a process called **convection**. In a similar way, this mass of rock is forced by the heat to circulate very slowly beneath the earth's crust. Over time, pressure from this movement has cracked the earth's crust, creating **plates**. The plates are then forced to move in various directions. Look at the plate tectonics map in Figure 3.24 to discover the direction of this movement today.

When plates move apart, rising liquid rock called **magma** is forced to the surface. There it cools, forming a new part of the earth's surface. When plates move towards one another, however, they either scrape together or one rides over the other. Geologists believe that the whole system of Canadian west coast mountains was formed by the collision of two plates.

Figure 3.24
Plate tectonics

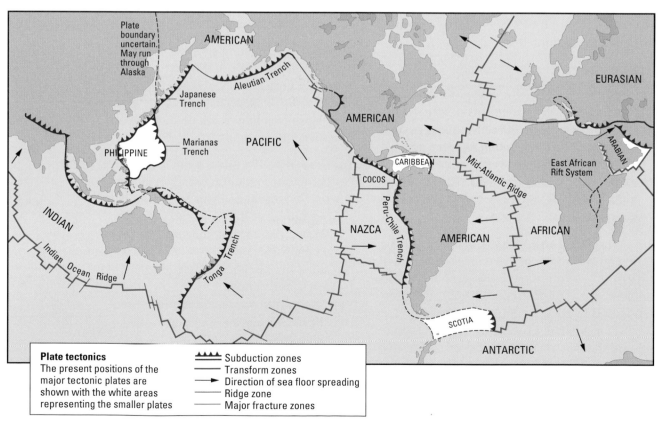

Plate tectonics
The present positions of the major tectonic plates are shown with the white areas representing the smaller plates

▲▲▲▲ Subduction zones
—— Transform zones
——▶ Direction of sea floor spreading
—— Ridge zone
—— Major fracture zones

27 Refer to Figure 3.24.
   a) Name the five largest plates.
   b) On which plate is Canada located?
   c) What is happening to the distance between Canada and Europe?
   d) Which plates meet near the west coast of Canada? In which direction are they moving?

One of the two plates you identified in part d) of activity 27 is heavier than the other. By the end of the Mesozoic era, these plates were moving towards one another. They finally collided. The lighter plate—the one beneath Canada—was forced up over the heavier one. This movement folded and uplifted much of the sedimentary rock on the surface. This created the **fold mountains** of the Western Cordillera.

Fold mountains are easy to identify because of the huge ripples in their rock structure. (Try pushing a tablecloth towards one end of the table to see this uplifting and folding effect!) The mountains of the Western Cordillera are sometimes described as young fold mountains because they were formed only 65 million years ago during the Cenozoic era. The Western Cordillera is shown in Figure 3.7 on page 28.

As the Pacific plate sank into the earth's hot interior beneath the North American plate, it began to melt. This caused much of the magma to rise upward and break through the earth's surface, sometimes in the form of spectacular volcanoes. Much of the Coast Ranges, including the coastal islands, were formed in this way. Many of the valleys that lay between the thrusts of sedimentary rock were also filled in by this rising molten rock.

As we discovered in the rock cycle, when rock is exposed to great heat it melts. The minerals of this rock then mix with minerals from other melting rocks to create metamorphic rock. When the Pacific plate began to melt under the North American plate, the rising magma came into contact with the sedimentary rock. As the magma pushed upward, minerals from the melted rock were squeezed into cracks in the surface rock. Today many valuable mineral deposits are mined from the metamorphic rocks of the Western Cordillera.

Figure 3.25 on page 46 is a profile of the Western Cordillera from west to east. There are three main sections. The Coastal Mountains consist of two main ranges running from north to south. Vancouver Island is separated by a trough of water flowing from the Pacific Ocean. On the other side, the rounded mountains of the Coast Ranges were formed by hardened volcanic rock. Moving eastward, the Interior Plateau consists of rolling hills with deep, sheltered valleys. This area contains igneous and metamorphic rock and many valuable minerals. The Okanagan Valley lies some 1000 m lower than the surrounding plateau. It is a rich agricultural region.

The Eastern Mountains also contain two north-south ranges. These are divided by the deep Rocky Mountain Trench, approximately 900 m above sea level. To the west of the trench are the Columbia Mountains. To the east lie the famous Rocky Mountains. Formed almost 65 million years ago, the Rockies rise to heights of nearly 4000 m. These fold mountains have huge slabs of sedimentary rock that thrust

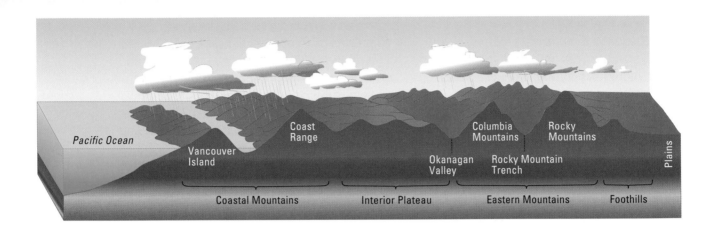

Figure 3.25
Profile of the
Western
Cordillera

eastward towards the Interior Plains. The Columbia Mountains are even older than the Rockies and much more folded. Although not as high, they rise to well over 3000 m. They contain more metamorphic rock than the Rockies, and therefore more valuable minerals. As a result, there is more mining activity in the Columbia Mountains than in the Rockies.

28 Using a minerals map, list the minerals mined in the Western Cordillera.

One of the oldest mountain systems in Canada is the **Appalachians**. Sediments from the Canadian Shield were deposited into the surrounding shallow seas. About 300 million years ago, at the end of the Palaeozoic era, the North American and European plates collided, causing these sediments to fold. As a result, the Appalachians are considered old fold mountains. Volcanoes and igneous intrusions were also created, resulting in many valuable minerals in the igneous, metamorphic, and sedimentary rocks.

Because of their age, the Appalachians can no longer be accurately described as mountains. Erosion has worn this range down so that elevations rarely exceed 500 m. Much of the landscape today consists of uplands with rolling, smooth hills and many glacial valleys. Some valleys are rich with deep glacial soils and are excellent for farming. Much of the coastline is highlighted by spectacular cliffs and sheltered harbours. In some places, the glaciers have cut deep into the valleys, creating **fiords** as the land plunges into the sea.

The **Innuitian Mountains** of the far north are the least known mountains in Canada. Like the Western Cordillera and the Appalachians, they are the result of the folding and faulting of the earth's crust during the Mesozoic era. Some of these mountains are spectacular, reaching heights of over 2500 m. They may also contain a wealth of minerals that are yet to be discovered.

29 Review the forces of erosion in Figure 3.17, then look at the photographs of the Appalachian landscape (Figure 3.8) and the Innuitian mountains (Figure 3.9) on page 29.

a) Which of Canada's mountain systems has experienced the most erosion? What evidence is there of this?

b) The Appalachians contain many valuable minerals. What evidence is there of this?

c) It is believed that the Innuitian Mountains contain valuable minerals. Why do geologists know so little about these mountains?

d) On an outline map, draw Canada's mountain rim. In a legend, describe each mountain region in a few sentences.

30 Collect magazine photographs showing different landforms in Canada. Write a caption identifying each photo and describing the landform.

31 Although the regions of Canada are unique, they all have the same geological beginning. Let's piece together the changes that took place over millions of years to create the distinctive Canadian landscape.

In Figure 3.26, seven statements are made about Canada's geological history. On a copy of this diagram, fill in each evidence box with the reasons why we know the statement is true.

Figure 3.26
Canada's geological history

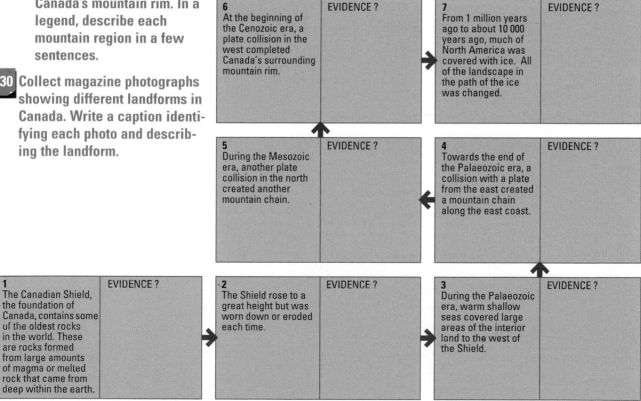

6 At the beginning of the Cenozoic era, a plate collision in the west completed Canada's surrounding mountain rim.
EVIDENCE ?

7 From 1 million years ago to about 10 000 years ago, much of North America was covered with ice. All of the landscape in the path of the ice was changed.
EVIDENCE ?

5 During the Mesozoic era, another plate collision in the north created another mountain chain.
EVIDENCE ?

4 Towards the end of the Palaeozoic era, a collision with a plate from the east created a mountain chain along the east coast.
EVIDENCE ?

1 The Canadian Shield, the foundation of Canada, contains some of the oldest rocks in the world. These are rocks formed from large amounts of magma or melted rock that came from deep within the earth.
EVIDENCE ?

2 The Shield rose to a great height but was worn down or eroded each time.
EVIDENCE ?

3 During the Palaeozoic era, warm shallow seas covered large areas of the interior land to the west of the Shield.
EVIDENCE ?

Figure 4.1
The Canadian winter landscape

Figure 4.2
Fog off the coast of Nova Scotia

Figure 4.3
A storm over the horizon of the Alberta prairies

We have seen how Canada's vast size has created a unique and diverse landscape. Similarly, Canadians across the country experience a wide range of weather patterns. In fact, as you read this chapter the weather outside your classroom is probably much different from the weather in another part of the country!

Weather is the combination of temperature, precipitation, cloud cover, and wind that we experience each day. **Climate** reflects the weather patterns in a particular region over the long term.

1 Look at a weather map of Canada in the newspaper. In a chart, record which parts of the country are the wettest, driest, warmest, and coldest on this date. Keep a record of this information on a weekly basis from now until you finish the Physical Diversity unit.

Factors that influence climate

Both weather and climate are the products of several influences: latitude, air masses, altitude, landforms, and nearness to water. Each of these factors has an impact on the two main components of weather and climate, temperature and precipitation.

Latitude

One of the most important influences on climate is latitude. How far north or south a region is from the Equator influences how cold or warm it is. The further away a place is from the Equator, the cooler it is. At 90°N or S latitude at the poles, it is very cold indeed!

2 a) Using an atlas, find the northernmost community and the southernmost community in Canada. Give their locations in degrees of latitude.
   b) How would you describe Canada's latitudinal position in the Northern Hemisphere?

The amount of heat energy, or **radiation**, that the earth receives depends on the angle of the sun's rays. Figure 4.4 shows equal widths of solar radiation striking the earth's surface at different latitudes. The radiation labelled *A* shows the sun's rays at higher latitudes like Canada. The radiation labelled *B* shows the sun's rays at low latitudes near the Equator.

3 Measure the width, in millimetres, along the earth's surface for each band of radiation. Which band of radiation covers more of the earth's surface?

The incoming solar rays in A and B represent the same amount of potential radiation. In A, however, the sun's rays are at a greater angle than in B. Therefore they cover a larger surface area of the earth. As a result, temperatures in A are cooler than in B because the same amount of radiation

Figure 4.4
Solar radiation on the earth's surface

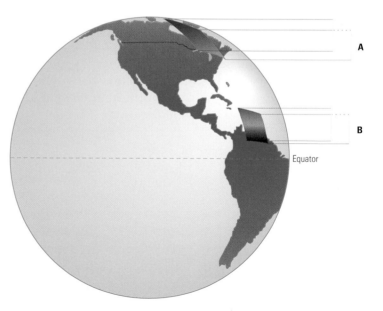

The sun's rays at the Equator are mostly perpendicular and therefore intense. Over Canada the solar band passes through more atmosphere where it is absorbed or reflected, and strikes the surface as an oblique ray. Because it is over a greater surface area, it is less concentrated.

must heat a larger area. This is why countries in northern latitudes, like Canada, have colder temperatures than places closer to the Equator.

How does latitude affect temperature at different times of the year? In Canada, we have four distinct seasons. The cold temperatures we experience in winter are in sharp contrast to the hot temperatures we enjoy in summer! What causes these seasonal changes?

The earth is tilted at an angle of 23.5°; this angle never changes. The North Pole always points to Polaris, the North Star. The earth rotates around the sun every 365.25 days. By June 21st, the Northern Hemisphere is tilted towards the sun. This means that the angle at which the sun's energy reaches places like Canada is less than at other times of the year. Therefore we receive our warmest temperatures during the summer.

By December 22nd the opposite occurs. Now the Northern Hemisphere is tilted away from the sun. The angle at which the sun's rays reach Canada is greater than at other times of the year. Therefore we receive our coldest temperatures in winter. (See Figure 4.5.)

Solar energy is also affected by the earth's **atmosphere**. When the sun's rays pass through the atmosphere, it absorbs up to 15 per cent of the radiation.

4 a) **When the Northern Hemisphere is tilted towards the sun, how does this affect:**
   i) **the angle at which the sun's radiation strikes Canada;**
   ii) **the temperatures Canada receives in summer?**
   b) **When the Northern Hemisphere is tilted away from the sun, how does this affect:**
   i) **the angle at which the sun's radiation strikes Canada;**
   ii) **the temperatures Canada receives in winter?**

5 **Refer to Figure 4.4. In which location, A or B, do the sun's rays pass through more atmosphere? How does this affect the temperature in each place?**

Heat energy is also reflected from the earth back into the atmosphere as light. This reflectivity is called **albedo**. In places where the albedo is high, most of the radiation is reflected as light; only a small amount is retained as heat. This means that

Figure 4.5
The earth's rotation around the sun

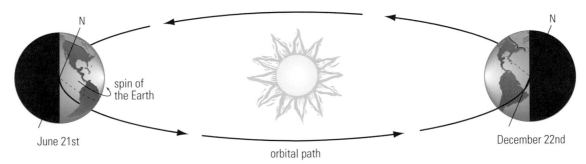

June 21st   orbital path   December 22nd

spin of the Earth

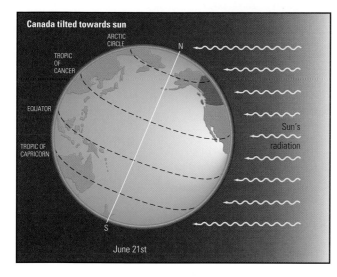

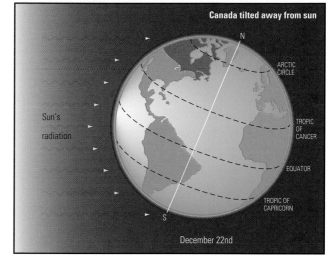

temperatures are lower in places with high albedo. Light, shiny, smooth surfaces have a higher albedo than dark, dull, rough surfaces. Snow-covered fields, therefore, have a greater loss of heat than dense forests.

6 **Which regions of Canada would have the highest albedo? Explain your answer.**

7 **Analyse the average monthly temperatures for July for each location in Figure 4.20 on pages 60–61. Use a grid similar to that in Figure 4.7 to construct a scattergraph that relates temperature to latitude. You will need to use an atlas gazetteer to find the latitudes.**

Air masses

The air in the earth's atmosphere is constantly on the move. Like a continuously running engine, air is pumped between the hot equatorial regions and the frigid polar regions. All of this air moves in huge vol-

umes called **air masses**.

The temperature and moisture content in any air mass is almost uniform throughout. Whether an air mass is warm or cold depends on where it originates. If it originates over the Gulf of Mexico near the tropics, for example, it is a warm air mass. Because it is formed over water, it also contains a lot of moisture.

Air masses are labelled according to

Figure 4.6
The position of Canada on June 21st and December 22nd

Figure 4.7
A scattergraph

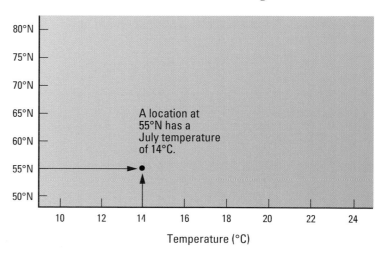

their temperature and moisture content. Each air mass has a two-letter label. The first letter indicates whether the air is wet or dry; the second letter indicates the temperature. The symbol cA, for example, indicates that the air mass is continental Arctic. This means it is very dry and very cold. Figure 4.8 indicates the different clas-

Figure 4.8
Air mass classifications

Moisture content

m = maritime (wet—formed over water)

c = continental (dry—formed over land)

Temperature

T = Tropical (hot—formed near the tropics)

P = Polar (cold—formed between 55° and 66°N)

A = Arctic (very cold—formed over the Arctic)

sifications for air masses.

8 Figure 4.9 lists some common air masses. Copy this table into your notebook. Complete the table by providing the meaning, origin, and description of each air

Figure 4.9
Air masses and their properties

LABEL	MEANING	ORIGIN	DESCRIPTION
mP	maritime, Polar	Formed over water between 55° and 60°N	Wet and cold
cA			
mT			
cT			

mass. **The first one has been done for you.**

Generally air masses originate in the south during the summer and in the north during the winter. In summer, warm, moist air from the Gulf of Mexico pushes northward into much of Canada. Most regions experience warm summer temperatures. Even Canada's Arctic region enjoys two months of relatively warm weather.

In winter, air masses from Canada's far north dominate. This cold, dry air pushes southward across much of Canada. The air masses that affect Canada in winter and summer are shown in Figure 4.10.

Air masses are influenced by the **jet stream**. This river of air moves from west to east at speeds between 300 and 400 km/h, at an altitude between 8000 and 15 000 m. The normal path of the jet stream is shown in Figure 4.11 on page 54. But it often moves farther north in summer and farther south in winter. In summer, the jet stream may allow hot and humid conditions from the Gulf region into Canada's interior. In winter, a more southerly flow of the jet stream may allow frigid Arctic air deep into the southern United States.

The direction in which air flows is generally from west to east. Direction is used to describe a wind. Most of the winds in Canada are called **westerlies** because they flow from the west.

The leading edge of an air mass is called a **front**. Where the fronts of two or more air masses meet, a battleground in the sky is created. This is because air masses do not mix. A mass of warmer (and lighter) air is always forced to rise above a mass of colder (and heavier) air. As the air

Winter Air Masses

----- Polar jet stream

▶ ▶ ▶ Primary storm tracks

Continental Arctic
- very cold -25 to -50°C
- dry

Maritime Arctic
- clouds, frequent showers or flurries
- visibility good except in showers

Maritime Polar
- milder than Arctic air

Pacific Maritime Tropical
- light winds, cooler than Atlantic air
- comes to North America from west or northwest

Atlantic Maritime Tropical
- comes to North America from south or southeast
- warm and humid

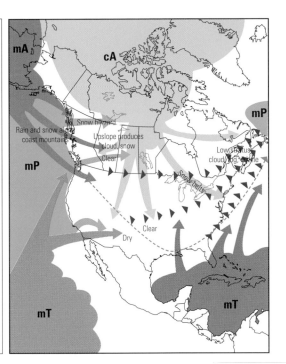

Summer Air Masses

----- Polar jet stream

▶ ▶ ▶ Primary storm tracks

Pacific Maritime Tropical
- warm and humid

Atlantic Maritime Tropical
- hot and humid
- frequent thunderstorms

Maritime Arctic
- continental air modified by open seas, lakes and swamps

Maritime Polar
- warmer than Maritime Arctic air

Continental Tropical
- hot, dry

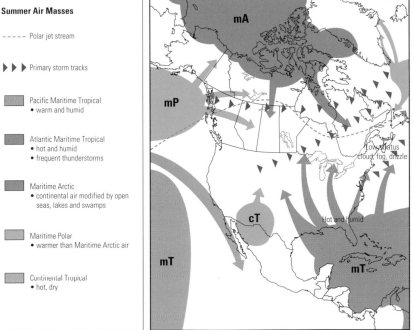

Figure 4.10
Air masses that affect Canada

Figure 4.11
Typical path
of the jet
stream in
North America
at an altitude
between 8000
and 15 000 m

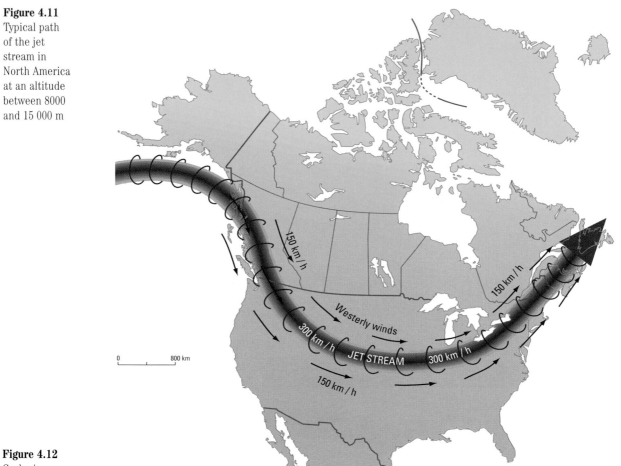

Figure 4.12
Cyclonic
precipitation

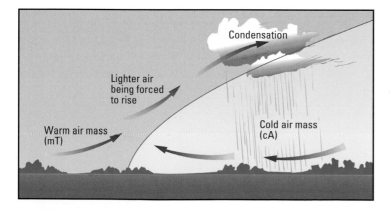

rises, it begins to cool. But cold air does not hold moisture as well as warm air. As a result, the water vapour in the cooling air condenses into droplets. These droplets join together to form clouds. Eventually they become too heavy for the air to hold and they fall to the ground in the form of rain or snow. This is called **cyclonic** or **frontal precipitation**. (See Figure 4.12.)

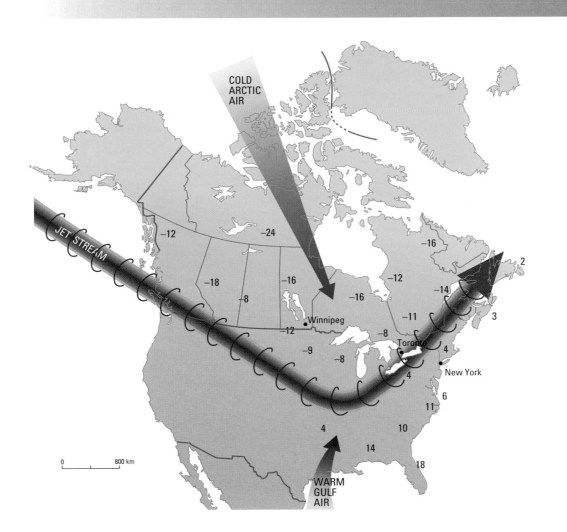

In Canada, cyclonic precipitation is most common in the southern parts of Ontario and Quebec. Rain and snow here is usually caused by warm, moist southern air meeting cold, dry northern air.

9   Figure 4.13 shows a typical path of the jet stream in February.

a) On an outline map of Canada, label Winnipeg, Toronto, and New York.
b) Draw a line between Winnipeg and New York. Indicate the area where the cold Arctic air and the warm Gulf air meet. Label this area the *front*.
c) On your map, indicate the weather conditions that would exist in each of the three cities.

Figure 4.14
Temperatures
across Canada
(°C)

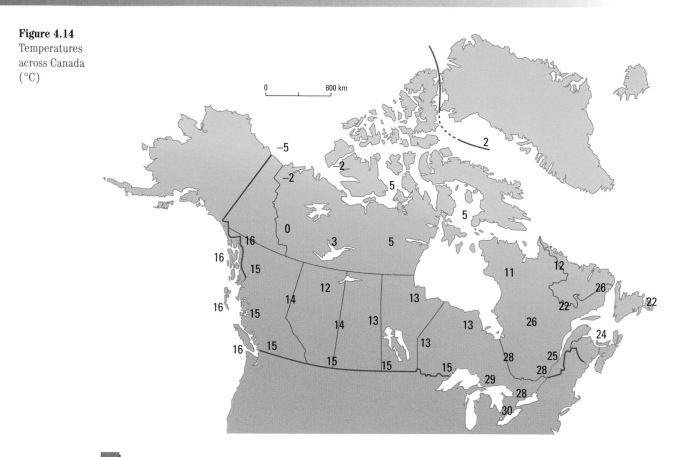

10 Figure 4.14 shows temperatures across Canada.

a) What time of year does this map represent?

b) Place a sheet of tracing paper over the map. Based on the temperatures, draw a line around each air mass you can identify. Label the air masses according to their likely place of origin, for example, cT.

c) Locate the following cities in an atlas. Based on Figure 4.14, estimate the temperature for each centre: St. John's; Toronto; Winnipeg; Yellowknife; Victoria.

d) Assume that the air masses are moving from west to east at 400 km per day. Using the map scale, predict the weather conditions for Montreal for the next three days. Include temperature and areas of rainfall along the front.

11 **Figure 4.15 represents two air masses flowing in opposite directions. Copy this figure into your notebook. Draw a line to show where the two fronts meet.**

Height (m)							
400	17	17	17	17	17	17	17
300	18	18	18	18	18	18	13
	DIRECTION OF FLOW						
200	19	19	19	19	19	14	14
100	20	20	20	20	15	15	15
					DIRECTION OF FLOW		
	21	21	21	16	16	16	16

Figure 4.15
Air masses flowing in opposite directions

12 a) **On an outline map of Canada, create a colourful weather map for broadcast on the television news. Use information and symbols from newspaper weather maps to help you.**
    b) **Prepare a script of the weather forecast for broadcast on the television news.**
    c) **Videotape your weather broadcast.**

Altitude

Altitude, or elevation, affects both temperature and precipitation. You might think that the temperature at the top of a mountain would be warmer because it is closer to the sun. In fact, the opposite is true. Temperature decreases as altitude increases. This is because when the sun's rays pass through the atmosphere, they have little effect on air temperature. The earth absorbs the heat energy. It then releases it into the air. So the farther up the air is from the ground, the cooler it is. Normally the temperature of dry air decreases 1°C for every 100 m of altitude.

If the air is saturated with water vapour and **condensation** forms, however, it retains more warmth. This is because heat is released during condensation. This air cools down at a lower rate of 0.6°C for every 100 m of altitude.

13 a) **You have decided to climb Bald Mountain, shown in Figure 4.16. If it is 20°C at sea level, what will the temperature be at i) Scenic View and ii) Ram's Rock?**
    b) **Calculate the temperature at the peak of Bald Mountain. Remember that condensation has taken place at Ram's Rock. The air is now wet from Ram's Rock to the peak.**

14 **Use an atlas to determine the altitude of the following mountain peaks in Western Canada. Assume that the temperature at sea level is 25°C. Calculate the temperature at: i) Mt. Waddington; ii) Mt. Ratz; iii) Mt. Logan. Assume the air is dry at each mountain peak.**

Just as air becomes cooler as it rises, it warms up as it falls. The rate of heating is usually 1°C per 100 m—the inverse of the rate of cooling. Sometimes, however, descending air heats up much more quickly. A well known example of this in Canada sometimes occurs on the eastern side of the Rocky Mountains. As the cold mountain air descends the eastern foothills towards Calgary, the temperature may rise dramatically—sometimes by as much as 20°C! Called a **chinook**, this warm wind brings welcome relief to cold winter days.

Figure 4.16
Climbing Bald
Mountain

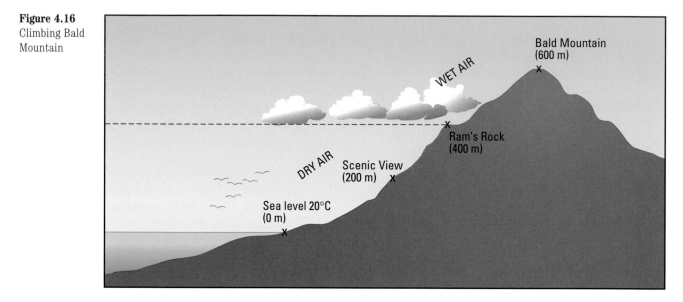

15 Figure 4.17 shows a profile of the Western Cordillera from Vancouver to Calgary. A represents Vancouver, where the temperature is 25°C. Calculate the temperature at each of these points. Assume the air is totally dry.

Landforms

Figure 4.17
Profile of the
Western
Cordillera

Landforms also affect patterns of precipitation. We have seen that most air moves across Canada from west to east. The large barrier of the Western Cordillera along the west coast produces some of the highest amounts of precipitation in Canada. As the wet Polar Pacific air masses reach these mountains, the air is forced to rise. This causes **orographic** or **relief precipitation** on the windward side of the mountains. (See Figure 4.18.)

Once the air passes over the top of the land mass it becomes quite dry. The leeward side of mountains is known as a **rain shadow**, or dry area.

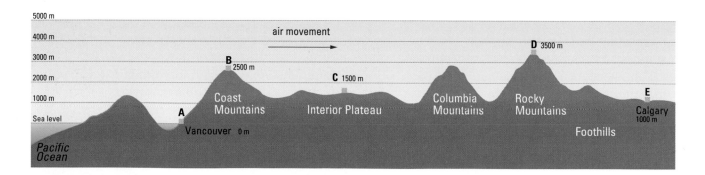

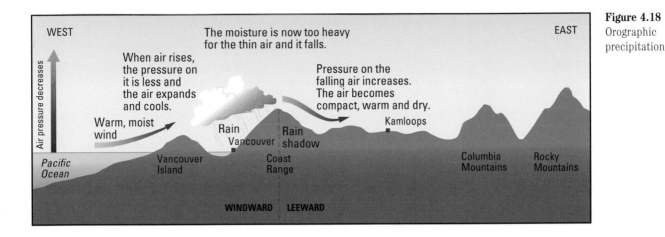

Figure 4.18
Orographic
precipitation

WEST

The moisture is now too heavy
for the thin air and it falls.

EAST

Air pressure decreases

When air rises,
the pressure on
it is less and
the air expands
and cools.

Pressure on the
falling air increases.
The air becomes
compact, warm and dry.

Warm, moist
wind

Kamloops

Pacific
Ocean

Rain
Vancouver

Rain
shadow

Vancouver
Island

Coast
Range

Columbia
Mountains

Rocky
Mountains

WINDWARD   LEEWARD

16 **Explain the cause of orographic precipitation.**

17 **Vancouver is located on BC's west coast, while Kamloops is situated in the province's interior. Calculate the precipitation totals for Vancouver and Kamloops in Figure 4.20. Explain the difference in precipitation each receives based on its location.**

Nearness to water

Large bodies of water such as oceans and lakes also influence climate. Water heats up and cools down much more slowly than land. In summer, a body of water remains cooler than the nearby land. As the water slowly warms, it stores heat. By the time winter arrives, the land has cooled down. The ocean, however, has retained its heat, so it is now warmer than the land.

The climate of Canada's west coast is strongly influenced by the Pacific Ocean. During the summer, coastal regions remain cooler than inland regions because of the colder ocean waters. In winter, however, the coast is warmer because of the heat retained in the water. This is called a **moderated temperature**. Figure 4.21 on page 61 shows why coastal areas have milder winters and cooler summers than inland areas do.

Figure 4.19
Spring flowers
blossom early
in coastal
locations like
Victoria

Figure 4.20
Climate
statistics

BRANDON, MB	J	F	M	A	M	J	J	A	S	O	N	D
Temp. (°C)	−19	−15	−8	3	11	16	19	18	12	6	−5	−14
Prec. (mm)	21	20	24	37	50	81	69	70	50	23	20	20

CHURCHILL, MB	J	F	M	A	M	J	J	A	S	O	N	D
Temp. (°C)	−28	−26	−20	−10	−2	6	12	11	5	−2	−12	−22
Prec. (mm)	15	13	18	23	32	44	46	58	51	40	39	21

COPPERMINE, NT	J	F	M	A	M	J	J	A	S	O	N	D
Temp. (°C)	−29	−30	−26	−17	−6	3	9	8	3	−7	−20	−26
Prec. (mm)	12	8	13	10	12	20	34	44	28	26	15	11

FORT GEORGE, PQ	J	F	M	A	M	J	J	A	S	O	N	D
Temp. (°C)	−23	−22	−16	−6	2	9	12	11	8	2	−5	−16
Prec. (mm)	28	21	30	24	37	52	86	73	78	76	68	54

FORT McMURRAY, AB	J	F	M	A	M	J	J	A	S	O	N	D
Temp. (°C)	−22	−15	−9	2	10	14	16	15	9	3	−8	−17
Prec. (mm)	23	19	21	21	36	64	75	77	59	28	25	25

FORT VERMILION, AB	J	F	M	A	M	J	J	A	S	O	N	D
Temp. (°C)	−24	−18	−11	2	10	14	17	15	9	2	−10	−20
Prec. (mm)	23	18	21	16	32	51	66	53	35	26	22	21

HALIFAX, NS	J	F	M	A	M	J	J	A	S	O	N	D
Temp. (°C)	−3	−4	0	5	10	14	19	19	16	10	5	−1
Prec. (mm)	141	119	113	112	109	94	94	96	117	120	143	126

KAMLOOPS, BC	J	F	M	A	M	J	J	A	S	O	N	D
Temp. (°C)	−6	−3	3	10	14	18	21	19	15	8	2	−2
Prec. (mm)	36	22	9	6	15	40	21	22	18	16	19	24

KAPUSKASING, ON	J	F	M	A	M	J	J	A	S	O	N	D
Temp. (°C)	−18	−15	−9	0	8	14	17	16	11	4	−5	−14
Prec. (mm)	55	45	54	53	80	95	85	87	90	71	83	60

LETHBRIDGE, AB	J	F	M	A	M	J	J	A	S	O	N	D
Temp. (°C)	−10	−5	−2	5	11	15	19	18	13	8	−1	−6
Prec. (mm)	24	19	24	43	51	78	44	47	37	18	17	22

OTTAWA, ON	J	F	M	A	M	J	J	A	S	O	N	D
Temp. (°C)	−11	−10	−3	6	13	18	21	19	15	9	2	−8
Prec. (mm)	55	55	59	65	68	80	85	85	80	68	74	73

PRINCE GEORGE, BC	J	F	M	A	M	J	J	A	S	O	N	D
Temp. (°C)	−12	−6	−2	4	9	13	15	14	10	5	−3	−8
Prec. (mm)	57	39	37	27	47	67	60	68	59	59	51	57

REGINA, SK	J	F	M	A	M	J	J	A	S	O	N	D
Temp. (°C)	−17	−15	−8	3	11	15	19	18	12	5	−5	−12
Prec. (mm)	19	17	21	21	40	83	55	49	34	18	20	17

SASKATOON, SK	J	F	M	A	M	J	J	A	S	O	N	D
Temp. (°C)	−19	−15	−9	3	11	16	19	17	11	5	−6	−14
Prec. (mm)	18	16	18	21	40	59	54	38	32	17	15	20

ST. JOHN'S, NF	J	F	M	A	M	J	J	A	S	O	N	D
Temp. (°C)	−4	−5	−3	1	6	10	15	15	12	7	3	−2
Prec. (mm)	153	163	135	121	99	95	89	102	120	138	163	174

TORONTO, ON	J	F	M	A	M	J	J	A	S	O	N	D
Temp. (°C)	−7	−6	1	6	12	18	21	20	16	9	3	−4
Prec. (mm)	50	46	61	70	66	67	71	77	64	62	63	65

VANCOUVER, BC	J	F	M	A	M	J	J	A	S	O	N	D
Temp. (°C)	3	5	6	9	12	15	17	17	14	10	6	4
Prec. (mm)	154	115	101	60	52	45	32	41	67	114	150	182

WHITEHORSE, YK	J	F	M	A	M	J	J	A	S	O	N	D
Temp. (°C)	−18	−14	−8	0	8	13	14	12	8	1	−8	−15
Prec. (mm)	18	14	15	11	13	27	35	37	25	19	23	20

WINNIPEG, MB	J	F	M	A	M	J	J	A	S	O	N	D
Temp. (°C)	−18	−16	−8	3	11	17	20	19	13	6	−5	−13
Prec. (mm)	26	21	27	30	50	81	69	70	55	37	29	22

Coastal regions have a **maritime climate**. The **temperature range** between the highest average temperature and the lowest average temperature is generally lower than in **continental climates**. Continental climates are usually found in the interior of large land masses. They are generally a long distance from large bodies of water. Continental climates experience hot summers and cold winters. This results in a larger temperature range than maritime climates.

Bodies of water also influence breezes. During the day, breezes flow from water to land. At night breezes flow from land to water.

Figure 4.21
Land and sea breezes

LOCATION	LATITUDE	WARMEST TEMP.	COLDEST TEMP.	TEMP. RANGE	CONTINENTAL OR MARITIME	EXPLANATION
Vancouver						
Winnipeg						
St. John's						
Churchill						

Figure 4.22
Weather chart, selected centres

Being near bodies of water may also affect the amount of precipitation a location receives as well as the time of year in which it occurs. Most of the water vapour that condenses to form precipitation has evaporated from oceans and large lakes. Places close to these bodies of water tend to receive more precipitation.

Figure 4.23
A convectional thunderstorm over the Alberta foothills

18 Copy the chart in Figure 4.22 into your notebook. Using the climate information in Figure 4.20 and an atlas map of Canada, complete the chart.

19 Describe the difference in temperature range for the locations in Figure 4.22 that are near large bodies of water and those that are inland.

20 Like Winnipeg, Churchill, Manitoba, is centrally located within Canada's land mass. It has very cold winters, but only mild summers. Explain why.

21 Consider the monthly precipitation totals for Vancouver and Winnipeg in Figure 4.20. Describe the major differences between the two locations.

Why are there such differences in precipitation? For most of the year, Vancouver's winds are the result of a flow of cold, wet Polar air from the northwest. As these winds hit the Cordilleran mountain range, orographic precipitation is produced. During the summer, however, the dominant air masses flow from the south and southeast. These air masses produce far less precipitation. The windward and leeward sides of the mountains are reversed: now Vancouver is in the rain shadow.

Winnipeg lies in the middle of the continent well away from any large body of water. In winter, it lies in the direct path of the very dry, very cold Arctic air masses. As a result, its monthly precipitation is limited. What little precipitation there is falls as snow. The temperatures are so cold that the snow remains throughout the winter.

In summer, Winnipeg receives warm, maritime tropical air from the Gulf of Mexico. Being in the centre of the continent, Winnipeg's summer temperatures are quite warm. As a result, Winnipeg receives **convectional precipitation** at this time of year. (See Figure 4.24.)

Convectional precipitation often occurs suddenly on hot summer afternoons and evenings. The moisture-laden air absorbs so much heat from the earth's surface that it is quickly swept up to great heights. As it rises, the air quickly cools. This results in a heavy downpour of rain.

Sometimes drops of rain are tossed upward into cooler air, where they freeze into ice particles. These particles may be tossed upward over and over again. Each time a new layer of ice forms. Eventually the ice particles become too heavy for the air to carry. They fall out of the sky as **hailstones**. In central Canada, summer hailstorms are quite common. Why do you think hailstorms are a concern to farmers?

Hurricanes are massive storms that produce extremely heavy winds and rain. To be classified as a hurricane, a storm must have wind speeds of at least 120 km/h. The main wind system in a hurricane extends out of a calm central eye for some 30 to 40 km. Hurricanes usually move at 15 to 25 km/h.

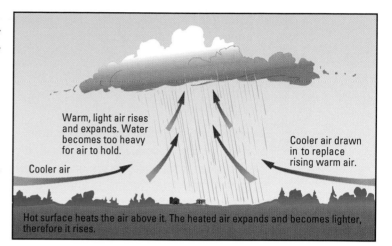

Warm, light air rises and expands. Water becomes too heavy for air to hold.

Cooler air

Cooler air drawn in to replace rising warm air.

Hot surface heats the air above it. The heated air expands and becomes lighter, therefore it rises.

Figure 4.24 Convectional precipitation

On average, only six hurricanes begin over the Gulf of Mexico each year; only two of these bring storm conditions to Canada, mostly to the Atlantic region. Figure 4.25 shows a hurricane drifting northeastward up the Atlantic coast.

Figure 4.25 The path of a hurricane

22 a) Locate the absolute centre of the hurricane in the satellite image in Figure 4.25. What tells us that the hurricane is moving in a northeast direction?
   b) What advantages do satellite images provide in the tracking of hurricanes?

23 Research the most damaging hurricanes experienced in Canada. Outline your findings in chart form. Include the name of the hurricane, the date, the areas affected, and the damage that resulted.

Like hurricanes, **tornadoes** are violent storms. While hurricanes sweep across large areas, however, tornadoes are more localized. Their destruction is confined to narrow bands where the tornado touches down. These powerful funnel clouds speed across the landscape at 50 to 100 km/h. When they touch down, they create a vacuum into which everything and anything can be caught up—from bicycles to mobile homes!

In Canada, tornadoes most commonly occur in the spring and summer following a period of intense heat. When hot, moist air from the Gulf of Mexico clashes with a cold front from the north, these devastating funnels of air can be created.

24 In Canada, tornadoes most commonly occur in the central provinces of Alberta, Saskatchewan, Manitoba, and Ontario. Explain why this is so.

Climate analysis

One way to gain a perspective on climatic differences across Canada is to study the climate data for different locations. This information is often provided in a **climagraph**. A climagraph is really two separate graphs rolled into one. A line graph shows monthly temperatures; a bar graph shows monthly precipitation. It will be easier to understand these graphs and analyse their information if we construct one of our own. Our climagraph will be for Saskatoon, Saskatchewan.

25 Start by drawing the frame for the graph.
   a) Draw a rectangle 20 cm high and 12 cm wide. Divide the width of the rectangle into twelve columns of 1 cm each. The columns represent the months of the year. Print the initial of the month across the top of each column, starting with J for January.
   b) The vertical line on the left of the graph represents temperature. From the base line, measure 10 cm up this line. Draw a horizontal line at this point. This represents the freezing point. Label this line 0°C.
   c) Each centimetre above the 0°C line represents an increase in temperature of 5°C. Each centimetre below the line represents a decrease in temperature of 5°C. Mark these intervals onto your graph. Be sure to include the minus sign (-5°C) for temperatures below 0°C.
   d) Draw a horizontal green line across the graph at the 5.6°C point. Label this line the **growing season**. This is the temperature at which most common grasses start to grow.

26 a) Using the climate data for Saskatoon in Figure 4.20, plot the temperature for each month.

b) In red, join the dots together to form a continuous line. You have now completed a **line graph** showing monthly temperatures for Saskatoon.

c) Shade the area between the temperature line and the growing season line in green. Shade only those areas *above* the growing season line. Can you explain why?

27 a) The vertical line on the right of the graph represents precipitation. The base line represents 0 mm. Each centimetre above the base line represents an increase of 10 mm. Mark these intervals along the vertical line.

b) Using the monthly precipitation figures for Saskatoon in Figure 4.20, plot the data on your graph. To do this, draw a straight line across the column for each month at the appropriate measurement. Remember that 1 cm of rain equals 10 cm of snow.

c) Shade in blue those columns with an average monthly temperature above freezing. This indicates that most precipitation was in the form of rain. Leave the columns with an average monthly temperature below freezing white. This indicates that most precipitation was in the form of snow. You have now completed a **bar graph** showing monthly precipitation for Saskatoon.

Now that we have prepared a climagraph for Saskatoon, we need to analyse the data.

28 a) What are the annual maximum and minimum temperatures? In which months do they occur?

b) What is the annual temperature range for Saskatoon?

c) How many months are there in Saskatoon's growing season?

d) For how many months are the temperatures below freezing?

29 a) What is the total annual precipitation? Write this figure at the bottom of your graph.

b) Does the precipitation fall evenly throughout the year or are there seasonal differences?

c) In which months does precipitation fall mainly in the form of snow?

d) Multiply the total for each of these months by ten to arrive at the approximate total annual snowfall in Saskatoon. Why is this figure only an approximation?

Now let's consider how the factors that influence climate affect the climate of Saskatoon.

Temperature

Latitude: Saskatoon has a latitude of 52°N. This is well into the northernmost portion of the globe. This produces extreme angles for incoming sun rays. There is also a high albedo in winter. Generally winter temperatures are quite cold; summer temperatures are warm.

Air masses: In winter, cold, dry air masses flow out of the Arctic. In summer, warm, moist air flows up from the south. Most air generally flows from west to east.

Landforms: Saskatoon is situated at an altitude of 501 m above sea level. This has only a limited effect on temperature.

Nearness to water: Saskatoon is located a fair distance from any large bodies of water and has a continental climate.

Precipitation

Latitude: Because of its northerly position and long winters, Saskatoon has five months in which most precipitation falls in the form of snow.

Air masses: Winter air masses are generally dry, producing small amounts of precipitation. Southerly flows in the summer contain more moisture, contributing to higher amounts of rainfall.

Landforms: The Western Cordillera causes Saskatoon to be in a rain shadow. Therefore the climate is generally dry.

Nearness to water: Situated near the centre of the continent, the land heats up quickly in summer. Convectional rainfall accounts for much of the summer precipitation. Saskatoon is near the path of the jet stream and so it also experiences cyclonic precipitation.

30 Copy Figure 4.26 into your notebook. Complete the chart using the information about the factors that influence Saskatoon's climate.

31 a) Form a group of five students. Each student must select a different location from the following list: Vancouver, BC; Coppermine, NT; Churchill, MB; Ottawa, ON; Halifax, NS.

b) Using the climate data in Figure 4.20, complete a climagraph for your location. Be sure to establish a standard format and colours within your group.

c) Once your climagraph is complete, prepare a climagraph analysis of your location using the questions provided for Saskatoon.

d) Working as a group, plot the five locations on a large outline map of Canada. In point form, describe the climate of your location at the appropriate place on the map.

Canada has several climate regions. Climate changes from one region to another are not sudden or distinct. Rather, changes in temperature and precipitation occur gradually.

Figure 4.26
Climate control analysis

LOCATION: _____		
CONTROLS	TEMPERATURE	PRECIPITATION
Latitude		
Air masses		
Land masses		
Nearness to water		

32 a) Working with your group from the previous activity, discuss where you think the boundaries of Canada's climate regions are. Draw these boundaries on your outline map. Give each region an appropriate name.

b) Compare your map with an atlas map of Canada's climate regions. How does your group's map compare with the map in the atlas?

33 a) Obtain climate statistics for your community or for a larger community in your region. Draw a climagraph using these statistics.

b) Analyse your climagraph using the questions provided for Saskatoon.

c) Complete a climate analysis for your community.

d) In which climate region is your community located?

e) State six ways in which the climate of your area influences human activity. Consider both business and recreational activities.

34 Examine a travel brochure for a recreational site in Canada. Describe how climate is promoted as a positive feature of the area.

35 Imagine you have the opportunity to move to another location in Canada *of your choice*. Based on climate, which location has the greatest appeal to you? Why?

The characteristics of the Canadian climate are typical of most northern countries. While summers are warm, and often quite hot, they are all too short. Winters, on the other hand, are long, and can be extremely cold. Northern climates like Canada's are called **nordic**.

1 a) **Using climagraphs and climate maps in an atlas, describe the climates of the following places: northern Norway; Iceland; northern Russia.**

   b) **How similar are these climates to the predominant climate regions of Canada?**

The natural impacts of climate

How does Canada's nordic climate affect the natural landscape? Climate has a significant impact on soil. It determines how wet or dry a soil is, which in turn affects the fertility of the soil. Together, climate and soil determine the **natural vegetation** of a region. Natural vegetation is the plant life that grows without interference from people. Different vegetation requires a different climate and different soil to grow well. Canada's varied climate means that soils and natural vegetation vary from coast to coast.

Figure 5.1
Winter snow-storms: a fact of life for Canadians

Soil

Soil consists of four main parts: minerals, humus, air, and water. **Minerals** are created when rock is broken down over long periods of time. Eventually the rock particles form sand, silt, or clay. These soils contain **nutrients** needed by plants to grow. **Humus** is the decayed remains of plant and animal life. Bacteria in the soil breaks down this organic matter, releasing nutrients into the soil. Air is a necessary element of soil because plants need air around their roots to grow. They also need water, not only for growth but for the processes of **weathering**. Weathering is the means by which rocks and other matter are broken down over time.

How does climate affect the type of soil found in a region? In regions where there is a great deal of precipitation, **leaching** occurs. As water moves down through the soil, it carries away the soil's nutrients. The soil that remains is unable to support plant life. The opposite occurs in regions with very dry climates. Moisture from the soil is drawn upward through **capillary action**. The water carries with it dissolved salts and minerals. These are then left behind in the **topsoil** as the water evaporates. Sometimes this creates a thick topsoil rich in minerals. In extreme conditions, however, hardened mineral deposits can be harmful to plant growth. The best soils are those with enough moisture—but not too much! They are rich in humus and living creatures such as earthworms, which create air spaces as they tunnel through the ground.

Soil forms layers called **horizons**. The A horizon, or topsoil, is rich in organic matter. It is usually dark brown or black in colour. The B horizon, or subsoil, is lighter in colour. It is a combination of the organic matter of the A horizon and the minerals of the C horizon that lies beneath it. The C horizon contains minerals from the bedrock and glacial deposits. It is often called the **parent material**. Figure 5.2 shows the three horizons in a simple **soil profile**.

2 Copy Figure 5.2 into your notebook. Label the characteristics of each horizon.

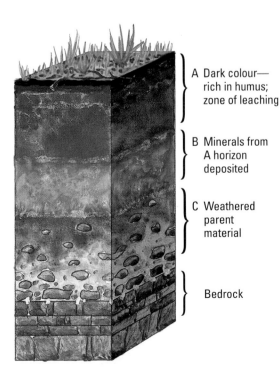

A Dark colour—
rich in humus;
zone of leaching

B Minerals from
A horizon
deposited

C Weathered
parent
material

Bedrock

Figure 5.2
A simple soil profile

Soil and natural vegetation regions

Figure 5.3
Soils and natural vegetation of Canada

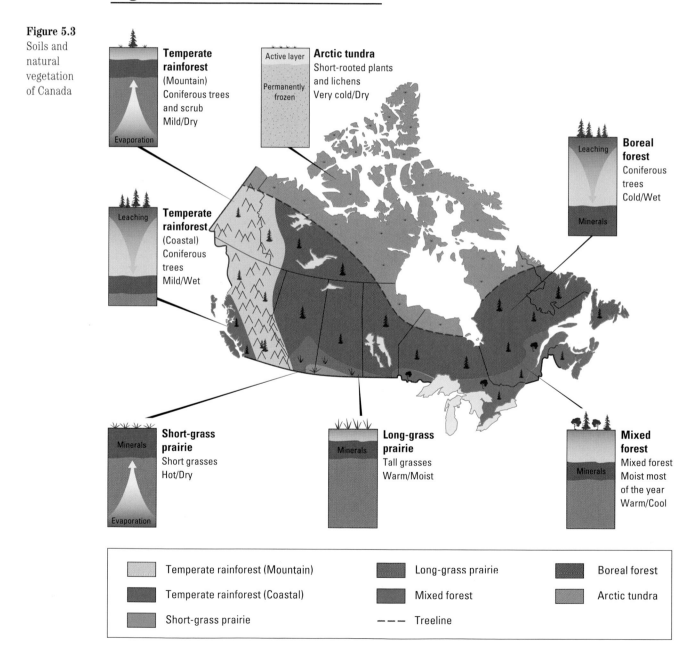

Temperate rainforest
(Mountain)
Coniferous trees and scrub
Mild/Dry
Evaporation

Arctic tundra
Short-rooted plants and lichens
Very cold/Dry
Active layer
Permanently frozen

Boreal forest
Coniferous trees
Cold/Wet
Leaching
Minerals

Temperate rainforest
(Coastal)
Coniferous trees
Mild/Wet
Leaching

Short-grass prairie
Short grasses
Hot/Dry
Minerals
Evaporation

Long-grass prairie
Tall grasses
Warm/Moist
Minerals

Mixed forest
Mixed forest
Moist most of the year
Warm/Cool
Minerals

Temperate rainforest (Mountain)
Temperate rainforest (Coastal)
Short-grass prairie
Long-grass prairie
Mixed forest
– – – Treeline
Boreal forest
Arctic tundra

Arctic tundra

The Arctic tundra region is found in the northernmost parts of Canada. This is the land of **permafrost**. Most of the ground is permanently frozen because of the extreme cold. Only the top metre of ground, called the **active layer**, thaws during the short summer. This allows for a brief growing season that lasts for six to eight weeks. (See the statistics for Coppermine, NT, on page 60.)

Little humus is found in this shallow soil. Only short-rooted plants, lichens, and bushes grow here. Most of the region is above the **treeline**, so there is little tree growth. The only place where trees are found is in sheltered valleys. Here the soil is a little deeper and the climate is less severe.

Boreal forest

The Boreal forest region is generally cold and wet. (See the statistics for Fort McMurray, AB, on page 60.) Although precipitation is not heavy, temperatures remain cool so there is little evaporation. Leaching washes the minerals deep into the soil horizon. Only coniferous trees, or evergreens, with their long roots are able to harvest the soil's nutrients. The region contains little humus. As a result, the soil is greyish in colour—hence the name podzol, meaning ash grey. Podzol soil is not very fertile. It contains lots of acids from the decaying needles of the coniferous trees.

The Boreal forest is the largest vegetation zone in Canada. The great forests of coniferous trees maintain their needle cover throughout the year. The needles

Figure 5.4
Autumn tundra landscape in the Pelly Mountains, Yukon

Figure 5.5
The boreal forest in the Western Cordillera

Figure 5.6
The temperate rainforest of British Columbia

Temperate rainforest

The climate of the temperate rainforest is mild throughout the year, with abundant precipitation. (See the statistics for Vancouver, BC, on page 61.) In the coastal areas, the climate is ideal for the growth of dense coniferous forests of red cedars, sitka spruce, and the famous giant Douglas fir. Many of the forested mountains contain old growth forests, heralded by many as valuable ecosystems to be protected from resource development.

The topsoil of the temperate rainforest in coastal regions is deep grey podzol. This soil supports extensive vegetation. In the mountainous interior, however, the climate is more extreme. The valleys are dry, and the soil here is similar to that found in the prairie grasslands. Irrigation is often necessary for agriculture. On the mountain slopes, the soil is thin and supports less vegetation than the valleys. (See the statistics for Kamloops, BC, on page 60.) Vegetation changes as altitude increases. The mix of coniferous and deciduous trees at lower elevations gradually gives way to fewer and smaller trees. The treeline marks the transition to sparse scrub vegetation. Near the snow-capped mountain peaks, the vegetation is similar to that of the Arctic tundra.

protect the trees from the harsh cold and lack of moisture during the long winter. In addition to the spruce, pine, and larch conifers, hardy deciduous trees, such as white birch, balsam poplar, and aspen, are found in the southern part of the region.

Short-grass prairie

The growing season in the short-grass prairie is warm and dry. (See the statistics for Lethbridge, AB, on page 60.) Minerals in the soil are drawn upward to the topsoil. Only short grasses and vegetation with short roots, such as cactus and sagebrush, grow here. Tree growth is limited to river valleys where there is more groundwater. As a result of the sparse vegetation, the amount of humus in the soil is limited. This results in a light brown soil, appropriately called brown grassland.

Long-grass prairie

The long-grass prairie is ideal for agriculture. Summers are warm, with reasonable amounts of rainfall. (See the statistics for Brandon, MB, on page 60.) The warmth and gentle rains keep the minerals in the soil, but not too far from the surface. Deep-rooted, tall grasses grow well in this region. The abundance of decaying organic matter makes the soil rich in humus. This dark brown or black grassland soil is called chernozem, which is Russian for "black earth." This is the region of Canada's world famous grain farms.

Mixed forest

The climate of the mixed forest is warm in summer and cool in winter. Precipitation is even all year round. (See the statistics for Toronto, ON, on page 61.) In southwestern Ontario, summer temperatures are a little warmer, and broadleaf deciduous trees like giant maples, oaks, and beech flourish. To the east and north there is a mixture of deciduous and coniferous trees. Today many of these forests have been cleared for urban development or agriculture.

Throughout this region, the topsoil is quite deep, and it is rich with minerals and

Figure 5.7
Short-grass prairie in Alberta

Figure 5.8
Long-grass prairie in Saskatchewan

Figure 5.9
Mixed forest
in Muskoka,
Ontario

c) Label one side of the line "Climate" and the other side "Natural Vegetation."

d) Using symbols or labels, indicate the different climates and natural vegetation found between Coppermine and Lethbridge.

e) Each degree of latitude is 111 km. Calculate the actual distance from north to south for each climate and natural vegetation region.

humus. This produces a brown or grey-brown podzol soil. With the addition of fertilizers, the soil is excellent for crops.

3   Copy Figure 5.10 into your notebook. Briefly describe each soil/natural vegetation region. Use the information provided in Figure 5.3 and the climate, soils, and natural vegetation maps in an atlas to help you. The Arctic tundra region has been completed for you.

4   a) In your notebook, draw a vertical line to represent a cross-section of Canada from Coppermine, NT, to Lethbridge, AB.

b) Mark every 5° of latitude along the line. The intervals should be drawn to scale, using an atlas map of Canada for reference.

The human impacts of climate

We have seen the impact that Canada's nordic climate has on soils and vegetation. It also has an impact on people. For example, cold climates limit the areas where people choose to live. Most Canadians live within 300 km of our southern border. Why do you think this is so?

Comfort temperature

Most people enjoy temperatures that are comfortable. In Canada, the **comfort temperature** is considered to be 20°C. When the temperature is below this we feel chilly. Then we either dress warmly or turn up the heat. When the temperature is above 20°C, we feel hot. We wear light clothing and turn

Figure 5.10
Soils and
vegetation
chart

REGION	CLIMATE	SUMMER/WINTER	SOILS	NATURAL VEGETATION
Arctic tundra	Cold Arctic	Very cold, dry winter; short, warm, dry summer	Shallow, infertile	Short-rooted plants, lichens, mosses, etc.

on the air conditioning to regain our comfort temperature. Temperatures below 20°C are a **deficit** to our needs, while temperatures above 20°C are a **surplus**.

One way to determine whether we have a deficit or a surplus temperature is to construct a **divergence bar graph**. The centre line of the graph represents the comfort level of 20°C. It has a value of 0. Horizontal bars drawn from the centre line outward on either side represent the surplus and deficit temperatures. (See Figure 5.11.)

Toronto is one of the most southerly of Canada's large urban communities. This suggests that it should have a good comfort temperature. Let's check the monthly temperatures of Toronto to see if this is true.

5 a) **Construct a graph outline similar to the one in Figure 5.11.**
   b) **Refer to the temperatures for Toronto in Figure 4.20 on page 61. Calculate the amount of surplus and deficit degrees**

for each month. April, for example, has an average temperature of 6°C. Since 20°C is the comfort level, in April Toronto has a deficit of 14°C (20°C – 6°C).

c) **Next to the month of April draw a horizontal bar on the deficit side of the comfort line to represent -14°C. Now do the calculations for May, and indicate your results on the graph.**

d) **Follow this procedure for all twelve months. Colour the bars on the deficit side blue to represent cold; colour those on the surplus side red to indicate warmth.**

e) **Total all of the deficit temperatures and all of the surplus temperatures. Subtract the total deficit figure from the total surplus figure. This is Toronto's comfort temperature index.**

f) **Write a summary of your findings. Do people living in Toronto spend more time trying to keep warm or cool off?**

Figure 5.11
Comfort temperature index

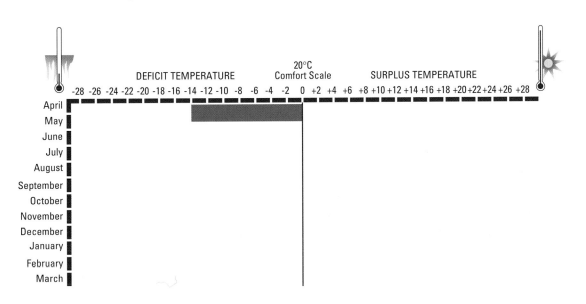

6 Choose a second location, from a different province, from the climate data on pages 60–61. Complete the process in activity 5 to produce a divergence bar graph for this location. NOTE: You may have to adjust the surplus/deficit scale along the top of the graph.

7 a) Form a group of three or four students. Calculate the comfort temperature index for each of the locations in Figure 4.20 on pages 60–61. It is not necessary to produce a graph for each location.

b) Place each of the comfort temperature index numbers on a map of Canada. Devise a method of showing the main differences between these numbers.

Consider the implications of temperatures that are either too warm or too cold. If it is too warm, for example, there are high energy costs for air conditioning. On the other hand, we can wear light clothing and spend more time outdoors. If it is too cold, we still have high energy costs to heat our buildings, and we have to wear heavy clothing. However, we can enjoy such sports as skiing and outdoor hockey. And we don't have to mow the lawn!

Of course, there are other impacts of living in a nordic country. How might our lifestyles be influenced by our northern location?

Figure 5.12
Warm *vs* cold: advantages and disadvantages

TOO WARM		TOO COLD	
Advantages	Disadvantages	Advantages	Disadvantages

8 a) Copy the chart in Figure 5.12 into your notebook. Working in groups of three or four, complete the chart by listing advantages and disadvantages of warm and cold temperatures.

b) Compare your chart with those of other groups in the class. Discuss whether you prefer a surplus or a deficit in temperature and why.

The geography of skiing

Our long winters provide Canadians with thousands of jobs, from manufacturing snow tires to selling vacations to tropical climates! But nordic countries also offer a lot of recreational activities. Skiing, tobogganing, ice hockey, skating, and snowmobiling are just some of the outdoor sports Canadians enjoy.

Recreational activities also boost our economy. Downhill and cross-country skiing have become increasingly popular in the last twenty years. The first rope-tow began pulling skiers uphill at Shawbridge, Quebec, in 1933. Today spectacular ski resorts dot the mountain slopes of the Western Cordillera and the Laurentians in Quebec. Even in Ontario, which has few highland areas suitable for really good skiing, there are over fifty ski resorts. All of these businesses create jobs for Canadians. The mountain resorts of British Columbia and Alberta also attract ski enthusiasts from around the world. This is a big boost to the Canadian tourism industry.

9 Figure 5.14 shows the ski hills at a ski resort.
a) Identify the contour interval on this map.

b) How high are the ski slopes?

c) The difference between the top of a hill and the bottom is called the **vertical drop**. What is the approximate vertical drop of this mountain?

d) Identify the features represented by the symbols labelled A to E.

e) Using tracing paper as an overlay, draw an outline of the wooded areas. Shade them green. Label the ski runs between the trees.

10 Drawing a profile of a mountain helps us to visualize the steepness of a particular slope. Using graph paper and the technique described on page 30, draw a profile of the slope called Snowballing between the letters X and Y. Use the map's scale (1:6000). The lowest point of your profile should be 250 m; the highest point should be 500 m.

If you are a skier, it is important to know if a particular run is too steep for your level of ability. It's not always possible to view an entire run from the bottom of the slope. So knowing the slope's **gradient** is useful. The gradient is the measurement of how much a slope drops over a given distance. It is usually stated as a ratio, such as 1 in 5. This means that the slope will drop 1 m over a horizontal distance of 5 m. The gradient can also be expressed as a percentage. A 1-in-5 slope is a 20 per cent gradient; a 1-in-4 slope is a 25 per cent gradient. The most severe slope is a vertical cliff with a 100 per cent gradient. This is too steep for even the most expert skiers! The Canadian government has regulated standard descriptions for ski hills according to their gradient. A sign at the top of each run bears a symbol showing how steep it is.

Gradient is calculated by dividing the vertical distance by the horizontal distance, or the **rise** by the **run**.

Figure 5.13
A ski resort in the Laurentians

Figure 5.14
A ski resort

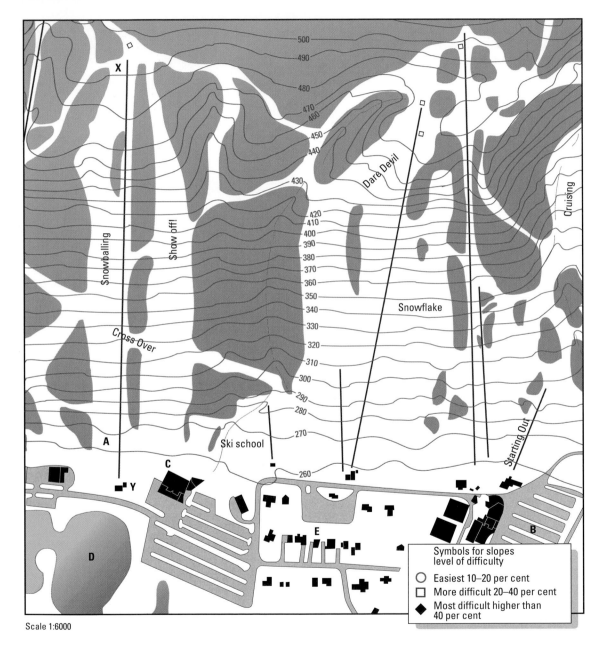

Scale 1:6000

$$\text{Gradient} = \frac{\text{Vertical distance (rise)}}{\text{Horizontal distance (run)}}$$

For example, $\frac{500}{1500} \times 100 = 33\%$.

11 a) Calculate the gradient for the run in Figure 5.14 called Snowballing.

b) Create an appropriate symbol for the degree of difficulty of the gradient on your profile of Snowballing.

c) Draw profiles of the other runs. Calculate their gradients. Classify each one with an appropriate symbol indicating the degree of difficulty.

Unit 3

RESOURCE CANADA

Canada is rich in resources. Resources are those substances that satisfy human needs or desires. There are two kinds of resources: natural and human. **Human resources** are the skills and abilities possessed by the people of a country. Canada is fortunate to have a well-educated and diverse population that can offer an abundance of human resources. **Natural resources** are those substances found in nature that people find useful or valuable. These include minerals, energy fuels, soils, natural vegetation, animals, and water.

Natural resources are either renewable or nonrenewable. **Renewable resources** can be replaced through natural means in a relatively short period of time. Sometimes these resources are harvested too quickly, however. Then they may lose their ability to replace themselves. In Canada, overfishing has severely reduced the ability of important fish species to renew themselves naturally. **Nonrenewable resources** cannot be replaced at all. Once they are gone, they're gone for good! Oil, for example, is nonrenewable because it takes millions of years for nature to produce petroleum from organic matter.

Cumshewa by Emily Carr/National Gallery of Canada, Ottawa

Food is one of our most important resources. We all need food to survive. Until the twentieth century, a majority of Canadians worked on farms producing the food needed to feed our nation. Over the twentieth century, however, the number of Canadians working in agriculture declined steadily. Today, less than 3 per cent of Canadians are farmers. Yet they manage to produce an abundance of food. In fact, farmers are so productive that Canada is a **net exporter** of food. This means that we export more agricultural products than we import.

In Canada, an agricultural operation is classified as a farm if it produces one of the following products for sale: crops, livestock, poultry, animal products, greenhouse or nursery products, mushrooms, sod, honey, or maple syrup products. Over 280 000 farms fit this definition. Over 40 per cent of these earn more than $50 000 a year. The average farm in Canada sells over $88 000 worth of agricultural products. Although few Canadians work in agriculture, we should all understand how much effort, skill, technology, and investment are needed to provide us with the variety and quality of foods we eat.

Canada's farmland resource

Canada is a large country with a relatively small population. As a result, there are 1.7 hectares (ha) of farmland per person in Canada. This rates quite favourably with cropland per person figures in other countries. (See Figure 6.1)

Figure 6.1 Farmland per person in selected countries, 1991

COUNTRY	FARMLAND (hectares/person)
Canada	1.70
United States	0.74
Russia	1.44
China	0.08
Japan	0.04
India	0.20
Bangladesh	0.08
Brazil	0.40
Germany	0.15
United Kingdom	0.11
France	0.34
Nigeria	0.29
Australia	2.70

Source: *World Resources*, 1994-95, Table 18.2.

1 a) **Calculate the total amount of farmland in Canada in square kilometres. To do this, multiply the farmland per person (1.7 ha) by the number of people in Canada (29 million). This gives the total number of hectares in farmland. To find out the number of square kilometres in farmland, divide the total number of hectares by the number of hectares in a square kilometre (100).**
   b) **Canada's total area is 9 976 000 km². What percentage of Canada's land area is farmland?**
   c) **By world standards, Canada is rich in food resources. How is this shown by the information in Figure 6.1?**

	A PERCENTAGE OF PROVINCE CLASSED AS FARMLAND	B LOCATION OF CANADA'S GOOD QUALITY FARMLAND (%)
Province/Territory		
Newfoundland	less than 1	less than 0.5
Prince Edward Island	50	less than 1
Nova Scotia	9	3
New Brunswick	6	3
Quebec	3	5
Ontario	7	15
Manitoba	14	10
Saskatchewan	46	35.5
Alberta	30	23
British Columbia	2	4
Northwest Territories and Yukon	0	0

Figure 6.2
Some facts about farmland in Canada
The figures in column A give the percentage of land area classed as farmland by province. The figures in column B show how good quality farmland (classes 1-3) is distributed on a province-by-province basis.

2 a) Copy Figure 6.3 into your notebook. Use the information in column A of Figure 6.2 and the maps in Figure 3.10 on page 30 and Figure 6.4 on page 84 to complete your chart.

b) Which **physiographic regions** contain little or no farmland?

c) Which two physiographic regions contain the most farmland?

d) Why is most of Canada not suited to agriculture?

3 a) Keep track of your diet for one day. List the agricultural activities that produce the variety of foods you eat. For example, dairy farming supplies the milk you drink.

b) Using Figure 6.4., identify those farm products that are grown i) in Canada, ii) outside Canada, and iii) both inside and outside Canada.

c) Approximately what percentage of the food you eat is "home grown"?

d) Give reasons to explain why we import some foods even though we produce them here in Canada.

PROVINCE	AMOUNT OF FARMLAND (%)	LOCATION OF FARMLAND IN THE PROVINCE	PHYSIOGRAPHIC REGION OF FARMLAND	MAJOR TYPES OF AGRICULTURE

Figure 6.3
Distribution of farmland and types of agriculture

Farmland location: the role of soils and climate

Figure 6.4
Major farm types in Canada *Categories are based on the predominant farm type in the region.*

Soils and climate are two factors that determine the location of Canada's farmlands. Good farmland needs fertile, well-drained loam soils spread across level to gently rolling plains. As we have seen in chapter 5, soils vary in fertility because of differences in bedrock, climate, and natural vegetation. Canada has two major agricultural soil groups: grassland soils and forest soils. Grassland soils have a higher natural fertility than forest soils. Of forest soils, those formed under mixed and deciduous forests are more fertile than those formed under coniferous forests.

One important climatic factor influencing the location of farmland is the amount and distribution of precipitation. Most of the crops grown in Canada require a minimum of 400 mm of precipitation annually. In areas where there is less than 400 mm, the land is better suited to grazing. However, where water is available from nearby rivers or lakes, crops can be grown under irrigation.

4 a) Find a precipitation map of Canada in your library resource centre. Identify

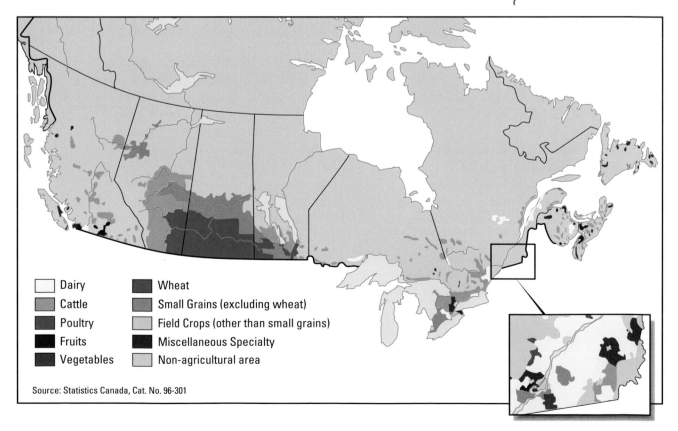

Dairy
Cattle
Poultry
Fruits
Vegetables
Wheat
Small Grains (excluding wheat)
Field Crops (other than small grains)
Miscellaneous Specialty
Non-agricultural area

Source: Statistics Canada, Cat. No. 96-301

the two regions in western Canada that are most likely to experience warm, dry seasonal conditions.

b) What percentage of total farmland in Canada would you estimate falls within these two areas?

c) According to Figure 6.4, what types of agriculture are found in these two regions? Suggest two reasons why these types of agriculture are suited to drier climates.

A second climatic factor influencing farmland location is the length of the growing season. The **growing season** is the number of days in the year with an average temperature above 5.6°C. This is the temperature at which plants begin to grow. Farmers successfully grow only those crops that can ripen within the growing season of their region. For example, the growing season for wheat in the Prairies is less than 100 days. Corn or soybeans, on the other hand, require over 150 days.

5 a) Copy Figure 6.5 into your notebook. For each location, record the number of months in which the temperature is above 5.6°C and the annual total precipitation is greater than 400 mm. You will find this information in the climate statistics in Figure 4.20 on pages 60–61.

b) To complete the sections on soil and natural vegetation, refer to pages 70–74. What soils are most suitable for agriculture? What climate conditions are most suitable for agriculture?

c) Based on the completed chart in Figure 6.5 and on Figure 6.4, which area of Canada would you say has the best farmland? Explain your choice.

A useful indicator of the growing season is **degree days**. Degree days are calcu-

PLACE	TYPE OF AGRICULTURE	GROWING SEASON	ANNUAL PRECIPITATION	SOIL	NATURAL VEGETATION
Brandon, MB					
Lethbridge, AB					
Regina, SK					
Coppermine, NT					
Toronto, ON					
Vancouver, BC					
Halifax, NS					
St. John's, NF					
Whitehorse, YT					

Figure 6.5
Distribution of agriculture

lated when the average daily temperature rises above 5.6°C. Every degree above 5.6°C is counted as one degree day. A spring day with an average temperature of 11.6°C equals six degree days (11.6 - 5.6 = 6). When all degree days for the year are totalled for places in Canada, a degree day map can be drawn, like the one in Figure 6.6.

Figure 6.6
Degree days in Canada

6 If a July day averages 22°C, how many degree days would this produce?

7 Study Figure 6.6.
   a) What degree day generally marks the northern limit of agriculture in Canada?
   b) Based on degree days, in what region of Canada do farmers have the greatest

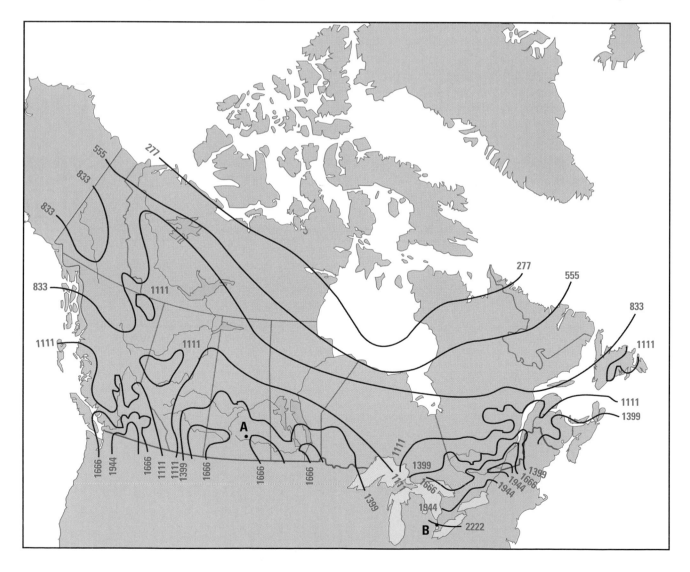

choice of crops to grow? Explain your answer.

8 Compare the degree days map with the agricultural map in Figure 6.4.
a) In general, what is the degree day limit for i) fruit in BC and Ontario and ii) wheat?
b) Why does this explain the much larger area of Canada suited to growing wheat rather than fruit?
c) Silage corn can be grown with a minimum of 1650 degree days. In what provinces can this crop be grown successfully?
d) Grain corn requires a minimum of 2200 degree days. Where can it be grown?

9 Explain why the degree days for point A and point B in Figure 6.6 differ.

10 Locate three photographs in this text that show why 93 per cent of Canada's land area is not suitable for farming. For each photograph, write a brief explanation of its location in Canada (province and physiographic region) and how it shows one or more reasons why much of Canada is unsuitable for agriculture. Be sure to provide the appropriate page reference in the text for each photo.

Quality farmland

The quality of farmland differs greatly across Canada. Farmland quality is based on its climatic and soil characteristics. The Canada Land Inventory for Agriculture (CLI) rates land from class 1, the highest quality, to class 6, the lowest quality. High-quality farmland is usually the most pro-

ductive. Column B in Figure 6.2 on page 83 shows the percentage of good quality, classes 1-3 farmland in each province.

11 Create a **divided bar graph** to show the data in Column B of Figure 6.2. Present the data in geographic order from west to east.
a) Draw a horizontal bar 10 cm long and 2 cm wide.
b) Label 0 per cent at the extreme left end and 100 per cent at the extreme right end of the bar. The total length of the bar represents 100 per cent; 1 cm represents 10 per cent.
c) British Columbia has 4 per cent of the good quality farmland in Canada. To show this, measure 0.4 cm, or 4 mm, from the left and draw a vertical line. From that line measure and mark the amount of quality farmland for Alberta. Repeat the process for the remaining provinces.
d) Once all the provinces are marked on the graph, colour and label each section. Give your graph a title.

12 a) Using Figure 6.2, organize the provinces into the following three groups according to the amount of quality farmland:
i) 16 per cent and over—large area of good quality farmland
ii) 15 to 5 per cent—average area of good quality farmland
iii) under 5 per cent—small area of good quality farmland.
b) On an outline map of Canada, use a colour code to plot the provinces with a i) large, ii) average, and iii) small area of good quality farmland.

c) Write a statement identifying the location of large areas of good quality farmland in Canada shown by your map.

Agriculture: past to present

The past

One hundred years ago, Canada was a nation of farmers. Nearly 75 per cent of Canadians lived in rural areas. More people worked in agriculture than in any other industry. Farm work was done by horse or human muscle. This meant one family could farm only about 40 ha of land.

Farm production was diversified, or mixed. This meant that each farm had a few dairy cows, hogs, chickens, and beef cattle and grew a variety of crops. A portion of the farm products were used directly by the farm family. Only the surplus was sold in local cities and towns.

The present

Today, Canada is a nation of urban dwellers. Over 78 per cent of Canadians live in towns and cities.

The majority of farms are specialized—that is, farmers concentrate on one type of farming. Both human and natural resources are used as efficiently as possible. Many farmers today are college graduates. They rely on their own knowledge as well as advice from agricultural research stations and colleges and the representatives of seed, fertilizer, and pesticide companies. Since many farms are highly mechanized and computerized, technical and computer skills are often essential for a successful farm operation.

Figure 6.7
Changes in agriculture in Canada

YEAR	TOTAL FARMLAND (ha)	NUMBER OF FARMS	AVERAGE FARM SIZE (ha)	FARM LABOUR	TRACTORS AND COMBINES
1901	25 700 000	511 000	50.3	718 000	na
1911	44 100 000	682 800	64.5	928 000	na
1921	57 000 000	711 100	80.2	1 025 000	47 455
1931	66 000 000	728 600	90.6	1 118 000	114 227
1941	70 200 000	732 900	95.8	1 074 000	178 765
1951	70 400 000	623 100	113.1	826 000	490 186
1961	69 800 000	480 900	145.2	649 000	705 400
1971	68 700 000	366 100	187.5	510 000	759 449
1981	65 900 000	318 400	207.0	508 000	818 716
1991	67 800 000	280 000	242.1	533 400	842 000

na = not available
Source: Statistics Canada, *Human Activity and the Environment*, 1986, pp. 69-71; 1994, pp. 220. Statistics Canada, *Agriculture at a Glance*, 1995, pp. 70, 94-95.

In recent years, science has contributed a lot to farming. **Genetic engineering** has created plants that resist frost and disease. Applications of weed sprays called **herbicides**, insect killers called **insecticides**, and artificial fertilizers have increased the yield per hectare. Genetics have also produced better livestock through the breeding of desirable characteristics into the next generation. Feed companies have improved the quality of their products. As a result, farmers now produce more and higher quality meat using less feed. One hundred years ago, a single farm produced only enough food to feed thirteen people. Today, one Canadian farmer produces enough food to feed ninety-one people!

13 a) **What trends can you identify in each category in Figure 6.7?**
   b) **What relationships between these categories help to explain each trend? For example, how has average farm size been influenced by the number of tractors and combines?**
   c) **Describe the trends and relationships in agriculture in your notebook.**

14 **Construct a multi-line graph to show the trend in i) the number of farms, ii) farm labour, and iii) tractors and combines. A multi-line graph is similar to a simple line graph except that two or more factors are graphed. A common scale is used for all three factors. Be sure to include a colour legend to indicate which line represents which factor. Use a vertical scale of 1 cm represents 100 000 units. Place the time in years along the horizontal axis.**

Farmers as business managers

To be successful, today's farmers must know how to manage a business. Seed, fertilizer, and machinery must be purchased months before farmers receive any income from their investment. In the case of livestock, it may be three years before farmers earn a return on their money. In addition to hard work and long hours, farmers must know about mortgages, operating loans, interest rates, markets, government grants, and cash flows. In addition, success requires long-range financial planning and an average investment of about $500 000 in equipment, livestock, and farmland.

Good decision making and suitable weather and market conditions are necessary to make a farm profitable. Profits allow farmers to support their families and keep their farms in good condition. Even so, farm incomes are generally much lower than the earnings of the average Canadian living in cities.

Farming inputs and outputs

Profits are determined by totalling the costs, or **inputs**, of the operation, then subtracting these from the earnings, or **outputs**. Figure 6.8 shows the percentage of farm inputs averaged for the whole of Canada and for Saskatchewan and Ontario, two of the leading agricultural provinces.

Farm outputs represent a variety of farm products. The top fifteen products produced on Canada's farms are shown in Figure 6.9. Although this list shows only fifteen out of over forty agricultural products,

Figure 6.8
Canada, Saskatchewan, and Ontario: farm inputs (%)

INPUT	CANADA (%)	SASKATCHEWAN (%)	ONTARIO (%)
Commercial feed	17	4	18
Machinery expenses	16	22	13
Interest on debt	13	15	10
Wages	12	6	15
Fertilizer	9	9	7
Rent	4	7	na
Pesticides	4	7	4
Seed	3	na	5
Electricity and telephone	3	na	4
Livestock purchases	na	na	4
Other expenses	19	25	20

na = not available
Source: *Canadian Global Almanac*, 1995 (Macmillan Canada).

Figure 6.9
Top farm outputs, 1994

ITEM	OUTPUT (millions $)	% OF TOTAL FARM RECEIPTS
Cattle	4 283	16.7
Dairy products	3 353	13.1
Wheat	2 429	9.4
Canola	2 161	8.4
Pigs	2 052	8.0
Poultry	1 282	5.0
Nurseries	904	3.5
Vegetables	833	3.3
Eggs	551	2.2
Potatoes	549	2.1
Corn	505	2.0
Soybeans	504	2.0
Barley	494	1.9
Tobacco	364	1.4
Fruits	202	0.8
All products	**25 602**	**100.0**

Source: *Canadian Global Almanac*, 1996 (Macmillan Canada).

they make up over 80 per cent of the total value of farm outputs.

15 a) Use the statistics in Figure 6.8 to produce bar graphs showing the farm inputs for Canada, Saskatchewan, and Ontario.
   b) Classify each input as either natural or human.
   c) Suggest two natural inputs that are not indicated in Figure 6.8.
   d) Suggest two reasons for the different percentages of inputs between Canada as a whole, Saskatchewan, and Ontario.

16 a) Use the statistics in Figure 6.9 to produce a bar graph showing the major products, or outputs, of Canadian farms.
   b) Into what two major categories can these outputs be grouped? Which group is more important?
   c) Name five other Canadian farm products that are not listed in Figure 6.9.

17 a) Suppose a farm family sold their $500 000 farm. First they paid off their outstanding debts totalling $200 000. Then they decided to invest the remaining $300 000 in low-risk securities paying 10 per cent interest. What would be the family's annual income from this investment?

b) Suppose that the farmer decided to work at a job in the city after selling the farm. The job pays $2000 a month. What would be the family's total annual income, including the income from their $300 000 investment?

c) Why do you think farmers continue to farm?

Simulation: planting the fields at Twin Maples Farm

The Ashlees have expanded their Twin Maples farm by purchasing 70 ha from their neighbour. They are planning to use the land to grow crops for market and to graze cattle. To decide which crops to plant, the Ashlees evaluated their current crops and then visited the crop specialist at the agricultural office and a seed supplier. They then spent several evenings with a crop-budgeting handbook and a calculator!

Figure 6.10 shows the crop-selection matrix the Ashlees used to decide which crops to plant in which fields. The necessary information for the four crops they selected is shown in Figure 6.11. The vertical axis lists the four crops being considered. The horizontal axis lists the factors or criteria used to judge the suitability of the crops for each field. Now you must help the Ashlees decide which crops to grow in which fields.

18 a) Work in groups of three or four. Draw a matrix similar to Figure 6.10 in your notebook. *Use a pencil*. Your answers may change later! Title your matrix *Field A*.

b) Study Field A in Figure 6.12 and the crop fact sheet (Figure 6.11). Complete the matrix by rating the crops for each factor. The most attractive rating is 4; the least attractive rating is 1. You will have to calculate the input costs for each crop before you can rate it. The profit average column has been done for you. Everyone in your group should complete a matrix.

Figure 6.10
Twin Maples crop selection matrix

WEIGHTING		X?	X?	X?	X?	X?		
CROPS	FACTORS TO CONSIDER	PROFIT AVERAGE	RATE OF SOIL EROSION	SOIL DRAINAGE	SOIL TEXTURE	INPUT COSTS	TOTAL POINTS	RANK
Alfalfa hay		3						
Barley		1						
Canola		2						
Grain corn		4						

Figure 6.11
Crop fact sheet

CROP	SOIL DRAINAGE	SOIL TEXTURE	RATE OF SOIL EROSION	INPUT COSTS /HA	AVERAGE PROFIT/HA (5-year average)
Alfalfa hay	Good drainage only	All types	Low	$547	$140
Barley	Best in good drainage Barely okay for imperfect drainage	Best in loam and clay Okay for sandy soil	Average	$453	$ 42
Canola	Best in good drainage Okay for imperfect drainage	All types	Average	$512	$130
Grain corn	Best in good drainage Okay for imperfect drainage	All types	High	$838	$145

Figure 6.12
Twin Maples
Farm, field
characteristics

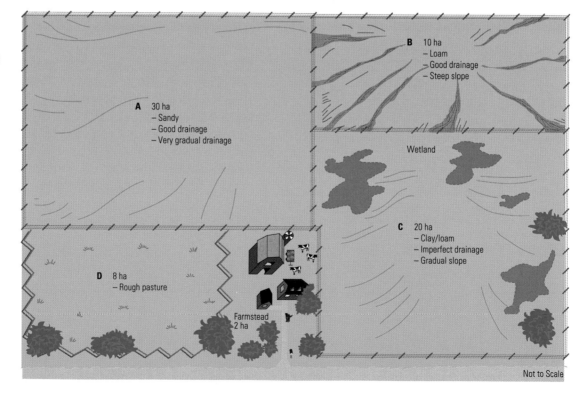

A 30 ha
– Sandy
– Good drainage
– Very gradual drainage

B 10 ha
– Loam
– Good drainage
– Steep slope

Wetland

C 20 ha
– Clay/loam
– Imperfect drainage
– Gradual slope

D 8 ha
– Rough pasture

Farmstead
2 ha

Not to Scale

c) Total the score for each crop by adding the points across the column. The crop with the highest score is ranked 1 and should be planted in Field A. Enter the rank for each crop in the last column.

d) Repeat the process for Fields B and C.

19 Raising livestock also involves decision making. Suppose a poultry farmer is considering modernizing by installing automatic egg-gathering and manure-handling equipment. What factors would have to be considered in making such a decision?

Types of farming

Canadian farms range from grain farms, which are the largest by area with an average of 460 ha, to mushroom farms, which have the highest average sales of any farm type at $885 500. Figure 6.4 on page 84 shows the distribution of major farm types in Canada.

Cattle, dairy, wheat, and small-grain farms are the leading farm types in Canada by number. In 1991, there were 178 000 farms in these four categories. This represents 64 per cent of all Canadian farms. Poultry, fruit, vegetable, and field crop farms are also important in certain regions of the country.

The type of farming that dominates in any area depends on many factors. The length of the growing season, the number of degree days, the amount and distribution of precipitation, and the fertility and texture of the soil are the important natural factors. In addition, farmers must consider economic factors. These include location, transportation, distance to markets, competition, price, cost of production, and their own knowledge and experience. If farmers make good decisions about what to produce, they will likely be successful. If they do not, they will likely go out of business.

Farm types can be classified in different ways. One way is based on the value of inputs and outputs for each hectare of land on the farm. Where inputs and outputs per hectare are high, the operations are called **intensive farms**. Such farms are often found in densely populated areas where land values are high. They require large amounts of labour and/or expensive equipment, and they have high yields per hectare. Farm types in Canada that are intensive include fruit, vegetable, dairy, poultry, and specialty crops such as tobacco and cut flowers. In many cases, these products are perishable—that is, they spoil quickly. **Extensive farms** are the opposite of intensive farms. They have much lower inputs and outputs per hectare and are usually located in areas with low population and lower land prices. They produce much lower yields per hectare. Their products are usually less perishable than those of intensive farms so they do not have to be processed or sold in markets as quickly.

Important farm types in Canada

Prairie wheat farms

Prairie wheat farms in Saskatchewan average 420 ha. They are among the most specialized farms in Canada. They produce wheat and other grains using large tractors and combines. On average, a Saskatchewan

Figure 6.13
A wheat farm in the Prairies

Figure 6.14
A cattle ranch in British Columbia

wheat farm sells crops worth $59 000 each year. But it takes over $440 000 to start up a typical wheat farm!

The conditions needed for ideal wheat production are a climate with a growing season of at least 90 to 100 days, a minimum of 400 mm of rain that falls mainly in the summer, a dry, sunny fall harvest period, and fertile soils over level land. Farm work is centred in the spring and fall with the planting and harvesting of the grain crop. There is little farming activity in winter.

Cattle raising

Cattle raising is an important activity in many parts of Canada. In Alberta and Saskatchewan, cattle are raised on large ranches in the dry grassland regions. Unable to grow wheat or other grains due to low rainfall and a hilly landscape, ranchers need less machinery and equipment than wheat farmers. But they must invest a lot of money in land, cattle, and buildings. On average, cattle farms require about $470 000 in start-up costs. The average income per cattle ranch in Saskatchewan is $74 000 and the average farm size is 640 ha.

The natural conditions for cattle ranching include a climate with rainfall of 200 mm or more in a landscape of rolling, grass-covered hills. In addition, ranches need valleys with water and soils suitable for growing irrigated hay and grains for feed and wells or watering places in the pastures for cattle. During the winter, cattle are either sold or fed on grains and hay until spring.

Dairy farms

Dairy farming is centred largely in Quebec and Ontario. These farms average 132 ha and have average yearly incomes of $142 000. Dairy products are highly perishable. Fresh milk must be sold quickly in nearby urban markets or processed into butter or cheese. Dairy farming requires a large investment in barns, hay and grain machinery, and milking and refrigeration equipment. On average, this costs $605 000 per farm! Work is steady year-round as the cattle must be fed, milked, and checked for diseases and pests on a daily basis. In addition, dairy farms often raise hay or grains as feed for the winter season.

The natural conditions needed for dairy farming include a climate with precipitation over 650 mm and relatively short, mild winters and warm summers. Pastures and hay grow best on clay loam soils, while grain fields require level lands with fertile soils.

Tender fruit farms

Tender fruit farms are found primarily in two regions in Canada, the Okanagan Valley in British Columbia and the Niagara fruit belt in Ontario. The average size of a Canadian fruit farm is 29 ha. The average annual income is $50 000. The capital invested in land, equipment, buildings, and orchards totals about $450 000. Work begins in the early spring and extends to the end of the fall harvest. Fruit growing requires large amounts of labour to plant, trim, spray, harvest, and maintain orchards. In addition, the crops are usually highly perishable and must be processed or marketed quickly. In both British Columbia and Ontario, fruit farms are disappearing as farmers sell their land at high prices to make way for urban development.

Tender fruit production is limited to areas with fertile, well-drained, sandy loam soils and a long growing season with mild winters. Sloping lands and terraces near lakes help to reduce late spring and early fall frosts that can damage tender buds and ripening fruit.

Figure 6.15
A dairy farm operation in Quebec

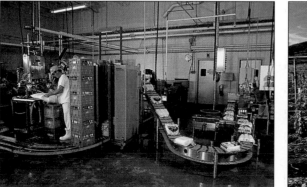

Figure 6.16
A tender fruit farm in the Niagara fruit belt

Vegetable farms

This type of farming is often known as **market gardening** or **truck farming** since the products are usually shipped fresh to urban markets by truck. In Canada, vegetable farming is found in a few small areas near Montreal, Toronto, and Vancouver. These farms average 55 ha in size and earn $115 000 per year. The work period is largely between spring planting and fall harvesting. A large amount of labour is needed to plant and harvest the various crops. Specialized machines are needed for ploughing, fertilizing, and harvesting since tender vegetables are easily bruised or damaged. Land values are also high. This accounts for the fact that the average vegetable farmer has invested $570 000!

Vegetable farming is most productive on fertile loam or peat soils that allow root crops like carrots and potatoes to grow easily. In addition, a moist climate and a source of irrigation water during the hot summers are necessary. The land should be level and well drained.

20 a) Copy Figure 6.18 into your notebook. Complete the chart using the information you have read here. Use your calculator to work out income per hectare and investment per hectare.

b) Produce two bar graphs showing the income per hectare and investment per hectare of the five farm types.

c) Review the terms *intensive farming* and *extensive farming*. Which of the five farm types would be considered intensive? Which would be considered extensive? Explain your answers.

d) If you were going to become a farmer, which type of farming would you choose? Explain your answer.

21 a) Find other photographs in this text that show different types of farming. For each photograph, indicate its location in Canada (province and physiographic

Figure 6.17
A vegetable farm in southern Ontario

Figure 6.18
Types of farms: a comparison chart

FARM TYPE	SIZE (ha)	INCOME ($)	CAPITAL INVESTED ($)	INCOME /HECTARE ($)	INVESTMENT /HECTARE ($)

region), the type of farming with supporting evidence, and reasons why this type of farm developed here. Be sure to provide the appropriate page reference in the text for each photo.

22 Explain why the prairie provinces are largely devoted to extensive wheat and cattle farming while Ontario and Quebec have intensive fruit, vegetable, and dairy farming. Use information from this text and your atlas to prepare your answer.

Changes in Canadian agriculture

Whether they grow wheat, tender fruit, or vegetables, or raise dairy or beef cattle, farmers are affected by many factors. Specialists are vulnerable to climate and market conditions. A summer hailstorm can destroy a peach crop. Competition on the world market can drive down wheat prices. A flood can wipe out a newly planted field of vegetables. These factors may have a short-term impact on a farming operation.

A more devastating factor, however, is a change in social attitudes. When society's attitudes change, the effects are usually experienced over the long term. Consider changing attitudes towards our diet and the foods we eat. Never before have Canadians been so concerned with what they should eat to maintain a healthy lifestyle. As a result, eating habits in Canada are changing. These changes have an important effect on Canadian farmers.

	% CHANGE
Vegetables	
Broccoli	+151
Cabbage	−26
Carrots	+13
Cauliflower	+6
Celery	+2
Cucumbers	+28
Lettuce	+12
Onions	+2
Peppers	+58
Radishes	+2
Rutabagas (Turnip)	−23
Tomatoes	−16
Fruits	
Grapes	+20
Grapefruit	−46
Oranges	−36
Meat and poultry	
Beef	−16
Pork	−14
Poultry	+31
Dairy products	
Margarine	−7
Butter	−30
Eggs	−15
Cheddar cheese	+43
Processed cheese	−6
Variety cheese	+45
Yogurt	+95

Source: *Farming Facts*, Statistics Canada, 1993.

Figure 6.19 Changing Canadian eating habits, 1981-1991 (kg/year)

23 Look at Figure 6.19.
   a) Pick three food items that increased in popularity. Why do you think these items are gaining popularity? Have

these items become more or less important in your family's diet?

b) Pick three food items that decreased in popularity. Why do you think these items are less popular today? Have these items become more or less important in your family's diet?

24 a) Which types of farms have benefitted from Canadians' changing attitudes towards diet? Which types have lost out?

b) What decisions do each of these groups of farmers face?

Case study: the Niagara fruit belt

The Niagara fruit belt is famous as a producer of tender fruit, such as peaches, sweet cherries, pears, plums, and grapes. Approximately 75 per cent of Canada's peaches and 90 per cent of its grapes are produced in this region.

The fruit belt lies in southern Ontario, between Hamilton-Grimsby and the Niagara River and the Niagara Escarpment and Lake Ontario. (See Figure 6.20.) This narrow strip of land possesses several advantages for fruit production. The soils vary, from well-drained, sandy soils best suited to growing peaches, to heavier, clay soils best suited for grape production. The climate is moist and mild compared with much of Canada. Lake Ontario cools spring temperatures just enough to delay fruit blossoming by a week or two, thereby avoiding the risk of late frosts. In the fall, the lake effect extends milder temperatures for a week or

Figure 6.20
The Niagara fruit belt

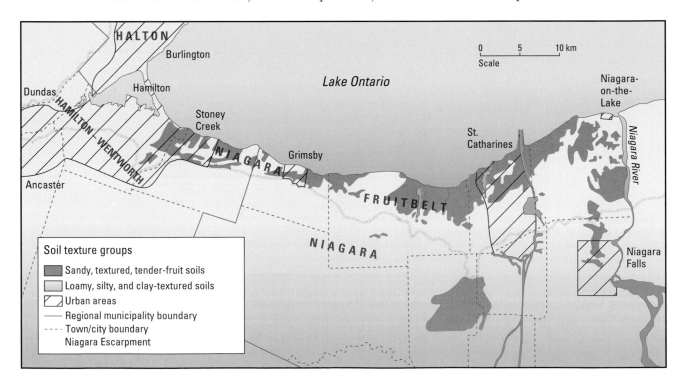

two, enabling grapes to fully ripen. With the exception of the Okanagan Valley in British Columbia, no other agricultural region in Canada enjoys these physical advantages.

Fruit farming is highly specialized. (See Figure 6.22.) The average fruit farm is less than 30 ha. Fruit farmers usually grow several types of fruit. These ripen at different times, spreading the harvest over a period of a few months. Work on a typical fruit farm begins in early spring. Pruning trees, tying vines onto trellises, and removing old clippings and other debris left over from the dormant winter are the first tasks of the season. When the ground is no longer frozen, dead or aging trees and vines are replaced and the ground is ploughed to kill weeds.

In early May, beehives are put out to pollinate the new blossoms. The orchards and vineyards are sprayed with insecticides and fungicides. The crops are sprayed again once the fruit begins to grow in June and early July. The first crop to be harvested is strawberries in early June, followed by cherries in late June, peaches and pears in August, and grapes in September and October. Labour for harvesting is expensive and in short supply. As a result, many fruit farms rely on migrant farm workers from outside Canada. Another trend is towards "pick-your-own" fruit farms. This saves labour and transportation costs and enables farmers to sell their crops directly to consumers at lower prices. But "pick-your-own" fruit farms are only suitable for ground crops, like strawberries, because inexperienced pickers may damage valuable fruit trees.

The future of the fruit belt

Two factors threaten the survival of this unique agricultural region: increased competition from American farmers as a result of the North American Free Trade Agreement and the loss of farmland due to urban expansion. In the 1980s, the grape growers and wineries, together with the provincial and federal governments,

Figure 6.21
The Niagara fruit belt from the air

Figure 6.22
Harvesting fruit by hand

launched a $48.5 million program to meet these challenges. First farmers reduced the amount of land in vineyards. (See Figure 6.23.) Next they switched from the lower-quality grapes used to produce juices, jams, and jellies to the higher-quality European varieties needed to produce premium wines. They also introduced ice wines. These are wines made from grapes that are allowed to freeze and thaw several times before they are harvested in early winter. Today Niagara ice wines are considered to be the world's best.

The plan was a success. The new Niagara wines became award winners, and their prestige soared both nationally and internationally. Sales of Niagara wines increased from $407 million in 1982 to $658 million in 1992. (See Figure 6.24.) Wineries introduced tourist programs, hosting such events as international jazz festivals and wine-tasting tours. One winery increased its sales from 3000 cases to 310 000 cases between 1988 and 1993!

The success of the grape industry has not gone unnoticed by farmers growing other fruit crops in the Niagara region. They are adopting more creative and aggressive marketing strategies for their products. The emphasis is on the high quality and superior taste of Niagara fruit. They are also taking advantage of the trend towards more nutritious snacks for children, such as fruit leathers and fruit chips.

Figure 6.23
Area of Niagara vineyards, 1977-1993

YEAR	AREA (ha)
1977	9 638
1978	9 644
1979	10 058
1980	10 064
1981	8 658
1982	8 878
1983	8 840
1984	8 843
1985	8 882
1986	8 750
1987	8 748
1988	7 520
1989	6 200
1990	5 422
1991	4 764
1992	5 046
1993	5 071

Source: Ministry of Agriculture and Food.

Figure 6.24
Sales and production of Canadian wines

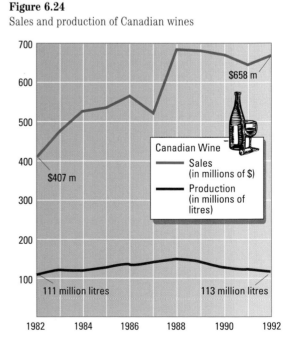

Source: Southam News Graphic, *Hamilton Spectator*, 3 September 1994

Still, it is difficult for many farmers to survive on the low prices their products fetch. In 1995, for example, sour cherries sold for about 7 cents a kilogram. This is about 53 cents a kilogram less than the cost of producing, harvesting, and delivering the cherries to processors.

If fruit farmers cannot be profitable, they will be forced to sell their land to developers. Housing subdivisions, shopping malls, and industrial parks will increasingly take over this valuable farmland. (See Figure 6.25.) A variety of programs and funds have been set up by the provincial government to keep farmers in business and to ban urban development on these valuable lands. Unfortunately, these programs vary and shift with the government in power. In May 1995, for example, the provincial government established a $20 million fund to help Niagara farmers. But in June, following a provincial election, a new government eliminated the fund. Many farmers fear they won't be able to save their farms. The result may be the "paving over" of the Niagara fruit belt.

25 Describe the factors that make the Niagara fruit belt a unique agricultural region in Canada.

26 a) What are the two most important challenges facing the fruit belt? Why are these a threat to the region?
b) What are the hopes for the future survival of the fruit belt?
c) Do you think the government should offer financial support to Niagara fruit farmers to ensure that the region is not lost to urbanization? Give reasons for your answer.

Loss of farmland in Canada

The loss of prime farmland to expanding cities is not unique to the Niagara fruit belt. Since the mid-1960s, much of Canada's best agricultural land has been covered over by subdivisions, shopping malls, roads, and other urban land uses. The amount of lost farmland varies from province to province. (See Figure 6.26.)

27 a) Suggest five land uses for converted agricultural land.
b) Use a calculator to figure out the number of hectares of lost farmland per year in Canada and in your province.
c) Assume this rate of farmland loss has continued from 1986 to the present. How much land will have been converted to other uses in Canada as a whole and in your province?

Figure 6.25
The changing area of Niagara fruit crops, 1951 and 1993

CROP	1951 (ha)	1993 (ha)*
Peaches	5700	2900
Cherries	1700	500
Pears	2300	1016
Plums	1900	606
Grapes	8300	5071

*Estimate

Source: 1951 Census of Canada and the Ministry of Food and Agriculture, 1993.

PROVINCE	CONVERTED LAND (ha)	AVERAGE FARM SIZE (ha)
Newfoundland	15	65
Prince Edward Island	1 197	110
Nova Scotia	3 047	100
New Brunswick	2 425	116
Quebec	24 912	90
Ontario	83 040	79
Manitoba	13 046	301
Saskatchewan	10 613	442
Alberta	51 691	364
British Columbia	45 330	124
Canada	**301 440**	**242**

Figure 6.26
Good quality land (classes 1-3) converted to urban use, within the last twenty years

28 a) **Based on the average farm size, calculate the number of farms that were lost in Canada during the last twenty years in Figure 6.26.**
b) **How many farms were lost in your province during the survey period?**
c) **Why is the loss of farmland in Ontario, Alberta, and British Columbia so high?**

29 **The two aerial photographs on page 103 illustrate the loss of farmland due to urban growth. This scene represents what is happening to farmland near many cities across Canada. Prepare two land use maps of the area shown in Figures 6.27 and 6.28.**
a) **Place the top half of a piece of tracing paper over the photograph taken in 1968. Draw a line to indicate the outside border of the photo and mark on the major roadways.**
b) **Major land uses include transportation, industrial, residential, commercial, agricultural, and recreational and open space. Outline each type of land use on the tracing paper. Choose a colour to show each land use and then lightly shade in your map. Give your map a legend and a title.**
c) **Repeat the process on the bottom half of the tracing paper using the photograph of urban development in 1995. Add any additional land use categories to your legend.**
d) **What land uses had consumed the farmland by 1995? Which of these uses had consumed the largest area?**

Simulation: farming on the urban fringe

Brookestone is a century-old farm. For generations the Melnick family has worked this land and gradually developed a high-yield dairy herd. Ten years ago, the Melnicks expanded their operation by purchasing a neighbour's farm. Their class 2 farmland continues to produce high-yield crops and their beef cattle sell well.

The Melnicks live only ten minutes from the city. They like being close to shopping and entertainment. Their teenage children are close to their school and friends. They live on a well-travelled highway, so their roadside vegetable stand has a steady flow of customers.

There have been some noticeable changes in the countryside surrounding Brookestone in recent years. A farm just to the east has become a golf course; another has become a luxury housing subdivision. Last week, two of the homeowners from that subdivision drove over to Brookestone

Figure 6.27
Site of the future Scarborough Civic Centre at the eastern edge of Metro Toronto in 1968
The site is just to the north of Ellesmere Road.

Figure 6.28
Urban development around the Scarborough Civic Centre in 1995
The Scarborough Civic Centre is the large white circular building in the foreground. The light rapid transit line (LRT) is seen across the centre of the photo.

to complain about the smell of manure coming from the farm. The previous spring, the same two owners had stopped the hired hand from spraying herbicides. The homeowners claimed the herbicides were drifting onto their property.

The Melnicks realize that the city will soon consume their area. A realtor suggested that they sell Brookestone now, even though they could continue farming here for another six to eight years. Since Brookestone is in the path of future city growth, the Melnicks have been offered over $6000 per hectare for their 167 ha property.

This is the third time a realtor has approached the Melnicks. Should they sell their farm now or wait a few more years? If they sell, what will they do for a living? This is a difficult decision for a farm family to make.

Melnick family profile

Mr. Melnick is forty-five years old and a full-time farmer. He has lived at Brookestone all his life. He is a graduate of the agricultural college and past president of the county dairy producers' association.

Mrs. Melnick is also a full-time farmer. She is forty-two years old. She is a university graduate with a degree in accounting. She is the executive director of the annual county fair.

The Melnicks' son is seventeen. He is in his last year of high school and plans to study agriculture at university. He wants to be a full-time farmer. He works on the farm year-round.

The Melnicks' fourteen-year-old daughter attends the local high school. She works part-time at the animal hospital and wants to become a veterinarian.

30 You must help the Melnick family make a decision about the future of their farm at Brookestone.

a) Working with a group of three or four students, list i) the arguments in favour of selling Brookestone now and ii) the arguments against selling Brookestone now. From these lists, determine four realistic options for the Melnicks' future.

b) How will the family determine which of these options is the best one for them? What criteria might they use to make their decision? Using a decision-making matrix similar to the one in Figure 6.10 on page 91, decide which option is best for the Melnick family. Be sure to include criteria, total points, and ranking columns in your matrix. When you have completed the matrix, write an explanation of the choice you made for the Melnicks.

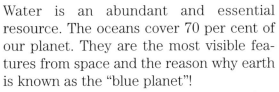
WATER

7

Water is an abundant and essential resource. The oceans cover 70 per cent of our planet. They are the most visible features from space and the reason why earth is known as the "blue planet"!

All living things need water to survive. In humans, water makes up 65 per cent of our bodies and 83 per cent of our blood supply. We use water to help digest food, to take in oxygen, to transport bodily wastes, and to control our body temperature. Daily access to drinking water is essential for everyone's survival. Our bodies need about 2.4 L of water each day to maintain good health. We can live for over a month without food, but we would survive only a few days without water!

Water is one of Canada's most valuable natural resources. It is vital for all ecosystems and for maintaining our quality of life. Water is used in almost every economic and recreational activity. Canadians are fortunate. We have more lake area than any other country in the world. We have 9 per cent of the world's total renewable freshwater. This equals 340 000 L of freshwater per person per day, more than any other major country in the world. The abundance of water in Canada can be seen on any detailed map and in the information in Figure 7.1.

With so much water, it should be no surprise that Canadians are third only to Australians and Kuwaitis in their average daily household water use per person, as shown in Figure 7.3. This is quite different

Figure 7.1
Land cover in Canada

LAND COVER	% OF TOTAL AREA
Forest	45
Tundra	23
Wetlands	12
Freshwater	8
Cropland	6
Ice and snow	3
Rangeland	2
Urban/Other	1

Source: Statistics Canada, *Human Activity and the Environment*, 1994.

from some nations in Africa and Asia that must survive on less than 10 m³ of water per person per year.

Figure 7.2
Canada: a land of abundant water resources

Figure 7.3
Average domestic water use per person

COUNTRY	ANNUAL USE (m³/person)
Australia	849
Kuwait	336
Canada	304
United States	244
Russia	134
Sweden	127
Japan	125
France	125
Germany	73
Israel	66
Mexico	55
Brazil	54
China	28
India	18
Nigeria	11
Bangladesh	6
Ethiopia	5

Source: United Nations, *World Development Report*, 1995.

1 Using the statistics in Figure 7.1, create a pie graph showing the different types of land cover in Canada. What percentage of Canada is covered in one way or another by water?

2 Using the statistics in Figure 7.3, create a bar graph comparing water use in different countries. Why might Australia, Kuwait, Canada, and the United States be greater users of water than the other countries?

3 Write a brief summary of Canada's fresh-water resources. Use the information from Figure 7.4 and the graphs you created in activities 1 and 2 in your answer.

The hydrologic cycle

The world's water supply is in constant motion through the **hydrologic cycle**. In the hydrologic cycle, water constantly evaporates from oceans, lakes, and other bodies of water to create moist air. Most evaporated water condenses and falls as rain over the oceans. However, winds carry some of the moist air over land. Here the water vapour condenses to form clouds; the water falls to earth as rain, hail, sleet, or snow. In desert areas, water droplets falling from clouds may evaporate before reaching the ground. In wetter areas, the water that falls may be absorbed by the soil or may fall into lakes or ponds. During times of heavy rain or spring snow melt, water flows over the land surface into stream channels, rivers, and lakes. This is called **runoff**. Part of this runoff evaporates back into the atmosphere, where it may again fall as rain. Eventually, much of

Figure 7.4
Distribution of the world's water
a) What percentage of the world's water is freshwater?
b) What percentage of this freshwater is usable?
c) Which two usable sources contain the most freshwater?

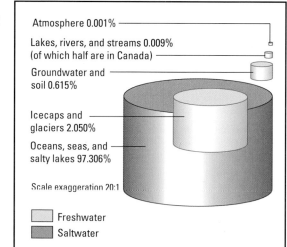

Atmosphere 0.001%

Lakes, rivers, and streams 0.009% (of which half are in Canada)

Groundwater and soil 0.615%

Icecaps and glaciers 2.050%

Oceans, seas, and salty lakes 97.306%

Scale exaggeration 20:1

☐ Freshwater
■ Saltwater

the remaining runoff returns to the oceans to complete the hydrologic cycle. (See Figure 7.5.)

The water that is absorbed into the pores and crevices of soil and bedrock is called **groundwater**. This water may be drawn up by plant roots and returned to the atmosphere through the process of **transpiration**. It may also reach the surface as spring water. Or it may seep slowly into the earth under the pull of gravity.

The amount of runoff and groundwater moving through the hydrologic cycle does not change much. Canada, for example, has 9 per cent of all of the world's runoff water and 20 per cent of its groundwater at any given time.

4 **Refer to Figure 7.5.**
  a) **Draw a sketch of the hydrologic cycle in your notebook. Be sure to include the ruled blank lines as they appear in the figure.**
  b) **Select terms from the word pool to correctly label your sketch.**
  c) **On your sketch, label five ways in which people use water as it moves through the hydrologic cycle.**
  d) **Explain why water is a renewable resource. You should refer to your sketch in your explanation.**

5 **Describe three things that can happen to precipitation in the hydrologic cycle after it falls to earth.**

Word Pool
Evaporation (1 blank)
Condensation (1 blank)
Solar radiation (1 blank)
Precipitation (2 blanks)
Infiltration (1 blank)
Groundwater flow (1 blank)
Runoff (1 blank)
Transpiration (1 blank)
Winds (1 blank)

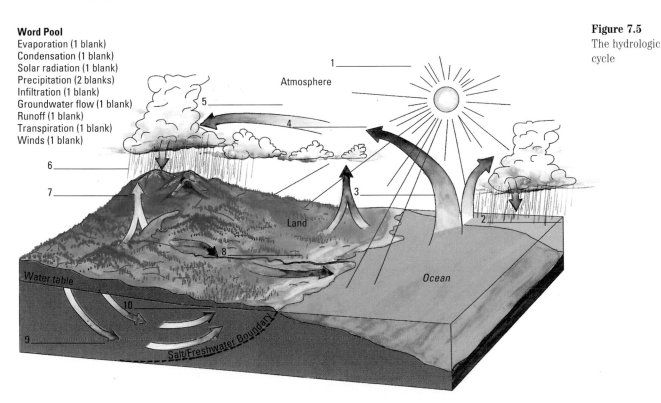

Figure 7.5
The hydrologic cycle

Groundwater

The different movements of groundwater within the hydrologic cycle are shown in Figure 7.6. It is estimated that two-thirds of the world's freshwater is stored below ground. Even in Canada, there is more water underground than on the surface. About 80 per cent of the water used in the rural areas of Canada comes from groundwater obtained from wells drilled into aquifers. Farms and ranches use this water to feed their livestock, poultry, and greenhouse plants and to sanitize equipment. In Prince Edward Island, 100 per cent of the water supply is obtained from groundwater. The urban centres in Yukon obtain 65 per cent of their water supply from groundwater. Cities in Saskatchewan rely on groundwater for 26 per cent of their water supply. This is because the supply of surface water cannot meet the needs of these communities.

Runoff and drainage basins

Precipitation that is not absorbed into the soil, evaporated, or transpired ends up as runoff. In southern Canada, about half of the precipitation flows over the surface as runoff, forming rivers, lakes, bogs, and other wetlands. This runoff moves at various speeds towards the lowest elevation at 0 m, or sea level. For example, rainwater may flow over the ground surface, enter a river, and flow quickly to the ocean. On the other hand, when precipitation falls as snow or ice, it may remain on the ground for several months before melting and becoming runoff. Where runoff flows into lakes or wetlands, it may take years before it reaches the ocean.

An area drained by a major river and its tributaries is called a **drainage basin**. Figure 7.7 shows the Cassidy River drainage basin. Around the edge of the basin is an

Figure 7.6
The groundwater system

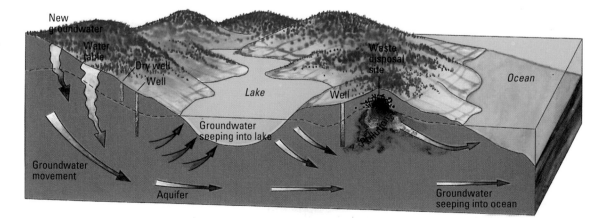

Water Table: Pore spaces are filled with water. This is the upper level at which groundwater is available to serve a well or feed a lake.

Aquifer: A porous rock layer that holds water and allows it to flow through freely.

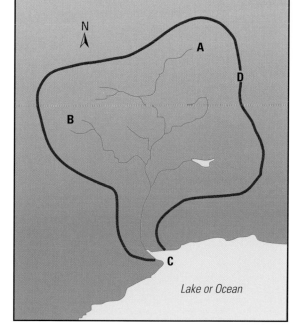

A SOURCE: Where a river begins.
B TRIBUTARY: Stream or river draining into a larger stream or river.
C MOUTH: Point where a river enters a lake or sea.
D WATERSHED: Dividing line between drainage basins.

N

A

D

B

C

Lake or Ocean

Figure 7.7
The Cassidy River drainage basin
In what general direction does the Cassidy River flow?

imaginary line known as the **watershed**. All runoff inside the watershed flows into the Cassidy River. Figure 7.9 on page 112 shows the areas of Canada that are within the drainage basins of the three oceans as well as Hudson Bay and the Gulf of Mexico.

6 a) Rank order the five ocean drainage basins in Figure 7.10 by area, from largest to smallest.
   b) Identify two places in Canada where water flows into three different drainage basins.
   c) Refer to a map of population distribution in Canada. Which drainage basin has the greatest total population?
   d) In which drainage basin is your community located?

Streams in a drainage basin

Streams differ in many ways. In the upper drainage basin near the watershed, they often contain less water, with rocky beds strewn with rapids. These "youthful" streams occupy V-shaped valleys. (See Figure 7.8a.) They erode downward into the highest part of the drainage basin.

As tributaries continue to flow into one another, the streams increase their water flow. This enables them to smooth out their beds and form wide curves, or meanders. (See Figure 7.8b.) These meanders cut into the stream banks and widen the valleys into a narrow U-shape. The stream is now in its "mature" stage.

In the lower drainage basin, the water from all the tributaries is concentrated into one channel with a large and regular flow. This channel has large meanders that become so curved that they are cut off to form horseshoe-shaped water bodies, known as **oxbow lakes**. (See Figure 7.8c.) During periods of high rainfall, the river may overflow its banks and flood its wide, level valley floor, or **floodplain**. The stream is now considered to be in its "old age" stage.

At its mouth, the stream may deposit large amounts of sand, silt, and clay, called **sediments**. If the lake or ocean is shallow and has no strong currents, these sediments may build up to form a large, marshy delta.

Figure 7.8
Types of streams in a typical drainage basin
A A youthful stream channel and valley
B A mature stream channel and valley
C An old-age stream channel and valley

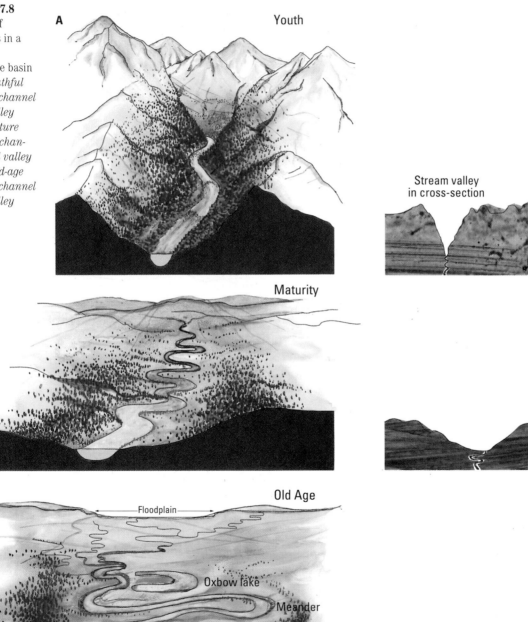

A   Youth

Stream valley in cross-section

B   Maturity

C   Old Age

Floodplain

Oxbow lake

Meander

Floodplain

7 Obtain a map of your province that shows rivers and other drainage features.
  a) Identify the river that drains the land around your community.
  b) Draw a sketch map indicating the route runoff takes from your community to a large lake or to the ocean.
  c) List the ways in which water is used as it flows to the lake or ocean shown on your sketch map.

Figure 7.9 shows the **water wealth** of each river basin in Canada. Water wealth is determined by the number of people that depend on a river flow of one cubic metre of water per second. For example, in the Pacific Coastal basin there are thirty-eight people per cubic metre of water flow per second. The fewer the number of people per cubic metre of water, the greater the water wealth.

8 Refer to Figures 7.9 and 7.10.
  a) On an outline map of Canada, draw the boundaries of the five ocean drainage basins. Label each basin.
  b) Draw two or three arrows to show the main direction of runoff in each drainage basin.
  c) Label Canada's ten largest lakes on your map and indicate into which ocean each lake eventually flows: Lake Superior; Lake Huron; Great Bear Lake; Great Slave Lake; Lake Erie; Lake Winnipeg; Lake Ontario; Lake Athabasca; Reindeer Lake; Lake Winnipegosis.

9 Refer to Figure 7.9.
  a) List the ocean basins in descending order, from greatest water wealth to least.

  b) Note the average water wealth for each basin. Which ocean basins have an average water wealth that is higher than the Canadian average? Which basins have an average water wealth that is lower than the Canadian average?

10 Figure 7.9 shows that there are great differences in water wealth within an ocean drainage basin. Name the two rivers in the Atlantic Ocean basin that i) have a greater water wealth than most of Canada, and ii) have less water wealth than most of Canada. How might these differences in water wealth affect human activity?

11 a) Which ocean drainage basins are most likely to have water shortages? Explain your answer.
  b) How might people living in these ocean basins cope with these shortages?

12 "Canada's river drainage pattern carries large volumes of water *away* from potential users." Is this statement true or false? Explain your answer with specific references to Figure 7.10.

Runoff rates

Most Canadian cities and industries are dependent on water from rivers and lakes. The **runoff rate**, or the amount of water moving over the ground, determines the size of the water supply. Runoff rates are affected by the slope of the land, temperature, vegetation cover, soil and rock types, and the intensity of precipitation.

Figure 7.9
Drainage
basins and
water wealth

OCEAN BASIN REGION	RIVER BASIN REGION	WATER WEALTH* INDICATOR	
		RIVER BASIN	OCEAN BASIN
Pacific	1 Pacific Coastal	38	
	2 Fraser-Lower Mainland	444	
	3 Okanagan-Similkameen	2 554	109
	4 Columbia	80	
	5 Yukon	9	
Arctic	6 Peace-Athabasca	99	
	7 Lower Mackenzie	6	17
	8 Arctic Coast Islands	1	
Gulf of Mexico	9 Missouri	1 167	1 167
Hudson Bay	10 North Saskatchewan	4 632	
	11 South Saskatchewan	5 364	
	12 Assiniboine-Red	26 000	
	13 Winnipeg	102	
	14 Lower Saskatchewan-Nelson	117	141
	15 Churchill	97	
	16 Keewatin	1	
	17 Northern Ontario	26	
	18 Northern Quebec	6	
Atlantic	19 Great Lakes	2 471	
	20 Ottawa	638	
	21 St. Lawrence	2 427	
	22 North Shore-Gaspé	75	583
	23 St. John-St. Croix	504	
	24 Maritime Coastal	426	
	25 Newfoundland-Labrador	61	
Canada		232	

*The number of people dependent on a flow rate of one cubic metre per second.

Source: Based on data from *Inland Water Directorate*, Environment Canada.

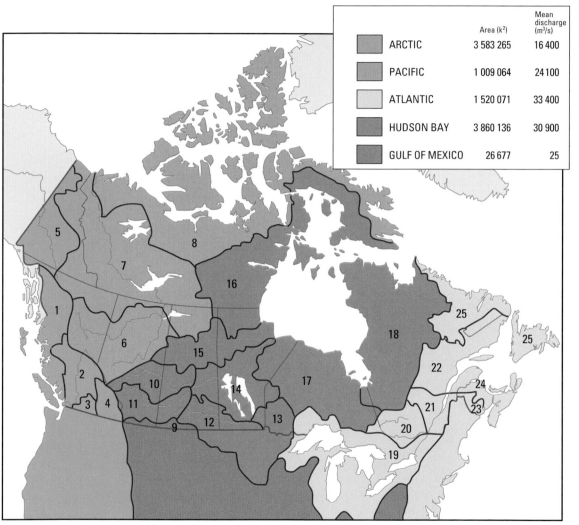

Figure 7.10
Canada's drainage basins

	Area (k²)	Mean discharge (m³/s)
ARCTIC	3 583 265	16 400
PACIFIC	1 009 064	24 100
ATLANTIC	1 520 071	33 400
HUDSON BAY	3 860 136	30 900
GULF OF MEXICO	26 677	25

13 Consider the following pairs of situations. Which condition in each pair would produce the most runoff? Explain your choices.

a) temperatures continually above freezing or temperatures continually below freezing

b) a coniferous forest or a freshly ploughed field

c) level plains or rolling hills

d) a rapid change from winter to spring or a gradual change from winter to spring

e) steady cyclonic rainfall or intense convectional rainfall

f) a city or a rural area.

14 What are the disadvantages of a high rate of runoff?

Snow accumulation, snow melt, and precipitation patterns influence when water runs off. These **runoff patterns** vary with the seasons. Data on runoff patterns are gathered by gauging stations located on rivers across Canada. Figure 7.11 provides temperature and precipitation data for each area. Figure 7.12 illustrates runoff data collected on selected Canadian rivers.

Figure 7.11
Climate data for selected rivers

15 Refer to Figures 7.11 and 7.12.

a) In what season do most Canadian rivers have the highest runoff? Why do rivers peak in this season?

b) Which river has the most delayed peak? When does this occur? What accounts for this delay?

c) How does the runoff pattern of the St. Lawrence differ from other rivers? Why?

d) How does the Somass runoff pattern differ from other rivers? Why?

16 a) Is the monthly precipitation pattern for the Thames River constant or varied? Compare it with precipitation data for the Somass or Black river areas.

b) Account for the seasonal runoff pattern in the Thames River.

	J	F	M	A	M	J	J	A	S	O	N	D	YEAR
South Nahanni area, NT													
Temperature (°C)	-28	-23	-15	-3	8	14	17	14	7	-2	-16	-25	-4°C
Precipitation (mm)	20	19	22	15	31	39	59	45	31	24	27	24	355 mm
Somass area, BC													
Temperature(°C)	1	4	5	8	12	15	17	18	15	10	5	3	9°C
Precipitation (mm)	278	246	187	93	50	36	24	39	90	194	294	321	1854 mm
Poplar area, SK													
Temperature (°C)	-15	-12	-5	4	10	15	18	17	11	6	-4	-11	3°C
Precipitation (mm)	16	12	18	22	48	65	45	37	30	14	14	20	340 mm
Black area, NT													
Temperature (°C)	-36	-37	-32	-23	-10	0	8	6	-1	-12	-24	-32	-16°C
Precipitation (mm)	3	4	3	7	6	10	23	37	22	16	7	5	144 mm
Thames area, ON													
Temperature (°C)	-7	-6	-1	6	12	18	20	20	15	9	3	-4	7°C
Precipitation (mm)	75	60	75	81	67	74	72	80	79	73	85	88	909
St. Lawrence River, ON													
Temperature (°C)	-10	-9	-3	6	13	18	21	20	15	9	3	-6	7°C
Precipitation (mm)	62	68	61	74	70	70	76	99	95	76	81	87	917 mm
Saint John River, NB													
Temperature (°C)	-11	-10	-3	4	11	16	19	18	13	7	2	-8	5°C
Precipitation (mm)	87	72	65	71	68	85	79	83	72	86	85	93	945 mm

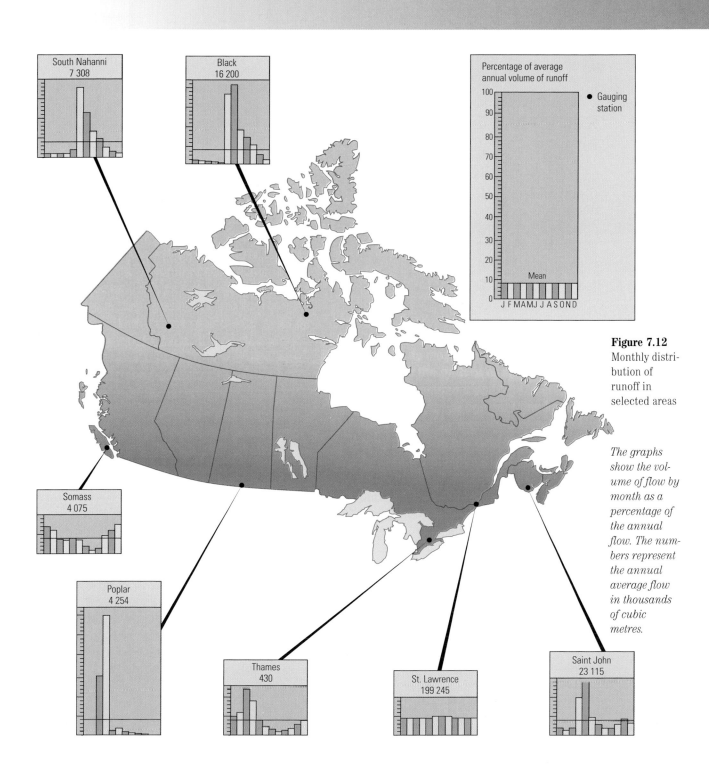

Figure 7.12
Monthly distribution of runoff in selected areas

The graphs show the volume of flow by month as a percentage of the annual flow. The numbers represent the annual average flow in thousands of cubic metres.

17 Describe and explain the pattern of seasonal runoff for the rivers in your area .

Runoff: human use and its impact

Canadians need access to water year-round. However, the amount of water we need changes throughout the year. In many communities, water usage peaks in July when demand can be as much as 36 per cent higher than in February.

18 Why is July the peak water demand month in most Canadian communities?

19 a) Which river in Figure 7.12 would be the best supplier of water for an industry needing large volumes of water year-round?
   b) Which river would be the poorest for irrigating crops?
   c) Which three rivers would be the least suited to industrial or agricultural use based on their runoff patterns? Explain.

20 How might a community located along a river deal with i) frequent floods and ii) a summer water shortage?

Classifying water use

Water use is classified as either **withdrawal** or **instream**. When water is removed from its natural location, it is withdrawal use. Water used in homes, farms, businesses, and industries is classified as withdrawal. If the demand does not remove the water from its natural location, it is instream use.

Fishing, swimming, canoeing, and shipping are examples of instream uses.

Figure 7.13 shows the main water uses in Canada. It indicates the total amount of water taken from streams and rivers as well as the amount of water consumed by the users and the amount returned to the source. In three of the five uses, the water is recirculated or recycled. In almost every case, however, the quality of recirculated or recycled water is reduced.

21 a) In chart form, identify ten ways in which water is used. Indicate whether each is a withdrawal or an instream use.
   b) Classify each of the major water users in Figure 7.13 as either withdrawal or instream use.

22 Refer to Figure 7.13.
   a) Calculate the amount of water consumed by each user in millions of cubic metres per year. For example, agricultural use consumed 2752 million cubic metres (3559 – 807 = 2752).
   b) Calculate the percentage of water taken from the water supply consumed by each user. Divide the amount of water consumed by the total amount withdrawn from the water supply, then multiply by 100. For example, the percentage of agricultural use consumed is 2752 ÷ 3559 x 100 = 77.3%.
   c) Which two uses have the highest percentage of water consumed? Explain why.
   d) Which two uses have the lowest percentage of water consumed? Explain why.

e) Which three users recycle or recirculate water? Explain why this is possible.

f) Which two users do not recycle the water they use? Give at least one reason why in each case.

23 Imagine the water supply in your community has been contaminated with toxic chemicals. For the next two weeks, everyone is limited to 25 L of water a day from the supply at the community centre. Residents have been issued ration cards.

In a group of three or four students, develop a plan to cope with water rationing. What water uses would you change or discontinue? How would you conserve the water you have? Are there ways to recycle or reuse some of the water? After your discussion, write an outline of your group's plan.

Problems with our water supply

Even with all of its freshwater resources, Canada faces problems with its water supply. These problems are created when our water resources are not properly managed or protected. In some cases, the water supply is too small to meet the demands placed upon it. In other cases, the quality of our water is reduced as a result of misuse or pollution.

Water shortages: agriculture

Although we have more freshwater than any other country in the world, some regions of Canada do not receive enough rain to meet their needs. Figure 7.14 shows Canada's water deficit regions.

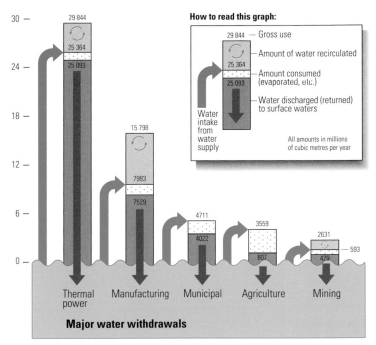

Figure 7.13 Water use in Canada

24 Refer to Figure 7.14.
a) In which river basins are there serious rainfall shortages?
b) Using Canadian climate maps, explain why these regions experience water shortages.
c) If agriculture is to succeed in areas of limited rainfall, what must be done? Why?

25 Using Figure 7.14 and your atlas, draw a half-page sketch map of Alberta and Saskatchewan. Include the provincial boundaries and the area with a water deficit greater than 20.3 cm annually. Identify and label the rivers that flow through this water-deficit area and the city of Medicine Hat.

26 a) Using Figure 7.16, draw a diagram illustrating the yearly flow for the South

Figure 7.14
Canada's water
deficit regions

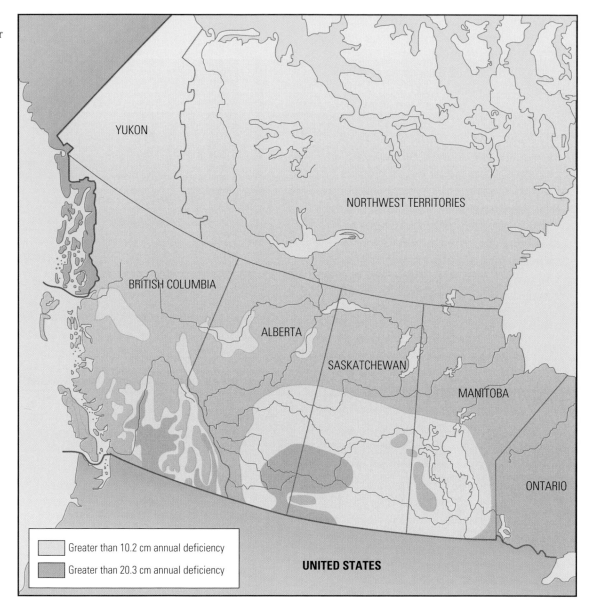

YUKON

NORTHWEST TERRITORIES

BRITISH COLUMBIA

ALBERTA

SASKATCHEWAN

MANITOBA

ONTARIO

Greater than 10.2 cm annual deficiency

Greater than 20.3 cm annual deficiency

UNITED STATES

Saskatchewan River at Medicine Hat.
(Use the bottom half of the page on which
you drew your sketch map of Alberta
and Saskatchewan.) Your diagram
should be similar to that in Figure 7.12.

b) The growing season in this part of
Canada is from June to September.
Would the South Saskatchewan River
be a suitable source of irrigation water
for crops? Explain your answer.

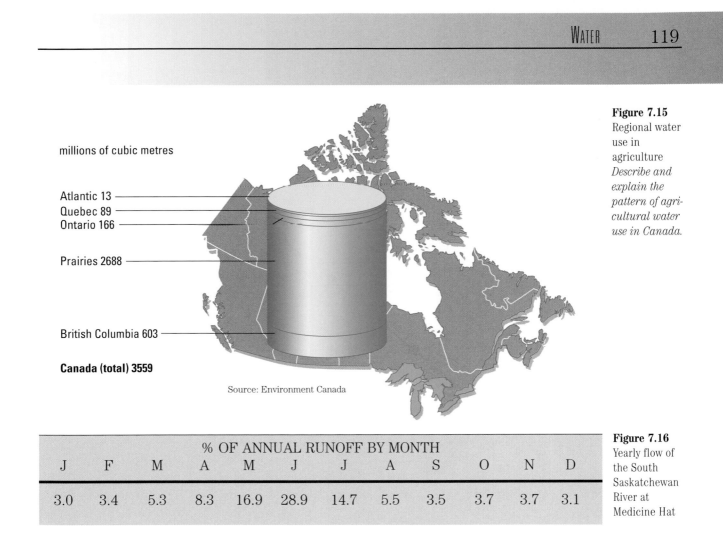

millions of cubic metres

Atlantic 13
Quebec 89
Ontario 166

Prairies 2688

British Columbia 603

Canada (total) 3559

Source: Environment Canada

Figure 7.15
Regional water use in agriculture *Describe and explain the pattern of agricultural water use in Canada.*

				% OF ANNUAL RUNOFF BY MONTH							
J	F	M	A	M	J	J	A	S	O	N	D
3.0	3.4	5.3	8.3	16.9	28.9	14.7	5.5	3.5	3.7	3.7	3.1

Figure 7.16
Yearly flow of the South Saskatchewan River at Medicine Hat

c) What could be done to ensure enough irrigation water is available throughout the growing season?

Dams and diversions

One way to overcome shortages is to build dams to store or divert water from areas of abundant water. Some dams store the excess flow of rivers during wet periods for use in drier seasons. This ensures that water is always available. Dams also divert water from one drainage basin to another.

In Canada, many of our major rivers carry the water north away from the heavily populated regions of the south. Damming these rivers diverts water into south-flowing rivers for use in power plants, industries, cities, and farms.

When water is diverted from one basin to another it is called **interbasin transfer**. The largest interbasin transfer in Canada is the James Bay Project. (See Figure 7.17.) This project began in 1971. It produces hydroelectricity using the large rivers flowing into James Bay. The water transfers occur where the flow of the

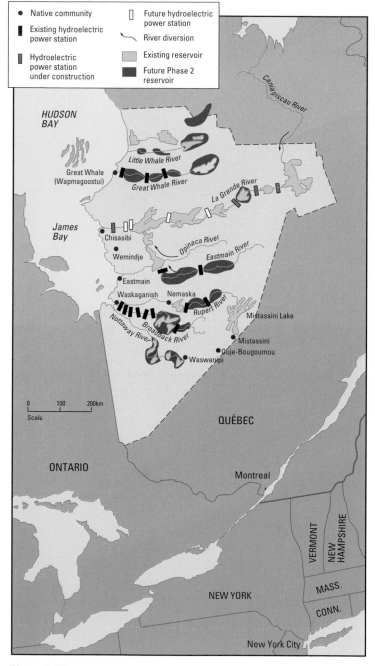

Figure 7.17
The James Bay Project: a major water transfer

Eastmain, Opinaca, and Caniapiscau rivers are diverted into La Grande Rivière. These diversions double the amount of water flowing in La Grande Rivière. So far, over $21 billion has been invested in dams, dykes, power stations, airports, roadways, and power lines to produce and transport hydroelectricity. This power is sold to markets in the United States as well as Quebec.

The second phase of the project is currently under construction. There were plans for a third phase, a giant $13-billion diversion project on the Grande Rivière de la Baleine and its tributary, the Petite Rivière de la Baleine to the north, and additional hydroelectric power stations on the Broadback, Nottaway, and Rupert rivers to the south. However, in November 1994, the Quebec government put this project on hold indefinitely. It would have flooded

Figure 7.18
Dam on the
James Bay
Power Project

3400 km^2 and seriously damaged the natural environment of the homeland of 10 000 Quebec Cree, who opposed the project.

27 Refer to Figure 7.17.
  a) Describe the location of the James Bay power project.
  b) Draw a sketch map of the project showing La Grande Rivière, the three rivers that were diverted to add to the runoff flow of La Grande Rivière, and the rivers involved in the second phase of the project.
  c) Why is this project a threat to the way of life of Native peoples living in the region?

28 Use your resource centre to find out more about the James Bay power project. Write a report outlining both the negative and positive aspects of the scheme.

Climate change and water supply

One of the major environmental changes facing Canada and the world in the twenty-first century is **global warming**. Many scientists believe that rising levels of carbon dioxide in the earth's atmosphere will bring major climatic changes to countries like Canada. One predicted change is an increase in global temperatures of 1.5° to 4.5°C over the next fifty years. To many Canadians, the idea of a warmer climate doesn't sound too bad! There would be shorter winters, lower heating bills, less snow to shovel, and less salt poured across icy roads to rust out the family car. But there is a dark lining to this cloud. Figure 7.19 illustrates some of the possible effects forecast by scientists working for Environment Canada.

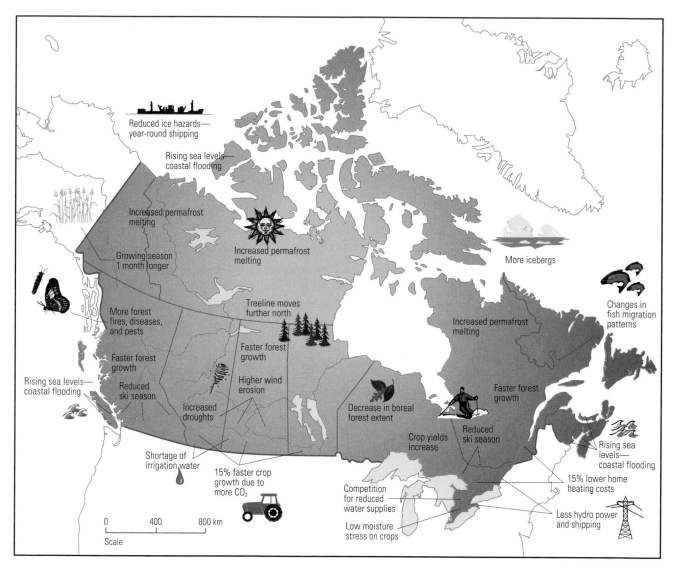

Reduced ice hazards—
year-round shipping

Rising sea levels—
coastal flooding

Increased permafrost
melting

Growing season
1 month longer

Increased permafrost
melting

More icebergs

More forest
fires, diseases,
and pests

Treeline moves
further north

Changes in
fish migration
patterns

Faster forest
growth

Faster forest
growth

Increased permafrost
melting

Rising sea levels—
coastal flooding

Reduced
ski season

Higher wind
erosion

Decrease in boreal
forest extent

Faster forest
growth

Reduced
ski season

Increased
droughts

Rising sea
levels—
coastal flooding

Crop yields
increase

Shortage of
irrigation water

15% faster crop
growth due to
more CO_2

Competition
for reduced
water supplies

15% lower home
heating costs

Less hydro power
and shipping

Low moisture
stress on crops

0   400   800 km

Scale

Figure 7.19
Possible effects
of global
warming

29 Refer to Figure 7.19
a) Make a list of good changes and bad
changes that may result from global
warming.
b) Write a letter to your Member of
Parliament expressing your concerns
about the effects of global warming in
Canada.

Canadian water exports: an issue

Climate change will affect the water supplies of the United States. Many studies predict that water levels in the Great Lakes
could drop as the climate warms. This is
because evaporation would increase
because of the higher temperatures.

Droughts would become more common in the Corn Belt—that area stretching from Ontario, Michigan, Ohio, Indiana, and Illinois west to Iowa and Minnesota. Climates would also become drier in the wheat-growing areas of the Great Plains that stretch from Saskatchewan to Kansas. Rivers in the southwestern United States, from Colorado and New Mexico west to California, would have lower runoff flows. This would result in more problems in a region that already suffers from serious water shortages. Lower river flows would mean less irrigation water for farmers in Arizona and California—water that is used to grow a wide variety of fruits and vegetables that are imported to Canada in the winter.

These changes would increase the pressure for Canada to export some of its surplus water to the United States. Many Canadians are opposed to such exports, however. They feel that Canada should be cautious about preserving such a precious resource. Once we begin to sell water, it would be difficult to reverse the decision, even if we experienced our own water shortages. Others see an opportunity to turn our excess water into a valuable export. Canada could earn money for surplus water that is currently unused. Furthermore, the United States would pay for the building of canals and pipelines to move the water south. Some of these facilities could bring water to the Prairies and southern Ontario. This would offset the possible effects of the drier climate created by global warming.

One scheme to export water to the US was proposed in the mid-1980s by a Canadian company. Called the Grand Canal Project, this $100 billion scheme would turn James Bay into a freshwater lake by building a dam to cut it off from the salty waters of Hudson Bay. (See Figure 7.20.) This freshwater would then be transported south into the Great Lakes. From there it would travel by canals and rivers to various parts of the United States.

30 a) Summarize the arguments for and against exporting Canadian water to the United States.
    b) Which side would you support on the issue of Canadian water exports? Explain your answer.

31 Refer to Figure 7.20.
    a) What large body of water will become a large freshwater reservoir?
    b) How will saltwater be kept out of the reservoir?
    c) What is the source of the freshwater that will fill the reservoir?
    d) Why is this water considered "waste water" today?

32 Prepare a presentation on the Grand Canal project. Your presentation should include:
    a) the purpose of the Grand Canal project
    b) a description of the route of the Grand Canal
    c) the role of the Great Lakes
    d) the regions of North America that would benefit from the project
    e) the advantages and disadvantages of the project
    f) the anticipated response of Canadian environmental groups.

Figure 7.20
The Grand
Canal Project

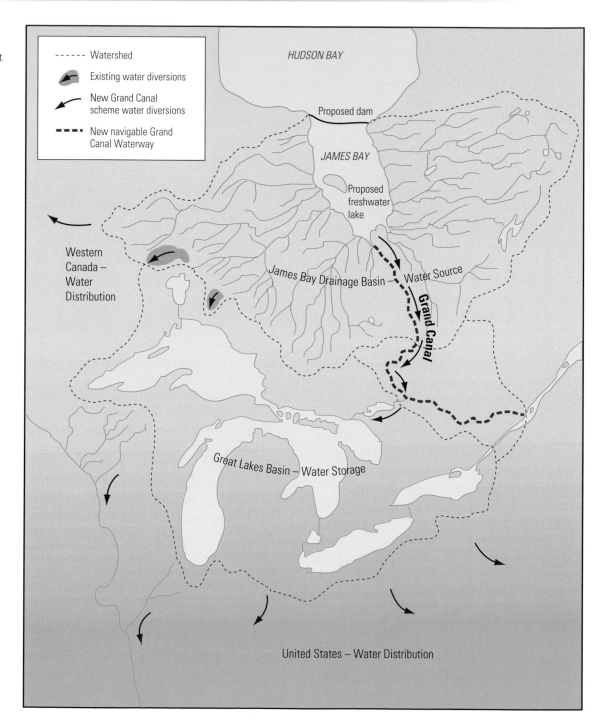

Watershed

Existing water diversions

New Grand Canal scheme water diversions

New navigable Grand Canal Waterway

HUDSON BAY

Proposed dam

JAMES BAY

Proposed freshwater lake

Western Canada – Water Distribution

James Bay Drainage Basin — Water Source

Grand Canal

Great Lakes Basin – Water Storage

United States – Water Distribution

The problem of water quality

In recent years, many environmentalists, as well as ordinary citizens, have become concerned about the safety of our drinking water. This is especially true for the millions of people who depend on the Great Lakes for water. Scientific studies have indicated that many rivers and lakes are contaminated with chemical poisons called **toxins**. Some toxins occur naturally. But most, like dioxins and PCBs (polychlorinated biphenyl), are produced by human activities. Common chemicals containing dioxins include wood preservatives, herbicides, electrical insulators, and hydraulic

Figure 7.21
Pathways of pollution

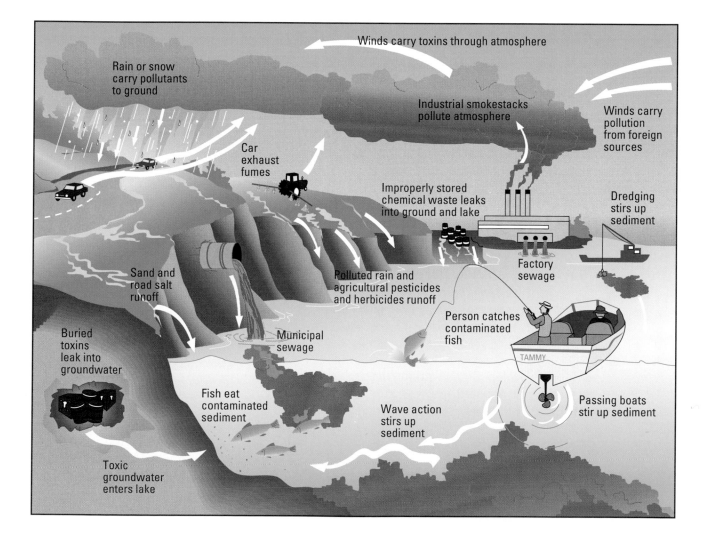

Winds carry toxins through atmosphere

Rain or snow carry pollutants to ground

Industrial smokestacks pollute atmosphere

Winds carry pollution from foreign sources

Car exhaust fumes

Improperly stored chemical waste leaks into ground and lake

Dredging stirs up sediment

Sand and road salt runoff

Polluted rain and agricultural pesticides and herbicides runoff

Factory sewage

Buried toxins leak into groundwater

Municipal sewage

Person catches contaminated fish

TAMMY

Fish eat contaminated sediment

Wave action stirs up sediment

Passing boats stir up sediment

Toxic groundwater enters lake

fluids. PCBs are found in electrical transformers and paper coatings. At one time, PCB-contaminated oils were used to control dust on gravel roads. Figure 7.21 illustrates the many ways that toxic and other harmful chemicals enter and move through the hydrologic cycle.

We now know that toxic chemicals are harmful to fish, wildlife, and humans. Continuous exposure to even small amounts of these chemicals can cause cancer, nerve disorders, and birth defects. These chemicals end up in our bodies when we eat fish and drink tap water from contaminated lakes and rivers. We also absorb poisons through our skin and breathe them into our systems through chemical-laden air. Scientists are still studying the effects on humans of long-term exposure to these toxins. It may be years before they have all of the answers. In the meantime, 16 per cent of Canadian households choose to buy bottled water rather than drink what they believe is unsafe tap water.

33 a) Use Figure 7.21 to describe the various ways in which toxic chemicals enter and pass through the hydrologic cycle.
   b) Suggest why the Great Lakes and the St. Lawrence River are contaminated.

34 Identify a lake, river, or stream in your area that is polluted.
   a) How can you tell that this water is polluted?
   b) What do you think is the cause of this pollution?
   c) What can be done to clean up this pollution?

Cleaning up the Great Lakes

The Great Lakes are a shared resource between the United States and Canada. Resolving the problem of toxic waste will require co-operation between these two countries. The International Joint Commission oversees issues of mutual concern. One of its major responsibilities is to carry out the Canada-US Great Lakes Water Quality Agreement. The purpose of the agreement is to improve the quality of the Great Lakes basin ecosystem. One of the first steps the commission took to clean up the lakes was to identify the most seriously polluted areas. Studies indicated there were forty-three such areas, mainly in industrial harbours and bays and rivers with many industries along their banks. The most seriously polluted areas are shown in Figure 7.22.

35 Look at Figure 7.22.
   a) Which one of the Great Lakes has the most serious toxic waste problem?
   b) Which single place has the greatest toxic waste problem? How did you reach this conclusion?
   c) Is more chemical contamination entering the Great Lakes from the American side or the Canadian side? How can you tell? Why do you think this is the case?

36 a) Draw a sketch map of the Great Lakes. Label each of the five major lakes.
   b) Draw in arrows to show the direction of water movement in each lake.
   c) Why do you think people who rely on Lakes Erie and Ontario for their water

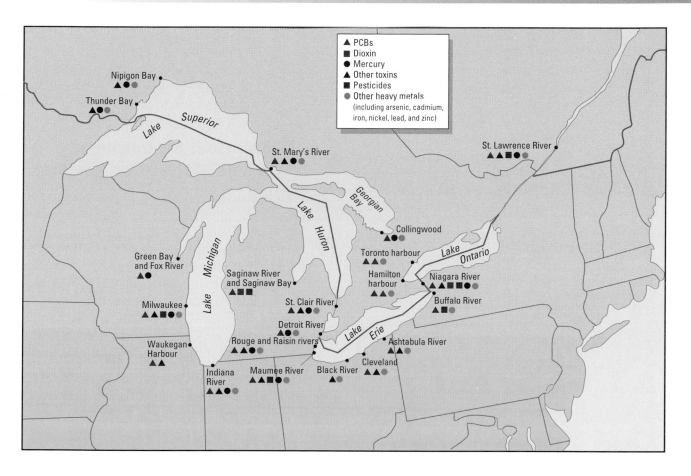

Figure 7.22
Toxic areas in
the Great
Lakes
*Why is an
international
problem like
Great Lakes
pollution more
difficult to
solve than a
national prob-
lem?*

supply are concerned about the safety of their drinking water?

37 "The Great Lakes basin is a water-rich area about to become a water-poor area." Explain this statement. Do you agree or disagree with it? Use data from Figure 7.9 and the maps from this chapter to explain your answer.

Once the most seriously polluted areas in the Great Lakes were identified, the commission had to draw up appropriate action plans. The first step was to track down the sources of the contaminants. The next step was to restrict the release of these toxins into the environment. The biggest step, however, was to clean up those areas that were already contaminated.

Environmentalists have had great success combatting Great Lakes pollution. In the 1960s and 1970s, scientists predicted Lake Erie was so seriously polluted that it would never recover. Today, through restrictions on untreated city sewage and the use of phosphorus-rich detergents, the lake has been taken off the endangered list. In the early 1970s, PCB levels in many of the Great Lakes were rising steadily. Today, however, these levels are on the decline. Still, for each success story, many other serious pollution problems remain. The task of cleaning up the Great Lakes is not over yet.

38 a) Why is the information in Figure 7.22 a source of concern for people living in the Great Lakes region?

b) Why does the information in Figure 7.23 give these people some hope for the future?

c) Although progress has been made, why is it too early to believe the toxic pollution problem is solved?

39 a) Working with a partner, prepare a draft of an environmental protection bill. Your bill should identify specific sources of contamination and suggest solutions to each problem. Include appropriate penalties that would be imposed on those who do not comply with the bill.

b) People concerned about water quality have formed action groups to make their concerns known. Do some research in your library resource centre to identify some of these groups. Choose one group and write a report on the solutions it proposes.

Simulation: evaluating a hydroelectric power project

The Albany River flows eastward from the Canadian Shield and drains into James Bay at Fort Albany. This river has been targeted for a massive hydroelectric power project. This will involve the building of four mega-dams along the river. These will create huge reservoirs that can be used to drive turbines to produce electricity. Ontario Hydro will be able to sell large amounts of this electricity to New York state, which is hungry for more power.

40 a) Working with a small group, prepare a presentation for one of the roles described in the briefing notes on pages 129–130. Discuss with your group what the impact of the power project will be on the group you represent. Make notes outlining your position.

b) Stage a mock inquiry in your classroom. Select one member from your group to present your position. The inquiry will be chaired by an impartial commissioner and a team of committee members.

c) After all the presentations have been made, the commissioner and the committee must summarize the pros and cons of the power project. They must then make a ruling on whether the project will go ahead as planned or be cancelled.

Figure 7.23
PCB concentrations found in gull eggs in the Great Lakes, 1974–1992

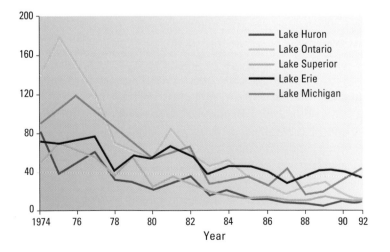

Legend:
— Lake Huron
— Lake Ontario
— Lake Superior
— Lake Erie
— Lake Michigan

Year

Briefing notes

A Native band leader: You represent 8500 Native people who live in the Albany River drainage basin. You make a living hunting, trapping, and fishing and you have always lived in balance with nature. You are concerned about the impact this project will have on your traditional way of life. You fear the project will destroy wildlife in the area and that you will be forced to relocate to make way for the large reservoirs. You believe that you have a right to live on this land. You do not want to be moved to a small town where your way of life will be lost. If this project goes ahead, you believe your band should be financially compensated.

The Minister of Indian and Northern Affairs: Although you are concerned with how the project will affect Native people, you believe that overall it will raise the standard of living in the region. The construction of the hydro project will provide jobs, which will reduce the amount of financial support required from the federal government. You recognize that Native people living in the area deserve compensation for the loss of their homeland and that they will need help once they are relocated. Privately, the Cabinet has agreed to a compensation package of up to $250 million. But you have been instructed to try to negotiate a smaller settlement, with payments made over several years. Above all, however, the government wants this project to go ahead!

A hydro commissioner from New York state: Your government is desperate for more power! The hydro authority has been forced to build more nuclear power plants, but these are unpopular with voters. Ontario has many rivers that could be used to generate clean, efficient power. You can buy power from these plants at a much lower rate than the cost of building more nuclear power plants. In addition, there would be no environmental threat to the state. This would be a popular move with the voters of New York state.

The director of Save Our River Environments (SORE): As the head of this environmental group, you oppose this power project. It will require the flooding of 200 000 km^2 of land. When the flooded vegetation rots, it will produce mercury levels in water three times higher than is safe for human consumption. Fish and wildlife will be harmed by these high mercury levels. In addition, artificially swollen rivers will carry more sediment. This will build up at Fort Albany, destroying rich beds of sea grass which are used by migrating ducks and geese. Shorelines will not be protected and will erode easily. Breeding grounds for wild fowl and spawning grounds for fish will be destroyed. Instead of building more power plants, Ontario Hydro should be more efficient and consumers should use less energy.

The regional director of the World Wildlife Fund: The World Wildlife Fund is concerned about the threat to wildlife in the region. The water flowing into James Bay in the winter when hydro demands are highest will be ten times greater than normal. This will kill many mammals that have a saltwater habitat. More freshwater in the winter will result in increased amounts of ice in the spring. This will hurt the Beluga whales, which like to nurse their young in the spring freshwater. Changes in water flow could also jeopardize polar bears and ringed seals. The WWF wants a ten-year environmental study to be conducted before this project gets the go-ahead.

A commissioner from Ontario Hydro: Ontario Hydro is running out of energy sources, but the population of the province is continuing to grow. You believe another power project is essential. This project would pay for itself because New York state needs more energy, too, and is willing to pay top dollar for energy from Ontario. This will help lower energy costs for Ontario users. While the Albany River project will cost $15 billion over the next twenty years, it should generate profits of $30 billion over the next fifty years. Hydroelectric power is also cost efficient. Nuclear power costs over three times as much, while coal-based power costs over six times as much! In addition, hydroelectric power is less harmful to the environment than coal or nuclear power.

FISHING

8

Canada has traditionally been rich in fish resources. Three oceans and hundreds of large freshwater lakes and rivers provide extensive marine environments for commercial and recreational fishing. This abundant natural resource was described by the explorer John Cabot in 1497 when he reached the shores of Newfoundland. In his journal, he wrote that the sea was "swarming with fish, which can be taken not only with net, but in baskets let down with a stone." His account soon attracted European fishers to these shores. Of course, Native peoples valued this resource long before Europeans arrived.

For centuries, Canada's fisheries have been the basis of hundreds of communities that dot the coastlines of the Atlantic and Pacific oceans. It is only in the 1980s and 1990s that this once renewable resource has become endangered by overfishing, pollution, and the possible effects of climatic change.

1 The average Canadian eats 6.8 kg of fish every year. People in other seafaring countries, such as Japan, Sweden, Britain, and Norway, eat twice as much.
  a) List the five foods you eat most often. Rank these by preference, with the most preferred food ranked number 1.
  b) In a group, share your list. Summarize the results by adding up the rankings for each food. The lowest total is the most preferred food. Where did fish and/or seafood rank in your group's list? Why do you think they received this ranking?

c) Why do you think Canadians eat so much less fish than people in Japan, Sweden, Britain, and Norway?

Since Canada has the longest coastline of any country in the world, it should not be surprising that it is also one of the world's leading exporters of fish. For over five centuries, the Atlantic fishery has been a way of life for thousands of people in Newfoundland, Nova Scotia, Prince Edward Island, New Brunswick, and eastern Quebec. Over 1000 communities along the Atlantic and Gulf of St. Lawrence shores have traditionally been dependent on fishing.

Figure 8.1
A fishing boat in St. John's, Newfoundland *Fish stocks were once abundant in Atlantic Canada but today many species are threatened by overfishing.*

On the west coast, the Pacific fishery of British Columbia is one of the world's richest. While it offers a variety of seafood, the west coast fishery is best known for one fish species: salmon. Canada also has a major inland, or freshwater, fishery. The Great Lakes, along with other major inland lakes such as Winnipeg, Manitoba, Winnipegosis, Athabasca, and Great Slave, provide the basis of this valuable fish resource.

2 Refer to Figure 8.2.
   a) How many Canadians are employed in commercial fishing?
   b) In small groups, brainstorm a list of jobs that are dependent upon or related to commercial fishing.

3 a) What percentage of the total production of fish is exported from each of the three fisheries?
   b) Why is so much seafood exported? Is this an advantage or disadvantage for Canada?

4 Refer to Figure 8.2.
   a) Which of the three fisheries would you consider to be the most important?
   b) Although only 18.5 per cent of the total catch comes from the Pacific fishery, it accounts for 29.4 per cent of the total value. What does this suggest about fishing incomes in the Pacific?

The Atlantic fishery

For over 400 years, boats and their crews from Britain, Portugal, France, and other nations have fished the waters off Canada's east coast. What conditions made this region one of the world's greatest fishing areas?

The marine food chain

Fish once thrived off the east coast as the result of physical conditions that are extremely favourable to **phytoplankton**. Phytoplankton is the basis of the marine food chain. These microscopic, single-celled plant organisms live in shallow seawater where sunlight can penetrate easily. They feed off mineral nutrients that result from decayed marine life. Microscopic, single-celled animal organisms called **zooplankton** feed on the phytoplankton. In turn, zooplankton serves as food for small fish like capelin and herring. Cod, haddock, and larg-

Figure 8.2
Canadian fisheries compared, 1994

FISHERY	NO. OF FISHERS	NO. OF FISH PLANT WORKERS	% OF TOTAL CATCH	% OF TOTAL VALUE	TOTAL PRODUCTION ($ millions)	TOTAL EXPORTS ($ millions)
Atlantic	61 3000	22 100	78.6	64.7	2100	1700
Pacific	20 100	3 200	18.5	29.4	880	780
Inland	8 500	700	2.9	5.9	230	180
Canada	**89 000**	**26 970**	**100.0**	**100.0**	**3210**	**2660**

Source: Department of Fisheries and Oceans Canada.

er marine animals such as seals and whales thrive on these small fish. Eventually these marine organisms die and decay. The supply of nutrients for phytoplankton is renewed and the cycle of life continues.

5 Draw and label a diagram illustrating the main links in the marine food chain.

The ocean waters off Nova Scotia and Newfoundland are less than 200 m deep. This is because the continent projects under the Atlantic Ocean, forming a **continental shelf**. (Figure 8.3 shows a cross-section through the continental shelf east of St. John's.) Some parts of the shelf are less than 150 m deep. These **fishing banks** are the places where fish gather to spawn and feed. Phytoplankton flourish here because the cold, nutrient-rich waters are at the surface where sunlight can penetrate the water. Ocean currents and fresh-water from the St. Lawrence stir up the water, making the nutrients available to the phytoplankton. Without this movement, the nutrients would settle on the dark

ocean floor well out of reach of the phytoplankton. Figure 8.4 shows the major fishing banks off the Atlantic coast.

6 On an outline map of Atlantic Canada, draw and label the major fishing banks shown in Figure 8.4.

The inshore fishery

There are two major types of fishing in the Atlantic—inshore fishing and offshore fishing. **Inshore fishing** uses small boats to fish in waters close to the coastline. **Offshore fishing** uses large vessels like trawlers to fish in waters far from shore. (See Figures 8.5 and 8.6.)

Inshore fishing boats remain within 20 km of shore and return to home port each day. The boats are launched from the hundreds of small harbours that dot the Atlantic coastline. About 80 per cent of all Atlantic fishing and 95 per cent of all fishing boats are inshore. Inshore boats are small, measuring

Figure 8.3
Fishing banks and the continental shelf

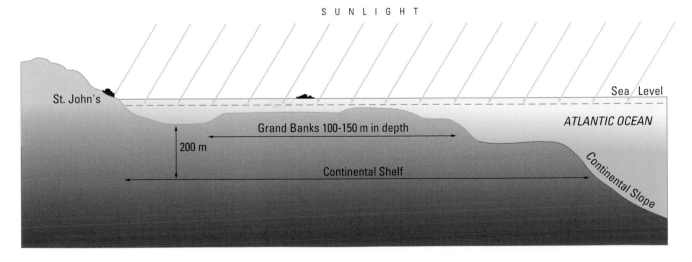

SUNLIGHT

St. John's

Sea Level

ATLANTIC OCEAN

Grand Banks 100-150 m in depth

200 m

Continental Shelf

Continental Slope

Figure 8.4
East coast
fisheries

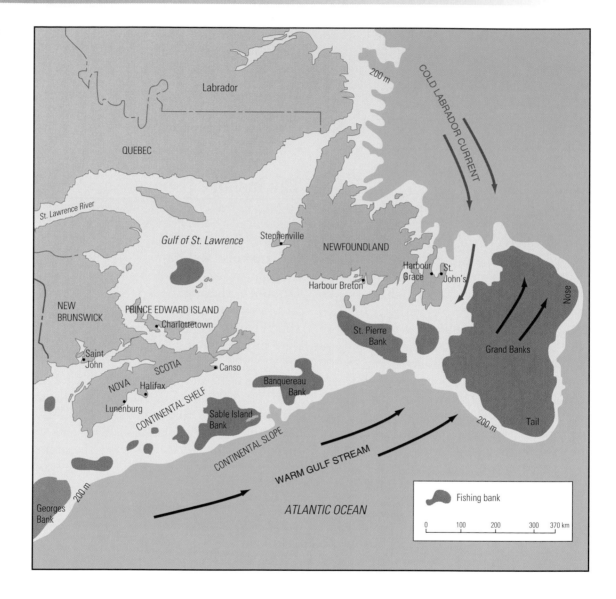

anywhere from 5 to 20 m in length. They require a small crew of one to three people.

Most inshore boats are independently owned and family run. The cost of a new, fully equipped boat can be $200 000, so most boats are older and have limited equipment. The inshore harvest includes lobster, shrimp, oysters, clams, herring, mackerel, haddock, pollock, redfish, hake, and halibut. But despite the variety of the catch, incomes are low and irregular. Most inshore fishers must supplement their incomes with other work or collect unemployment insurance during the off season.

Figure 8.5
Inshore fishery boats in a small harbour

Figure 8.6
A large ocean-going boat of the offshore fishing fleet

7 a) **What conditions made Atlantic Canada ideally suited for inshore fishing?**

  b) **What skills do you think are necessary to be a successful inshore fisher?**

  c) **Suggest reasons why inshore fishing is dying out in many parts of Atlantic Canada.**

8 **Describe what a typical day in the life of an inshore fisher might be like.**

Case study: fishing for shellfish

In dollars per kilogram, lobster is the most valuable seafood caught in Canada. (See Figure 8.7.) Most of the catch is taken within 2 to 5 km of the shores of Nova Scotia, New Brunswick, Prince Edward Island, the Magdalene Islands, and the island of Newfoundland. Because it is so valuable, the lobster fishery is strictly regulated. Lobster fishers must be licensed and must follow conservation measures. These include restrictions on minimum size, limits on the lobster-fishing season, quotas on the number of lobsters caught, and returning egg-bearing females to the ocean.

When the lobster season opens, fishers rush to set their traps in the best locations. The box-like traps are made with wooden slats and twine mesh. They are baited with cod heads, herring, or mackerel and lowered to a rocky bottom, usually within sight of the shore. The traps are weighted to keep them in place and then marked by the owner's numbered and coloured buoy. Traps must be checked for their catch daily. They are raised either by motorized winch or by hand line.

FISH SPECIES	ATLANTIC QUANTITY (t)	ATLANTIC VALUE ($000)	ATLANTIC ($/t)	PACIFIC QUANTITY (t)	PACIFIC VALUE ($000)	PACIFIC $/t
Cod	22 719	29 605	1 303	3 500	2 300	657
Haddock	6 955	13 965	2 008	0	0	0
Herring	206 772	27 676	134	40 218	80 000	1 989
Salmon	136	685	5 037	65 351	250 460	3 833
Scallop	91 382	138 646	1 517	107	504	4 710
Lobster	41 323	353 369	8 551	0	0	0
Shrimp	48 661	99 205	2 039	4 185	15 577	3 722
Crab	64 897	272 827	4 204	5 645	24 158	4 280
Total all species	**686 627**	**1 108 187**	**1 614**	**300 083**	**536 395**	**1 787**

Source: Department of Fisheries and Oceans Canada.

Figure 8.7
Quantity and value of fish caught in the Atlantic and Pacific fisheries, 1994

Approximately 65 per cent of the lobster catch is sold live in Canada, the United States, and Europe. The live lobsters are held in slatted wooden crates. These are placed either in indoor tanks supplied with running ocean water or in tidal ponds. These are enclosures that are created by damming a natural sea cove. The rest of the catch is either canned or processed as frozen meat.

In the 1960s, a new species of shellfish was "discovered" by inshore fishers—snow crab. This seafood rapidly gained popularity with consumers. The harvesting and production of snow crab expanded in the 1980s, creating a new source of income

Figure 8.8
Atlantic lobster and snow crab catch, 1950-1992

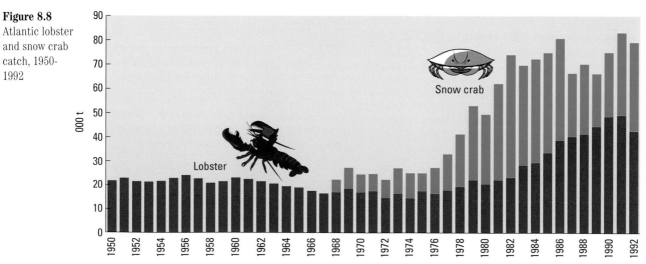

for the Atlantic fishery. Those fishers who have licences are earning high incomes. Yet licences are restricted to protect against overfishing. This has led to controversy as more fishers want to share in the wealth of this resource.

9 The lobster fishery has its own special equipment. Describe how rocks, buoys, and cod heads might be used in lobster fishing.

10 a) Name the provinces that are involved in the lobster fishery. Describe where most lobster fishing areas are located and mark these on an outline map of Atlantic Canada.
   b) Why is the lobster an ideal species for inshore fishers?

11 Refer to Figure 8.8. Describe the pattern of lobster fishing between 1950 and 1992.

12 a) Explain how the conservation regulations ensure that Canada's lobster resource is managed wisely.
   b) What effect have these regulations had on the lobster catch since 1975? Explain.

The offshore fishery

The offshore fishery operates out at sea within Canada's 370 km fishing limit on the rich fishing banks of the continental shelf. While at its peak only 15 per cent of fishers worked in the offshore fishery, it accounted for 90 per cent of the total Atlantic catch. Boats used in the offshore fishery range in size from 20 to 50 m. Most are trawlers equipped with the latest technology. They use huge nets that drag along the ocean floor to scoop up thousands of kilograms of fish. (See Figure 8.6.) Inshore fishers complain that the trawlers' huge catches are responsible for the decline in the number of fish at the shore.

Offshore trawlers are able to withstand many of the hazards created by the stormy weather of the North Atlantic. This enables them to operate year-round. The ships set out from the larger centres on the Atlantic coast, staying at sea for two or three weeks. The boats have their own processing equipment, which enables workers to prepare some of the fish for market on board. These offshore vessels are owned and operated by large companies that catch, process, and market the fish.

13 List the main characteristics of the offshore fishery.

14 Fog can be a major hazard for the fishery on the Grand Banks. Fog results when a warm, moist air mass meets a cold, moist air mass.
   a) Refer to Figure 8.4 on page 134. What are the names of the two ocean currents that converge off the east coast of Newfoundland? Why are each of these currents shown with different coloured arrows?
   b) Where do these currents originate? How does this account for the temperature of each one?
   c) How do these currents explain why this is one of the foggiest regions on earth?

15 Another hazard of the Atlantic fishery is icebergs. Draw a sketch map to show where icebergs originate and the route they take to reach the Grand Banks. Why would icebergs frequently be seen off the coast of Newfoundland but seldom off the coast of Nova Scotia?

Case study: the *Scotia Eagle*

Jimmy McKerlie is one of eighteen crew members on the *Scotia Eagle*. When he leaves Battery Point for the distant fishery called Sable Island Bank, it will be a couple of weeks before he returns. Jimmy is the fourth generation of McKerlies to be a fisher, but he is the first to work in the offshore fishery.

The *Scotia Eagle* was built by a Halifax shipyard in 1977 at a cost of $5 million. The trawler is 47 m long and has a depth of 5 m. Like other modern trawlers, the *Scotia Eagle* is a sturdy ship designed to handle the stormy and icy conditions so common in the North Atlantic.

When the *Scotia Eagle* reaches Sable Island Bank, some 225 km away, an echo sounder locates the fish by transmitting a sound that is reflected by the sea floor back to the trawler. Anything that interferes with the transmission, like a school of fish, is recorded by the echo sounder and displayed on a screen. A giant, cone-shaped net called an otter trawl net is used to catch the fish. (See Figure 8.9.) Heavy rollers on the bottom lip help the net roll along close to the ocean floor. Large floats hold the top of the net up so the fish are scooped up as the net moves through the water. After three or four hours the net is brought up using a winch. The catch is released onto the working deck. The fish are then processed on board and stored in a refrigerated room that can hold up to 182 000 kg of fish and ice.

Like the rest of the crew of the *Scotia Eagle*, Jimmy works in two shifts, rotating every six hours. This enables the trawler to operate continuously. Last year Jimmy spent 245 days at sea and earned $24 000. When

Figure 8.9
The otter trawl method of offshore fishing
How does the otter trawl net stay open vertically and horizontally?

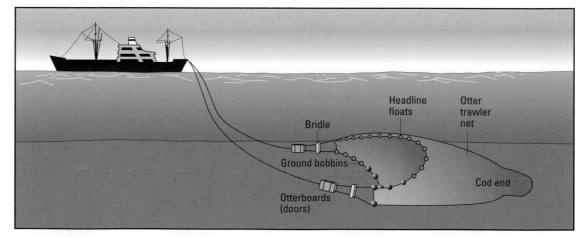

Bridle

Headline floats

Otter trawler net

Ground bobbins

Otterboards (doors)

Cod end

he worked on his father's inshore boat, the weather restricted them to about 100 fishing days a year. Last year the average net income in the inshore fishery was $6000.

16 If the *Scotia Eagle* can cruise steadily at 20 km/h, how many hours will it take to reach its destination?

17 If you were in the fishing industry, would you prefer to work in the inshore or the offshore fishery? Explain your choice.

Processing Atlantic fish

At one time, Canadians were limited to fish that was either dried, salted, or canned. Today, the small fish plants once found along the Atlantic coast have been replaced by large, modern processing plants. A wide range of high-quality fish products is produced. To meet changing demand, a large part of the catch is cooked and sold as single or multiple-serving frozen food. This convenience food meets the demands of the modern household for labour- and time-saving meals.

The National Sea Products High Liner plant near Lunenburg, Nova Scotia, is one of the largest fish processing plants in the world. It occupies more than 3 ha of land and employs about 1000 people. The plant, which usually operates year-round, is supplied by five company-owned stern trawlers and six scallop draggers. Fish are also purchased from independent inshore fishers and from foreign trawlers in the offshore fishery.

National Sea Products is a **vertically integrated company**—that is, it controls all aspects of the fishing process, from catching to processing to marketing. (See Figure 8.10.) When the boats reach the National Sea Products docks, the fish are inspected and sorted according to species, size, and quality. They are then washed and refrigerated. Once on the processing line, the fish are filleted and processed in one of three ways. Some are iced and sent fresh to buyers. Others are frozen for eventual distribution to supermarkets, fish and chip chains, and restaurants. The remainder are made into a variety of precooked convenience foods, such as fish sticks, fish burgers, and fish nuggets.

A fleet of refrigerated transport trucks distributes the fish products across North

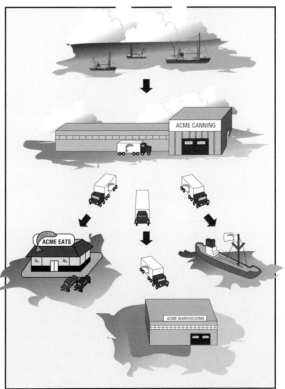

Figure 8.10
A vertically integrated company

America. Products destined for overseas markets are transported by ship. All of High Liner's processed fish products are sold in Canada. Sixty-five per cent of raw fillets are destined for the domestic market, while the remaining 35 per cent is exported to the United States.

Canadians consume less fish per person than people in other fishing nations like Britain and Japan. Canada's physical size may have originally been a contributing factor to this. Prior to 1945, fresh fish was available only in port or coastal cities. Many of Canada's large cities were too far inland for fresh fish to be delivered without spoiling. Remember, in 1945 there was no air freight shipment, fast-freeze processing, or refrigerated transport! To ship fish, it had to be salted, smoked, or dried. In inland communities, this did not compete well with local fresh pork, beef, and poultry.

Although our fish consumption is still low by comparison, Canadians are changing their eating habits. As a result of technology, we can now buy fresh boned and filleted fish no matter where we live. We are also more aware of the fat content in our diets. As a result, lean sources of protein, like fish, are becoming increasingly popular.

18 a) Construct a flow chart showing the stages of operation of the National Sea Products company.
   b) What are the advantages for a company if it is vertically integrated?

19 a) Find out the fat content of a 100 g serving of each of the following: pork loin, chicken breast, ground beef, and cod fillet. Rank these items in order beginning with the lowest in fat content.

b) Go to your local supermarket. List the various ways in which seafood is offered for sale in the store. Interview the seafood manager. Find out where the store purchases its fresh seafood and the portion of seafood sold fresh, frozen, and processed. Prepare a poster or display showing the results of your survey.

The collapse of the cod fishery

Cod was always the mainstay of the Atlantic fishery. This is especially true for the fishing communities dotted along the rocky coastlines of Newfoundland and southern Labrador. For almost 500 years, the fishery not only supported the fishing fleets of Canada, but also those of many European countries. Fishing methods were simple by today's standards. The boats were small. The catch was preserved in salt in the holds of foreign vessels or sun-dried on fish flakes in coastal communities along the Atlantic.

All of this began to change in the 1960s. Huge factory trawlers came into use as demand for fish increased with the world's growing population. The trawlers processed the catch on board. Giant dragnets scooped up fish of all species and sizes—anything that lay in their path. More countries, such as Russia, Japan, Korea, and Poland, joined the fishery. By 1970, the United Nations was considering extending national fishing limits from 22 km to 370 km, a move that would give Canada greater control over the continental shelf. The rush was on! Fishing fleets hurried to grab all the fish they could before the limits were extended. The catch of cod off Newfoundland skyrocketed to 800 000 t— three times the traditional level. (See Figure 8.11.)

To save the cod and other overfished species, Canada extended its fishing limits to 370 km on 1 January 1977. The Canadian fishing industry heaved a sigh of relief. Canada now had the right to control the quotas, size, tonnage, seasons, and equipment used to catch fish found within this 370 km area. The foreign catch was greatly reduced. The fishing industry hoped that new methods of resource management would give the fish time to increase their numbers. Over the next decade, evidence suggested that cod stocks were rebounding. But by the late 1980s, it was clear that the stocks were not rebuilding as quickly as anticipated. By 1992, cod stocks were less than 2 per cent of their sustainable level. (See Figure 8.12.) The government had to make a dev-

astating announcement: the cod fishery had collapsed and fishing for northern cod was banned for two years. But in 1994, the ban was extended indefinitely as scientists could find little evidence that the cod stocks were recovering.

Why did the cod disappear? Overfishing by both Canadian and foreign offshore fleets seemed to be the most obvious reason. The quotas had been too high and the size of the breeding stocks had been overestimated. The fishing industry, too, may have failed to report the full catch. Fishing methods were also to blame. The dragnets that had scraped the ocean floor had damaged plant and animal life on the fishing banks, thereby disrupting the food chain that supported the cod stocks. Changes in the flow patterns of the Labrador Current and the Gulf Stream may also have caused the fish to migrate elsewhere. The growing number of fur seals, which were protected from hunting in the 1980s, may also have played a part as the

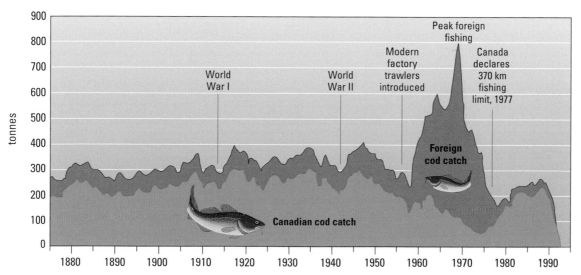

Figure 8.11
The decline of the northern cod fishery

seals feed on cod. As their numbers increased, they placed even more pressure on the cod stocks.

20 Refer to Figures 8.11 and 8.12.
a) In what decade were foreign fishing fleets overfishing in the northwest Atlantic?
b) Why were foreign fleets able to conduct such massive fishing operations during this period?

c) What was happening to the quantity of northern cod during this same decade? Why did this change go largely unnoticed? What were the consequences?

21 a) Draw a chart like Figure 8.13. Using the line graph in Figure 8.11, record the data.
b) Explain why Canada extended its territorial limit in 1977. Your completed chart should help you with your answer.

22 a) Evaluate the effect the extension of Canada's offshore territorial limits should have had on each of the following:
i) offshore and inshore fish stocks
ii) the number of offshore and inshore fishers
iii) the number of fish plant workers
iv) the size of fishing vessels and the technology they used
v) the amount of fish consumed by Canadians.
b) Did the extension of the fishing limit have the expected effects? Explain your answer.

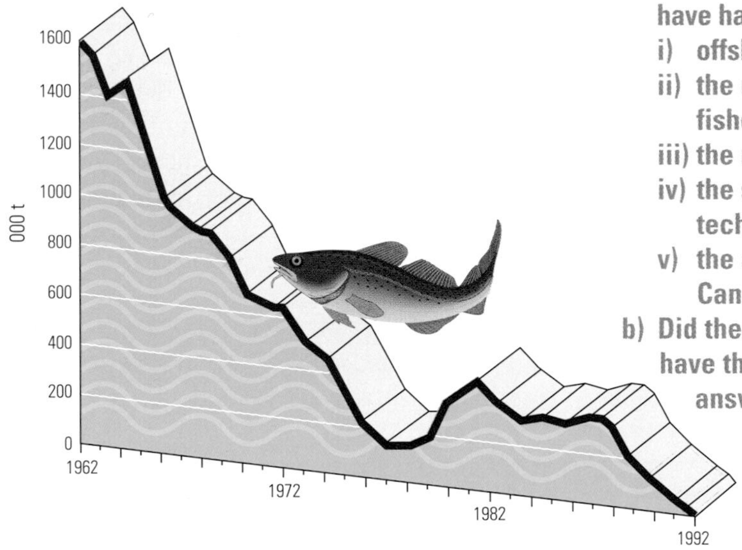

Figure 8.12
Northern cod stocks, 1962-1992: Will the cod ever recover?

Figure 8.13
Charting the decline of the cod fishery

YEAR	DOMESTIC CATCH (000 t)	FOREIGN CATCH (000 t)	DIFFERENCE
1940			
1950			
1960			
1970			
1980			
1990			
1992			

Simulation: defending Canada's offshore fishery

In 1992, the cod fishery in the northwest Atlantic Ocean east of Newfoundland on the Grand Banks was closed to all Canadian fishing. Fishers in Newfoundland have been devastated by the collapse of the fishery. Their livelihood is gone, and there are few other opportunities to earn a living. They have been further angered by the activities of foreign fishing fleets. Overfishing by Spanish and other fishers threatens the stocks of other species, such as turbot, a low-value fish once ignored by fishing fleets. These foreign boats catch fish just outside Canada's 370 km economic zone on the "Nose" and "Tail" of the Grand Banks. (See Figure 8.4 on page 134.) In the meantime, Canadian fishers are limited by quotas and other restrictions.

Spanish fleets have been fishing on the Grand Banks for hundreds of years. Most European fishing banks have already been overfished and destroyed, so there are no other places for the Spanish to fish. The North Atlantic Fisheries Organization (NAFO), made up of all nations fishing in this part of the world, sets quotas for turbot. In 1994, the quota was 50 000 t. Canada caught 4000 t. The European Union, including Spain, caught 50 000 t. Other countries added to this total, and the quota was exceeded by several thousand tonnes. Environmentalists and scientists believe that to protect turbot stocks, the total catch should be reduced to half of the 1994 quota.

Canadian fishers have demanded that the federal government take action against overfishing by foreign fleets. Legally, Canada does not have the right to interfere with fishing boats beyond its 370 km limit. On the other hand, under the UN Law of the Sea, Canada is expected to manage and preserve the fish stocks on the Grand Banks.

Between January and April 1995, a series of incidents between Canadian authorities and Spanish fishing fleets erupted. In one instance, Canada seized a Spanish fishing trawler outside the 370 km limit. On board authorities discovered undersized turbot and illegal fishing nets. Spain demanded the release of the trawler as well as a halt to further interference from Canada. Canada demanded an agreement that would prevent the catching of protected fish species and the use of illegal fishing nets by foreign fleets. How should this situation be resolved?

23 Form groups of six. Assign each member one of the roles described below. Each student should review the briefing notes for her/his particular role. As a group, try to reach a consensus to resolve this fishing dispute.
   a) Copy Figure 8.4 on page 134 onto a piece of paper. Note the purple areas on the map are less than 200 m deep. These are the traditional fishing grounds of the shallow continental shelf.
   b) From several points along the coast, measure Canada's 370 km limit and mark it with a dot. Join the dots together to create a line representing Canada's zone of control. Label the line.
   c) How much of the continental shelf is outside Canadian control? What can you conclude from this?

Briefing notes

The Canadian fisheries minister: You represent Canada's interests and particularly those of Newfoundlanders who rely on the fishery. Canada has strict quotas for fish caught by its fleets within the 370 km limit, therefore Canada is not responsible for the overfishing. Spain, a member of the European Union, has overfished the fishery off its own coast. It has also been fishing illegally in the waters off Britain. Now Spanish trawlers are about to destroy the fish resources of the Grand Banks. Although Canada does not have a legal right to interfere with fishing fleets beyond the 370 km limit, it must gain control over the fish that migrate across the 370 km limit if their stocks are to survive. This must be achieved through an international agreement with the European Union or the United Nations. If such an agreement cannot be reached, the entire fishery will be destroyed. Canada blames Spain alone for the overfishing, however, not the EU. Canada does not want to jeopardize its trade with Europe.

A Newfoundland fisheries representative: You want a total ban on all fishing fleets operating on the continental shelf off Canada's east coast. The ban cannot be limited to that part of the shelf that lies within Canada's 370 km limit. It must include the Nose and Tail of the Grand Banks, which lie beyond this limit. This is the only way that migratory fish such as turbot will not be overfished to the point of extinction. Thousands of unemployed fishery workers see this as their only hope for the future.

The Spanish fisheries minister: You want to make it clear that Canada has no right to interfere with Spanish trawlers fishing in international waters. Any illegal boarding of ships outside the limit is considered piracy and Spain will respond accordingly. You feel the EU should support Spain's rights in this dispute. You strongly disagree that Spanish trawlers are responsible for overfishing on the Grand Banks. You feel the blame lies with Canada, whose fishing fleets have plundered the fish stocks within the 370 km limit throughout the 1980s and now want to blame Spain.

A Spanish fisheries representative: For centuries, Spanish fleets have travelled to the Grand Banks to catch cod and halibut. When Canada declared a 370 km limit, a large part of the Grand Banks was no longer open to Spanish fishers. Only the areas known as the Nose and Tail of the Grand Banks were left. Now Canada wants to take these areas away, too. If this happens, Spanish fishers will no longer have a trade, since there are no other fishing banks open to Spanish trawlers.

A European Union representative: You must act in the best interests of Spain. The Spanish fleet has a legal right to catch fish beyond the 370 km limit. Any actions by Canada outside this limit can be considered piracy according to international law. You know that Canada does not want to jeopardize its trade relationship with the European Union through its actions in this dispute. In addition, Canadian tourists visiting Spain are not required to obtain visas or special entrance passes. These are two bargaining chips you can use in your negotiations.

A NAFO representative: As a member of the North Atlantic Fisheries Organization, you want a final resolution to this dispute. International law states that countries only control fish stocks within the 370 km limit. In the open seas, no country has the right to interfere with the ships of any nation. But you are also concerned about rapidly declining fish stocks. Many fishing banks have been overfished to the point that the stocks will never recover. You are concerned this is about to happen on the Grand Banks. You believe that Canada and Spain share blame for the destruction of the cod fishery. You want to get the two sides to reach an agreement that will save the fishery. You also want all countries to observe the quotas NAFO establishes.

24 Use your library resource centre to find out what agreement was actually reached by Canada, Spain, and the European Union in April 1995 to resolve the fishing dispute.

The Pacific fishery

Salmon is the most important catch in the Pacific coast fishery. The five varieties of salmon—chum, pink, spring, coho, and sockeye—account for 20 to 35 per cent of the total quantity and 40 to 60 per cent of the total value of fish caught on the Pacific coast. Other fish and seafood in the Pacific catch include halibut, cod, herring, flounder, oysters, and clams.

Salmon is a unique fish. Its life cycle starts and ends in the cold, freshwater rivers of the west coast. Its mid-life, however, is spent in the salty waters of the north Pacific. The fast-flowing mountain streams, created by snow melt and heavy rains, help the salmon migrate to the ocean. Once there, they find an ample supply of food as they grow and mature. In two to three years, they return to the rivers where they were born. As they do, the commercial harvest begins.

25 Look at Figure 8.14.
   a) Describe the stages in the life cycle of the Pacific salmon.
   b) At what stages do commercial and sports fisheries harvest salmon? At what stage are salmon relatively safe from human interference?
   c) Why is its unique life cycle a problem for the survival of the salmon?

26 a) Draw a map of Canada's Pacific coast similar to the one for the Atlantic coast in Figure 8.4. Using an atlas, label the following items on your map: two ocean currents and their relative temperatures; the continental shelf; two major Canadian coastal cities; three rivers that flow into the Pacific Ocean.
   b) Compare your Pacific coast map with Figure 8.4. Why do the physical conditions of the Atlantic coast produce more fish than the Pacific coast?

Figure 8.14
The life cycle of the Pacific salmon

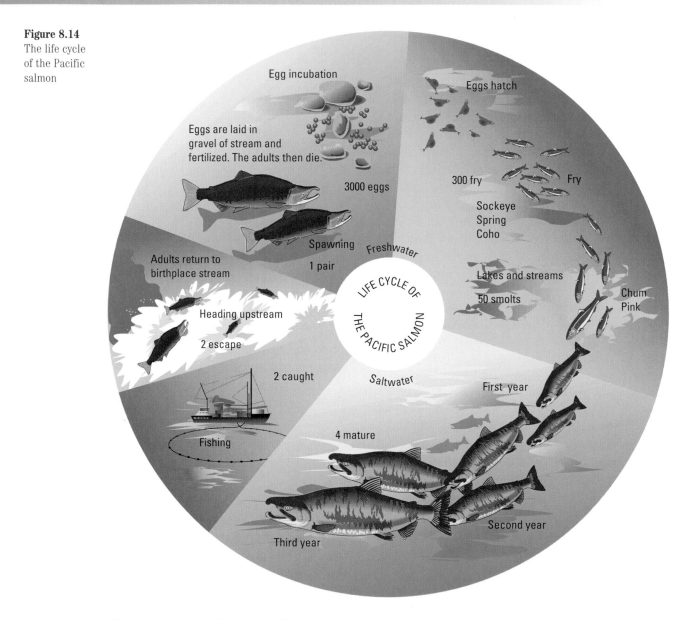

Case study: harvesting salmon

There are three methods of harvesting salmon. **Gill nets** and **purse seines** are generally used on the inshore salmon migration routes near the mouths of salmon-spawning streams. **Troll lines** are concentrated offshore, although they are sometimes used inshore as well.

A gill net hangs like a curtain with floats attached to the top and lead weights attached to the bottom to ensure that the net hangs vertically. Salmon swim into the net and become entangled. As the net is wound onto a drum on board the boat, the salmon are removed from the net by hand. This method accounts for approximately 27 per cent of the salmon caught.

Purse seining is an encircling technique that draws the net together to trap the fish. (See Figure 8.15.) The purse seine net has floats on the top and weights on the bottom to keep the net vertical. A wire cable runs through the net bottom so the net can be drawn together around the fish. When a school of salmon is located, a smaller boat takes one end of the seine and begins to encircle the fish. Once the small boat reaches the seine boat, the wire cable is winched and the bottom of the seine is closed, creating a bag-like net around the fish. The net is raised alongside the boat, and the fish are placed into containers or in the ship's hold.

Troll boats have six stainless steel lines suspended over the side. Each line is weighted, fitted with ten to twelve lures, and set at different depths. When salmon are hooked, the lines are retrieved by power-driven reels. The salmon are removed by hand as the line comes aboard the troller. About 23 per cent of the salmon catch is taken by troll boats.

27 a) What percentage of salmon fishing is i) inshore and ii) offshore?

b) Which of the three fishing methods accounts for the largest percentage of the salmon catch? Why is this the most popular method?

28 a) Draw and label a sketch of the troll-line method of salmon fishing.

b) Why is this method used mostly in the offshore fishery?

Figure 8.15
Purse seining

Salmon habitat under attack

Salmon are sensitive to human activity in their **habitat**, or natural environment. The unique life cycle of the salmon means that these fish live in several different habitats, from spawning beds in rivers to the vast ocean.

Traditionally the Fraser River has supported Canada's greatest salmon resource. About 25 per cent of BC's salmon catch has come from the Fraser. Its estuary, located at the mouth of the river where tides flow in and out, is a vital part of the salmon habitat. This is where freshwater and seawater mix. Migrating adult salmon gather here before swimming upstream to spawn. Young salmon migrating downstream pause to feed in the marshes and to adjust to the change from freshwater to saltwater.

Today, however, the estuary is home to over 2 million people as well as to industries like lumber and pulp and paper mills. The human activities that take place here have seriously damaged the salmon habitat. But the changes to the natural environment are not limited to the estuary alone. Upstream the salmon habitat is also threatened, as are other salmon-producing rivers in BC.

Logging

Logging has a greater impact on salmon habitat and stocks than any other human activity. Forty per cent of all logs harvested in British Columbia are hauled up the Fraser estuary to New Westminster. In addition, the 1700 ha of the Fraser River estuary are used for log storage near the mills.

Logging has a profound effect on the habitat of the Pacific salmon. Cutting forests on mountain slopes increases soil erosion. Eroded mud and silt then cover the gravel stream beds where salmon lay their eggs, thereby destroying the vital spawning habitat. Log drives also destroy spawning beds, and log jams and debris block fish migration routes.

Draining estuary wetlands

The lower Fraser River was once an area of extensive marshland. Much of this has now been dyked, dredged, and filled to allow the construction of causeways, wharfs, and marinas. Draining and landfilling marshes reduces the flow of the nutrients and food salmon require for growth.

Pollution

Herbicides and pesticides used in agriculture in the Fraser Valley enter the river system and pollute the water. In the estuary, organic wastes from sewage and meat-packing plants and pulp and saw mills decompose. This reduces the amount of oxygen in the water and kills fish.

Dams

River dams obstruct salmon migration routes. Although the Fraser has no dams, many other rivers in the region do. The result is decreased salmon stocks. Today, construction of large-scale power and flood-control dams in BC has been stopped.

River diversions

Diverting water for industry and irrigation harms the salmon habitat. Summer demands for irrigation water peak at the same time that juvenile salmon migrate downstream. The resulting low water levels and warmer water temperatures doom many salmon to an early death.

29 a) Describe the habitats required by the Pacific salmon during its life cycle.

b) Why might changes to salmon habitats not attract much public attention?

30 a) For each illustration in Figure 8.16, write a caption that explains how this is a threat to the salmon's habitat or survival.

b) Draw sketches of two other factors that threaten the salmon fishery. Include a caption to explain each sketch.

Figure 8.16
Threats to the west coast salmon fishery

Figure 8.17
Human activities and the life cycle of the salmon

SKETCH	ACTIVITY	STAGE OF LIFE INTERRUPTED	HOW SALMON ARE HARMED	POSSIBLE SOLUTIONS
A				
B				
C				
D				

31 Copy Figure 8.17 into your notebook. Using Figure 8.16, complete the chart by describing the threats to the salmon fishery and their possible solutions.

32 a) Using an atlas, sketch a map of the Fraser River system. Label the major tributaries, cities, and the estuary.
   b) Salmon spawn in the upper Fraser River and its tributaries. Mark these salmon-spawning areas on your map.
   c) Review the factors that threaten the salmon habitat. Outline five pieces of legislation that you would like to see enacted to protect the salmon in this region.
   d) Outline your suggestions in a letter to the Department of Fisheries and Oceans.

Crisis in the salmon fishery

In recent years, scientists have warned that stocks of almost all species of Pacific salmon are decreasing and could suddenly disappear, just as northern cod did off the Newfoundland coast. By 1996, these warnings had become reality. The number of salmon returning from the Pacific Ocean to the rivers of British Columbia had reached an all-time low.

How did the salmon fishery reach this state of crisis? Several factors combined to create what many experts have called an ecological disaster. New technology has meant that commercial fleets can catch in hours what they used to take days to catch. Deep-sea **drift-nets**, commonly used by Japanese, Korean, and Taiwanese fleets, have added to the problem. These kilometre-long nets hang from large floats. Their primary purpose is to catch tuna and other large fish in the open seas. Unfortunately, they scoop up everything in their path, including salmon. Poor management of the resource has added to the problem of overfishing. Talks between Canada and the United States over the Pacific Salmon Treaty collapsed in 1995. The treaty is supposed to regulate salmon quotas between American and Canadian fishers. Without the quotas, fleets from both sides had been trying to maximize their catches. Even nature itself has contributed to the problem. A slight increase in ocean temperatures has resulted in a population explosion among mackerel, which feed on young salmon.

Commercial fleets harvest about 90 per cent of the salmon each year. The rest is evenly divided between the sports fishery and Native fishers. The number of sports fishers has increased, from 1 million in 1983 to over 1.5 million today. Native peoples, who have guaranteed rights to fish for BC salmon for food and traditional purposes, have also increased their catch. Both groups, however, opposed reduced quotas on their catch.

In response to the crisis, the federal government announced in March 1996 that the commercial salmon fleet would be reduced by almost 50 per cent. The plan calls for more than 1500 fishing boats to be placed in dry dock over the next few years. The Fraser River, which is a main waterway for millions of salmon, was among the areas that were shut down. Among the five West Coast salmon species, the premium sockeye salmon is the most seriously depleted. It was estimated that only 1.5 million sockeye salmon would return to the Fraser River in 1996. This was not enough to ensure that the salmon stocks would replenish themselves. Experts believe that the commercial fishery for sockeye salmon is no longer sustainable.

33 What factors led to the crisis in the Pacific salmon fishery?

34 Find out the current status of the Pacific salmon fishery. Prepare a report in which you update the situation since the shutdown was announced in March 1996.

The freshwater fishery

With its abundance of freshwater lakes, it is not surprising that Canada has a major freshwater fishery. The biggest fishery is centred in the Great Lakes, with Lake Erie being the largest producer. Other fisheries operate on Lake Winnipeg, Great Slave Lake, and hundreds of smaller lakes across the country. These lakes contain over 180 different fish species. Of these, whitefish, perch, pickerel, trout, and bass are among the major species sent to market. Figure 8.18 lists the fish caught by commercial fishers by weight and value and the important producing provinces.

The freshwater fishery provides jobs for over 9000 crew members and fish-processing workers. Trawlers fish on the larger lakes, while smaller boats are used elsewhere. Boats fish close to the shore where the best feeding and spawning habitats are. They operate out of small harbour communities with local fish-processing facilities. Their catch is sold fresh or frozen to the United States, Japan, and Europe.

In some parts of Canada, recreational fishers now catch more than twice the amount of fish by weight than commercial fishers do. Sport fishing is an important economic activity for many communities. It fuels the tourist industry in places like northern Ontario and Manitoba. Fishing is also an important source of income for some Native communities in the North.

Pollution and habitat destruction in the Great Lakes fishery have reduced the catch or edibility of many fish species. Toxic substances that are discharged into

FISH SPECIES	QUANTITY 1991 (t)	QUANTITY 1992 (t)	QUANTITY 1993 (t)	QUANTITY 1994 (t)	VALUE 1994 $(000)	$/t 1994	LARGEST PROVINCE 1994
Alewife	1 355	1 089	1 200	1 272	1 515	1 191	New Brunswick
Arctic char	52	4	64	0	0	0	NT*
Carp	801	494	470	650	238	366	Manitoba
Chub	318	699	643	622	269	432	Ontario
Lake trout	568	481	626	261	568	2 176	Ontario
Perch	6 472	5 699	5 289	3 425	11 556	3 374	Ontario
Pike	3 172	3 266	2 151	1 791	1 232	688	Manitoba
Sauger	2 542	3 061	1 587	1 345	439	326	Manitoba
Smelt	9 184	5 769	5 778	4 862	2 185	449	Ontario
Sucker	4 878	3 061	1 587	1 345	439	326	Manitoba
Walleye	3 713	1 711	978	2 373	9 048	3 813	Manitoba
White bass	939	405	400	552	1 519	2 752	Ontario
Whitefish	9 023	9 038	8 060	9 486	11 220	1 183	Ontario
Yellow pickerel	3 577	5 997	5 489	5 188	20 423	3 937	Ontario

*for 1991–1993

Figure 8.18
Commercial catch of freshwater fish in Canada, 1991–1994

the lakes often contaminate the fish. Efforts to clean up the Great Lakes have been under way in Canada and the United States since 1970. The levels of many dangerous substances have been greatly reduced. Laws now require any new industries around the Great Lakes to conduct environmental impact studies to ensure that they do not harm fish habitats.

35 Lake Erie is only 64 m deep. The other Great Lakes are three to six times deeper. Explain how depth helps make Lake Erie the most profitable lake for fishing. (HINT:

Figure 8.19
Great Lakes fishing boats at Tobermory, Georgian Bay, Ontario

You may wish to review the description of the Atlantic fishery.)

36 The location of the Great Lakes is a major advantage for marketing fish. Explain why.

Aquaculture

Aquaculture is the raising of marine life in a controlled environment. Often called fish farming, aquaculture breeds and raises fish in tanks, ponds, and reservoirs. Since the fish are fed regularly and are safe from their natural enemies, they mature rapidly and successfully. Salmon, trout, mussels, and oysters are the leading seafood raised in Canada through fish farming. (See Figure 8.20.)

Aquaculture is a growth industry in Canada. In 1984, it produced $7 million worth of fish. By 1994, this figure had jumped to $297 million! By the year 2000, aquaculture is expected to produce over $630 million worth of seafood. Over $450 million of this will be exported to the United States, Japan, and other countries. Figure

8.26 shows the regional value of aquaculture in 1994.

The growth of aquaculture is largely the result of overfishing. Our fish supplies are threatened, but the demand for fish products is growing. Aquaculture may help to ensure that supply meets demand.

37a) Why might aquaculture be called the future of the world's fishing industry?
b) What is the future of aquaculture in Canada based on trends in the last fifteen years?
c) Why is Canada well suited to aquaculture?

Case study: salmon farming in New Brunswick

Salmon farming meets all of the criteria for successful aquaculture. Salmon is a high-priced commodity in a market in which demand exceeds supply. It is easily marketed fresh, frozen, or smoked. Canadians have the expertise to breed, hatch, and rear salmon in captivity. One of the coun-

Figure 8.20
Aquaculture in Canada, 1994

SPECIES	PRODUCTION QUANTITY (t)	VALUE ($ 000)
Salmon	33 326	244 337
Trout	5 892	33 250
Mussels	6 898	7 645
Oyster	7 767	9 133
Total	**54 487**	**296 853**

Figure 8.21
Aquaculture production by region, 1994

REGION	$ 000	LEADING SPECIES BY VALUE
Atlantic	123 369	Atlantic salmon, mussels, oysters
Central	17 717	Lake trout
Pacific	155 767	Salmon, oysters
Total value	**296 853**	

try's most successful salmon farming ventures is in New Brunswick.

The first successful marine production of Atlantic salmon began in the southwest region of New Brunswick around the Bay of Fundy in 1978. It was a co-operative venture supported by private enterprise and the federal and provincial fisheries departments. The first production of cultured salmon in 1979 yielded 6 t. In the early 1980s, four more farms were established. Production of smolt (young salmon) for use in the farms began in 1986 by two Atlantic fish companies. By 1987, smolt sales to salmon farmers almost met the growing demand. By 1988, local industries were supplying the salmon farms with feed, nets, cages, and other equipment. As a result, the industry experienced slow but steady growth. By the mid-1990s, production exceeded 12 000 t and enriched the New Brunswick economy by $100 million annually.

Today there are seventy-one Atlantic salmon farms in the region. The greatest concentration is in Lime Kiln Bay along the mainland. However, farms are also located adjacent to Deer, Campobello, and Grand Manan islands in the Bay of Fundy. This region of New Brunswick contains sheltered bays and coves that are protected from the prevailing northwesterly winds and seas. This creates water conditions that are acceptable for salmon growth. Ocean temperatures are moderate, with a maximum of 12 - 15°C in summer. Winter temperatures rarely fall below -0.7°C, the temperature at which the salmon's blood freezes and the fish die. The strong tidal currents provide an efficient water exchange and high oxygen levels for the fish.

Only a few areas have acceptable conditions for raising salmon year-round. Upper Passamaquoddy Bay off the Bay of Fundy is a marginal area because it lacks these key requirements. New strategies and technological breakthroughs may allow salmon farming to take place in colder temperatures in the future.

Figure 8.22
Salmon farms in New Brunswick

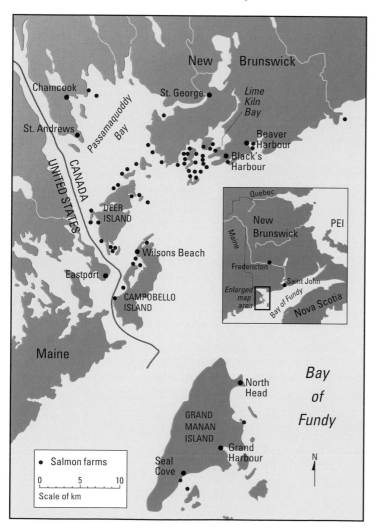

Cultured salmon are spawned in saltwater and eggs and milt are fertilized at a freshwater hatchery during October and November. By safely incubating the salmon eggs at temperatures warmed to 8 to 10°C, hatching may occur as early as January or February. The fingerlings, or young salmon, are fed throughout February and March. They then develop into parr. The following spring the parr turn into smolt that are ready to be transferred to saltwater sea pens or cages in April or May. For the next sixteen to twenty-four months the salmon are cultivated to market size—about 3 to 5 kg. Under controlled conditions, the growth of cultured salmon is much faster than wild salmon. The initial hatching process can be completed in less time by warming the water. The growth of smolt can be compressed into one or two years instead of the three to five years required by salmon in the wild.

The salmon are cultivated in floating sea pens or cages. The pens enclose between 500 m³ and 6500 m³ and can hold varying numbers of fish, depending on size and stage of development. The fish swim endlessly in their enclosures, thereby developing the same muscle structure as their wild counterparts. The salmon are fed a diet of high-protein pellets. The result is a high-quality product that is comparable to salmon caught in nature.

Like any animals in close confinement, cultured salmon face the threat of disease. Strong currents help to carry away waste products that might otherwise accumulate and threaten the health of the salmon. Overcrowding can result in stress for the salmon, which in turn can lead to disease. Overcrowding also attracts parasites. Therefore it is important that the pens contain only the number of fish that can successfully survive.

Predators are another threat to the salmon farms. Birds frequently seek out their next meal in the salmon enclosures. Seals pose an even greater danger. They can claw through the nets and enter the cages, damaging or killing many fish while the survivors escape. Predator nets are made of a large-mesh weave of coarse material that forms a barrier about 1 m outside the fish enclosure. These are effective measures against birds, but sonic seal-scaring devices are also needed to ward off these determined predators.

The salmon industry has created many economic benefits for the region beyond the farms themselves. The production of smolt, fish feed, sea cages, and nets creates jobs. The industries that supply the fish farms add another $100 million to the economy annually. There is also growth in the research and development of salmon farming techniques designed to suit the unique conditions of Atlantic Canada's waters. Thus the salmon industry makes a substantial contribution to the economy of southwestern New Brunswick.

38a) How did salmon farming boost the fishing communities of southwestern New Brunswick?

b) What advantages does this part of Atlantic Canada have for the development of this industry?

c) What factors limit the growth of salmon farming in the region?

Canada is a land of forests. Stretching from the Atlantic to the Pacific oceans, forests cover 45 per cent of the country's total land area. Forests have had a profound effect on Canadian life. They have shaped our trade and commerce as well as our art and literature. Many people would argue that our forests symbolize Canada. Our national flag proudly bears a maple leaf. The beaver, another Canadian symbol, makes its home in the vast boreal forests.

Canada's forest resource

Canada supplies an abundance of forest products to countries around the world. In fact, Canada is the world's leading exporter of softwood, newsprint, and wood pulp. (See Figure 9.2.) This makes forestry an important element in the Canadian economy. But our forests are not only valuable as a source of revenue. In recent decades, the Canadian public has come to appreciate forests for their recreational value. We have come to understand that forests are a renewable but fragile resource to be enjoyed and preserved. This has led to conflict. On the one hand, conservationists and environmentalists want to limit logging of Canadian forests. On the other hand, the forest industry wants to continue to reap the benefits of this renewable resource. During the 1980s and 1990s, the two sides have openly clashed at Clayoquot, Meares Island, Carmanah Valley, and Stein Valley in British Columbia and in Temagami in Ontario.

1 a) **List ways in which Canada's forests are used for commercial purposes.**
   b) **List ways in which forests are used for recreational purposes.**

Types of forests

Canada's forests are made up of either coniferous or deciduous trees, or a mix of both. (See Figure 9.4.) About 90 per cent of Canada's forests are coniferous. Deciduous forests, most of which have been cleared for farming and urban development, make up less than 1 per cent. Most of the remaining forest land is mixed.

Coniferous trees have evergreen needles and soft wood. Their seeds are produced in the cones that hang from their

Figure 9.1
The landscape of the Canadian boreal forest

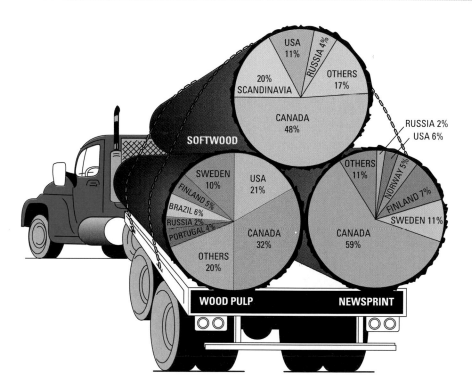

Figure 9.2
Canada's forestry exports

branches. The waxy, needle-like leaves hold moisture during the long, cold, dry winters. When spring arrives, the needles are already in place, ready to manufacture food during the short growing season. **Softwood** coniferous trees, such as spruce, pine, fir, and cedar, are ideal for making pulp and paper, lumber, and plywood products.

- Canada has nearly 10 per cent of the world's forests.
- More than 900 000 Canadians earn their livelihood through the forest industry.
- There are more than 7600 logging firms, sawmills, pulp and paper mills, shingle mills, and other forestry-related businesses.
- The world's largest producer of newsprint, Abitibi-Price, is a Canadian company.
- About half of all forestry production is exported to other countries.
- Canada supplies 48 per cent of the world's softwood.
- Canada ranks first in the world as an exporter of forest products, second in wood pulp production, third in lumber production, and fourth in paper production.
- Forests accounted for 13 per cent of Canada's total exports and earned $28.6 billion in 1993.

Figure 9.3
Some forest facts

Figure 9.4
Coniferous and deciduous trees

Coniferous

Winter   Summer

Deciduous

Winter   Summer

Deciduous trees have broad leaves and very hard wood. They shed their leaves each fall and remain dormant throughout the winter. In spring, new buds appear and the trees come into bloom once again. **Hardwood** deciduous trees, such as birch, maple, cherry, and walnut, are valued by furniture and flooring manufacturers. Others, like ash, are used to make baseball bats and hockey sticks.

Coniferous forests flourish in Canada because of the cool, moist climate. The warmest parts of Canada, southwestern British Columbia and southern Ontario, have annual average temperatures of 10°C. In Figure 9.5, only those types of vegetation above the 10°C line are found in Canada. These include deciduous forests, west coast coniferous rainforests, boreal forests, and mixed forests. The vertical lines on the graph indicate the amount of precipitation needed to support each type of vegetation. The very wet areas of coastal British Columbia receive enough precipitation to support coniferous rainforests. Southern Quebec and Ontario, along with New Brunswick, Nova Scotia, and Prince Edward Island, are moist enough to support mixed and deciduous forests. The boreal forests, which cover so much of Canada, are best in a climate with an annual temperature below 5°C. Because of lower evaporation rates, the trees are able to survive in areas that receive less than 300 mm of precipitation.

2 **Refer to Figure 9.5.**
   a) **Give the general range of temperatures and precipitation needed to support i) the coniferous rainforest; ii) the boreal forest; iii) the deciduous forest.**

b) **The coniferous rainforest and deciduous forest regions require more precipitation at higher temperatures. Explain why.**

Forest regions

The Canadian Forest Service divides the country into distinct forest regions. Differences in temperature, precipitation, growing season, soils, and landforms all determine the type of forest found in a region. The forest regions and their percentage of Canada's total land area are shown in Figure 9.6 on page 161.

Boreal forest

The boreal forest is subdivided into three regions: boreal forest, boreal forest and tundra, and boreal forest and grassland. All three regions are underlain by infertile, acidic, podzolic soils that are often thin and poorly drained. The boreal forest region contains mainly small- to medium-sized coniferous trees. These trees have adapted to the short, cool summers, long, cold winters, moderate amounts of precipitation, and short growing season that are typical of this part of Canada.

The boreal forest and tundra region lies between the true boreal forest and the northern treeline. It has a colder, windier, and drier climate and is underlain by large areas of discontinuous **permafrost**, or permanently frozen ground. All these factors mean the trees in this region are short, thin, and more widely scattered than those

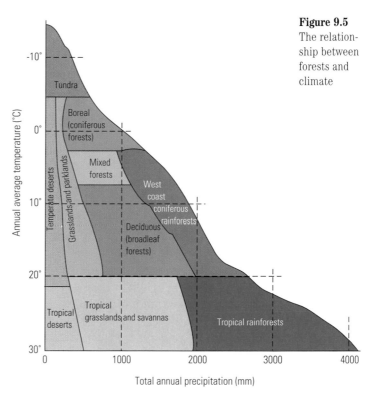

Figure 9.5
The relationship between forests and climate

to the south. The volume of wood and the number of tree species also decreases towards the treeline.

The boreal forest and grassland region is the transition zone between the forest and the grasslands of the drier southern prairies. Here the forest thins and the trees become smaller. Areas of tall grasses and shrubs become more common. Even though the total amount of precipitation is similar to areas further north, there is less water available for tree growth. This is because the warmer temperatures cause higher evaporation rates. At the southern edge of the region, trees are found only along wetter, more protected river valleys.

West coast coniferous rain-forest

The west coast coniferous rainforest is the most productive forest region in Canada. It is one of the few remaining old-growth temperate rainforests in the world. The region is limited to the western slopes of the Coast Range Mountains where rain-bearing winds from the Pacific drop most of their moisture. The coniferous trees grow to an enormous size and great heights because of the high precipitation, moderate temperatures, and long growing season. The Douglas fir, sitka spruce, and western red cedar found here are much taller and thicker and grow more rapidly than those found in the Montane and Columbia forest regions in the interior. The volume of wood per hectare exceeds 100 m^3, the highest of any forest region in Canada.

Columbia coniferous forest

This coniferous forest region is found on the wet, western slopes of the high interior mountains of British Columbia. Although it has similar species to the west coast rainforest, the trees are shorter and smaller. This is because the region receives less rainfall, has a shorter growing season, and has steeper, more rugged mountain slopes. It ranks second only to the west coast coniferous rainforest in its volume of wood per hectare.

Montane coniferous forest

The Montane region occupies the low-lying plateaus and valleys of the interior of British Columbia. These forests lie in the rainshadow of the Coast Ranges and so receive less precipitation. As a result, the trees are smaller than those of either the west coast or the Columbia forest regions. This is evident in the volume of wood per hectare values in Figure 9.8.

Deciduous forest

This is the only region in Canada with the hot summers, short winters, abundant precipitation, long growing season, and fertile soils deciduous trees need to flourish. Much of the original oak, maple, beech, and walnut trees once found here have been cleared for farming and urban development. This is why the volume of wood per hectare is so low. Only a few small areas of this unique Canadian forest have been preserved in their natural state.

Great Lakes-St. Lawrence mixed forest

This is a transition region between the boreal forest to the north and the deciduous forest to the south. Temperatures are cooler, the growing season shorter, the precipitation lower, and the soils less fertile than in the deciduous forests to the south. As a result, coniferous trees grow among less hardy deciduous trees, creating a mixed forest. In many places, the better drained, more fertile soils are occupied by deciduous trees. The conifers grow in areas of poorer drainage, thinner soils, and greater exposure to winds.

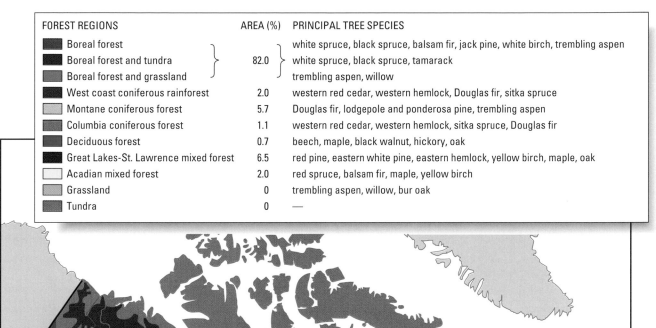

FOREST REGIONS	AREA (%)	PRINCIPAL TREE SPECIES
Boreal forest		white spruce, black spruce, balsam fir, jack pine, white birch, trembling aspen
Boreal forest and tundra	82.0	white spruce, black spruce, tamarack
Boreal forest and grassland		trembling aspen, willow
West coast coniferous rainforest	2.0	western red cedar, western hemlock, Douglas fir, sitka spruce
Montane coniferous forest	5.7	Douglas fir, lodgepole and ponderosa pine, trembling aspen
Columbia coniferous forest	1.1	western red cedar, western hemlock, sitka spruce, Douglas fir
Deciduous forest	0.7	beech, maple, black walnut, hickory, oak
Great Lakes-St. Lawrence mixed forest	6.5	red pine, eastern white pine, eastern hemlock, yellow birch, maple, oak
Acadian mixed forest	2.0	red spruce, balsam fir, maple, yellow birch
Grassland	0	trembling aspen, willow, bur oak
Tundra	0	—

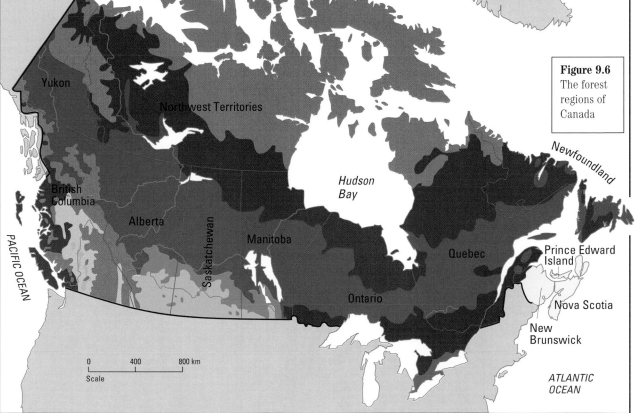

Figure 9.6
The forest regions of Canada

Figure 9.7
Comparing
forest regions

FOREST REGION	TREE TYPE	PRINCIPAL SPECIES	AREA OF EACH REGION	PROVINCES/ TERRITORIES

Acadian mixed forest

This is also a transition region between deciduous and coniferous forests. The tree species in this region differ from those in the Great Lakes forest, however, because they are better suited to the cooler and wetter climate of the Atlantic coast. Otherwise the size of trees and the volume of wood per hectare is similar to the Great Lakes mixed forest.

Figure 9.8
Wood productivity by forest region

3 Copy and complete Figure 9.7 in your notebook.
   a) For each region, list the tree type as coniferous, deciduous, or mixed and

give two or three species commonly found there.
   b) Rank the total area of each region, beginning with 1 as the largest and ending with 8 as the smallest.
   c) In the last column, list the provinces and territories that contain each forest region.

4 Create a bar graph to show the percentage of land area of Canada's major forest regions from the legend in Figure 9.6.

5 a) There is great variation in forest regions and tree species within British Columbia. Using Figure 9.6, give evidence to support this.
   b) What factor is largely responsible for these variations?

6 Refer to the forest regions map (Figure 9.6 on page 161) and the annual precipitation map (Figure 9.10 on page 164).
   a) The southern parts of Alberta and Saskatchewan receive less than 400 mm of precipitation annually. What type of natural vegetation is found here?
   b) A large area that spans parts of northern Alberta and northern Saskatchewan also receives less than 400 mm of precipitation. Why is this area covered in boreal forest even though it receives the same annual precipitation as the grasslands to the south?

FOREST REGION	WOOD VOLUME (m³/ha)
Boreal forest	25-75
Boreal forest and tundra	1-25
Boreal forest and grassland	1-25
Montane coniferous forest	50-100
West coast coniferous rainforest	100+
Columbian coniferous forest	75-100
Deciduous forest	1-25
Great Lakes-St. Lawrence mixed forest	25-75
Acadian mixed forest	25-75
Grasslands	0
Tundra	0

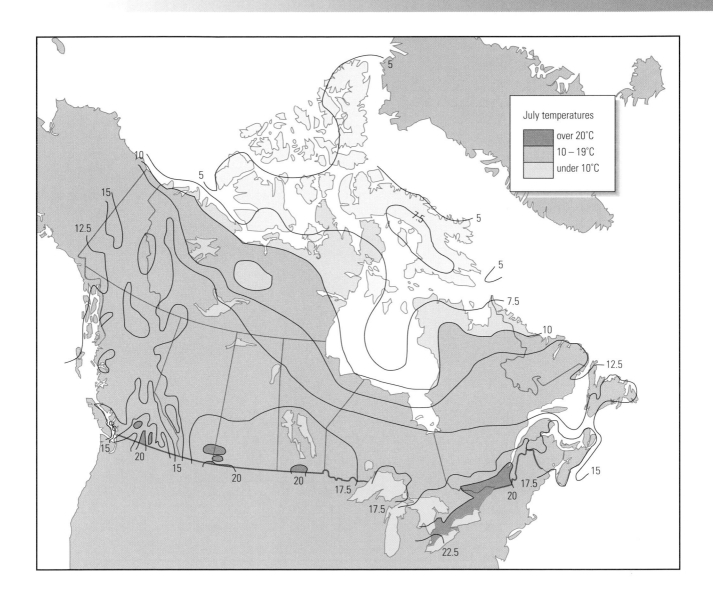

Figure 9.9
Isotherms for July

7 Refer to Figure 9.9.
   a) Identify the temperature of the July isotherm that closely matches the northern limit of forests (the treeline) in Canada.
   b) What July isotherm marks the approximate northern limit of the mixed forest region?
   c) What July isotherm marks the approximate northern limit of the deciduous forest region?
   d) Explain the relationship between temperature and forest distribution in Canada.

Figure 9.10
Annual precipitation in Canada

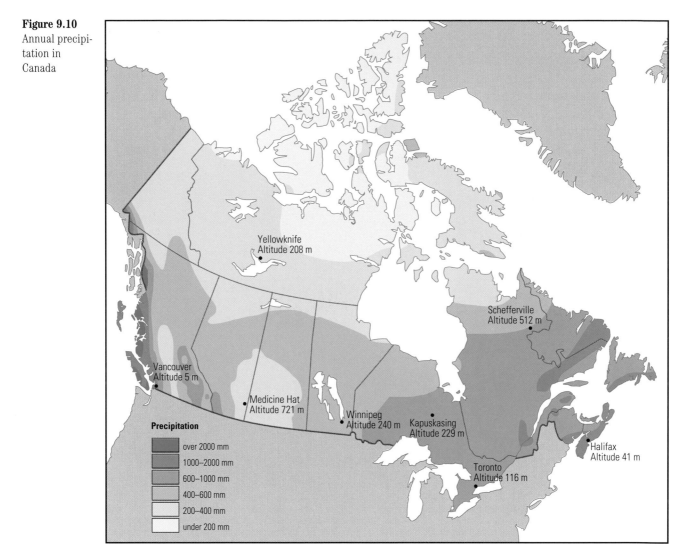

Yellowknife
Altitude 208 m

Schefferville
Altitude 512 m

Vancouver
Altitude 5 m

Medicine Hat
Altitude 721 m

Winnipeg
Altitude 240 m

Kapuskasing
Altitude 229 m

Halifax
Altitude 41 m

Toronto
Altitude 116 m

Precipitation

over 2000 mm
1000–2000 mm
600–1000 mm
400–600 mm
200–400 mm
under 200 mm

8 a) Copy Figure 9.11 in your notebook. Complete the chart for Corner Brook and Tofino using the information in Figures 9.6 and 9.12. NOTE: The *annual temperature range* is reached by subtracting the temperature of the coldest month from that of the warmest month.

b) What relationship is there between precipitation and temperature and wood volume per hectare as indicated in Figure 9.8?

c) Which area would attract the highest bids for long-term logging rights? Why?

9 a) Construct a hythergraph for climate stations A and B using the data in Figure 9.13 on page 166. Mark the temperature

PLACE	FOREST REGION	PRECIPITATION	ANNUAL TEMPERATURE RANGE	NUMBER OF MONTHS WITH AVERAGE TEMPERATURE ABOVE 5.6°C	AVERAGE WOOD VOLUME PER HECTARE

intervals along the vertical axis and the precipitation amounts along the horizontal axis. To plot the temperature and precipitation for January for Station A, find the point that represents the temperature along the vertical scale, then move horizontally to the right to the point that represents the precipitation total along the horizontal scale. Put a dot at this point and label it January. Repeat this process for the other months of the year. Join the dots togeth-er with a straight line. Identify and label the name of the climate location.

b) Repeat this process for Station B using a different colour line. NOTE: When plotting more than one station, be sure to join the first set of dots before mark-ing a second set on the graph.

c) Lightly shade in the growing season for each station using different colours.

d) How many months have an average temperature above 5.6°C at Station A? At Station B?

Figure 9.11
Climate and tree growth

Figure 9.12
A hythergraph of the climates of Corner Brook, Newfoundland, and Tofino, British Columbia

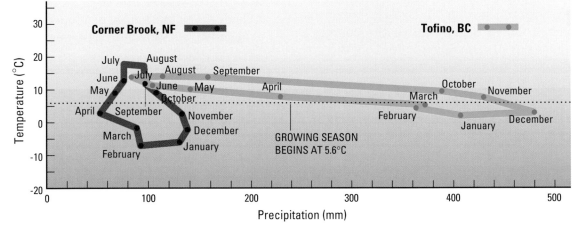

The temperature and precipitation values for each month are plotted on the graph using the temperature scale along the vertical axis and the precipitation scale along the horizontal axis. Straight lines join the dots together. The shape created by the lines shows climatic variations. Tofino's long, narrow, horizontal graph indicates a wide difference in monthly precipitation but a small difference in temperature during the year. The dotted line represents the temperature at which plants begin to grow (5.6°C), making it easy to see which months lie within the growing season. The growing season at Corner Brook, for example, begins in late April and extends into the first week of October.

Figure 9.13
Climate data

STATION A	J	F	M	A	M	J	J	A	S	O	N	D
Annual temperature –0.6°C	–22.4	–18.3	–11.4	–0.4	7.7	14.0	17.9	16.3	10.2	3.8	–7.5	–17.4
Total precipitation 449 mm	18	16	21	25	38	59	72	62	55	31	29	23

STATION B	J	F	M	A	M	J	J	A	S	O	N	D
Annual temperature 8.7°C	0.5	3.0	4.6	8.0	11.5	14.3	16.6	16.3	13.7	9.6	4.5	2.0
Total precipitation 2246 mm	313	234	189	149	77	69	52	73	127	301	314	348

Forest inventories

Harvesting the wealth of Canada's forests provides jobs for one in sixteen Canadians and produces 3 per cent of the country's total value of economic production. But not all of our forests are suitable for harvest. Figure 9.14 gives an inventory of forest land by province. **Productive forests** are those that can be harvested profitably. They are found in the warmer, wetter regions where large trees grow quickly in dense forests. They are close to roads, railways, and waterways for easy shipment to markets. **Unproductive forests** are just the opposite. They are found in isolated areas where the climate is colder. Here the trees are smaller and further apart. There are few, if any, transportation routes, which means harvesting these forests is too costly to be profitable.

10 Create a map of Canada to show productive forest lands. Refer to Figure 9.6 on page 161.
   a) Shade in the west coast coniferous rainforest, the Montane coniferous forest, and the Columbia forest.
   b) Locate the boreal forest region. Draw a line across the middle of the region from Atlantic Canada to the Yukon. Shade in the area south of this line.
   c) Shade in the Great Lakes-St. Lawrence forest region to the west of Lake Superior. Draw a line across the middle of this region eastward from Georgian Bay to the St. Lawrence River in Quebec. Shade in the area north of this line.
   d) Shade in all of the Acadian forest region.
   e) Describe the general pattern of productive forests shown on your map. Identify four factors that explain why these are Canada's most productive forest lands.

PROVINCE	TOTAL FOREST LAND (km²)	PRODUCTIVE FOREST LAND (km²)	VOLUME OF USABLE WOOD ON PRODUCTIVE FOREST LAND (1 000 000 m³)		
			TOTAL	SOFTWOODS	HARDWOODS
Newfoundland	225 240	112 710	527	488	39
Prince Edward Is.	2 940	2 780	26	16	10
Nova Scotia	39 230	37 670	254	153	101
New Brunswick	61 060	59 540	646	434	212
Quebec	838 950	539 910	4 243	2 951	1 292
Ontario	579 950	422 040	3 622	2 320	1302
Manitoba	262 770	152 390	911	609	302
Saskatchewan	288 060	126 330	827	434	393
Alberta	382 140	257 050	2 683	1 709	974
British Columbia	605 650	517 390	9 936	9 245	691
Yukon	275 490	74 700	632	567	65
Northwest Terr.	614 370	143 210	446	315	131
Canada	**4 175 850**	**2 445 720**	**24 753**	**19 241**	**5 512**

Source: Statistics Canada, *Canada Year Book*, 1994.

Figure 9.14
Forest inventory, 1994

11 Refer to Figures 9.14 and 9.17.
  a) Name the three provinces with the greatest area of productive forest.
  b) Name the three provinces with the greatest volume of usable timber.
  c) In an organizer, compare the forest resources of British Columbia, Quebec, and Ontario. Consider characteristics such as tree types, productive forest as a per cent of total forest land, wood volume per hectare, volume of wood harvested, and value of forest products sold. Use specific figures in presenting your information.

12 a) Form groups of four students. List as many products as you can think of that come from Canada's forest industry. Categorize each product as either softwood or hardwood. For each category, list the forest region(s) that could provide the wood needed to make the products and the provinces where these regions are found.
  b) Using a large outline map of Canada as a background, create a poster to illustrate the information your group has collected.

Jobs in the forest industry

Forests are an important source of jobs for Canadians. In 1994, 367 000 people were directly employed in forest products industries. An additional 508 000 Canadians were indirectly employed providing products and services for forestry companies and their workers. This means that approximately one Canadian job in ten depends on forestry! A Canadian Forest Service study showed that in 1993, 309 communities across the country directly depended on forestry for more than 50 per cent of their jobs. Another 1068 communities had 10 to 50 per cent of their jobs based in forestry.

Employment in the forest industry is divided into four main sectors: logging, paper and allied products, wood industries, and furniture industries. (See Figure 9.15.) Logging includes activities such as felling trees and collecting and hauling logs to the mills. Paper and allied products include pulp and paper manufacturing and the recycling of used paper into new paper products. Wood industries include sawmills, planing mills, and shingle mills, and the manufacturing of veneer and plywood. Furniture industries include the making of all types of wooden or partly wooden furniture.

The distribution of employment in forestry is closely related to the size of productive forests. Figure 9.15 shows jobs in the main sectors of the forest industry by province. The majority of jobs in British Columbia and Alberta are in logging and wood industries. In Ontario, Quebec, and Atlantic Canada the balance shifts to paper industries. While British Columbia is con-

Figure 9.15
Employment in the forest industry, 1993

PROVINCE/ TERRITORY	LOGGING	WOOD INDUSTRIES	FURNITURE INDUSTRIES	PAPER AND ALLIED PRODUCTS	TOTAL FOREST INDUSTRY
Newfoundland	1 200	478	32	na	1 710
Prince Edward Island	na	272	0	na	272
Nova Scotia	2 000	2 235	304	3 425	7 964
New Brunswick	4 400	4 620	290	6 291	15 601
Quebec	14 600	34 149	20 683	43 203	112 635
Ontario	10 000	29 185	33 284	42 794	115 263
Manitoba	500	2 474	2 184	1 755	6 913
Saskatchewan	800	1 445	182	na	2 427
Alberta	2 900	6 793	2 850	2 479	15 022
British Columbia	26 100	42 283	2 564	18 207	89 154
Yukon/NT	na	na	na	na	na
Canada	**62 500**	**123 934**	**62 373**	**118 154**	**366 961**

na - not available/confidential – usually means the number is so small that it is not reported.
Source: Canada Yearbook.

sidered to be the top forest province, both Quebec and Ontario employ more people in forestry.

The number of jobs in the forest industry fluctuates. Like many industries based on natural resources, forestry experiences **boom-and-bust cycles**. When times are good, more houses are built and more books and newspapers are sold. The demand for forest products rises. This in turn creates more jobs. In times of recession, fewer houses are built and there may be less demand for paper products. When this happens, forest workers are laid off as paper and lumber mills cut back on production or go out of business altogether.

Jobs are also affected by worker productivity. New machines and methods of logging and processing wood have increased productivity and reduced the number of jobs. (See Figure 9.16.) The shift towards fewer but more highly skilled workers will continue. Only the largest, most modern mills will be able to survive in a competitive global economy. Older, smaller mills will be forced out of business, leaving one-industry forestry towns to a gloomy fate.

The amount of wood harvested is closely related to forest productivity. British Columbia, for example, has the largest volume of wood by province. It is also the largest harvester. (See Figure 9.17.) The total value of all forest products shipped in 1993 was almost $45 billion. Of this total, about $27 billion was exported. These figures illustrate the importance of forestry to the Canadian economy.

YEAR	WOOD HARVESTED (millions m³)	EMPLOYED PERSONS	WOOD HARVESTED PER EMPLOYEE (m³)
1970	121	65 562	1845.6
1971	119	60 146	1978.5
1972	124	57 163	2169.2
1973	143	66 072	2164.3
1974	138	68 328	2019.7
1975	115	58 642	1961.0
1976	139	56 933	2441.5
1977	145	60 510	2396.3
1978	156	63 917	2440.7
1979	161	66 084	2436.3
1980	155	64 174	2415.3
1981	144	61 467	2342.7
1982	127	52 210	2432.5
1983	155	58 792	2636.4
1984	167	59 816	2791.9
1985	168	59 401	2828.2
1986	177	54 628	3240.1
1987	191	61 172	3122.3
1988	190	60 233	3154.4
1989	188	61 947	3034.9
1990	163	56 865	2866.4
1991	162	55 942	2895.9
1992	165	55 113	2993.8

Source: Canadian Forest Service.

Figure 9.16

Forest industry jobs over time
A recent study by the Canadian Forest Service predicted employment in Canadian pulp and paper mills will drop by 15 000 to 20 000 jobs by the year 2004.

13 List four forestry jobs that would be classified as direct employment and four that would be classified as indirect employment.

Figure 9.17
Volume and value of forest products, by province, 1993

PROVINCE	VALUE OF FOREST PRODUCTS SHIPPED ($ millions)	VOLUME OF WOOD HARVESTED (million m³)
Newfoundland	na	2.2
Prince Edward Island	na	0.2
Nova Scotia	900	4.2
New Brunswick	2 200	8.8
Quebec	11 500	32.3
Ontario	10 300	23.2
Manitoba	600	1.5
Saskatchewan	450	4.4
Alberta	2 300	14.2
British Columbia	15 600	78.0
Canada	**44 500**	**169.3**

na = not available

14 Refer to Figure 9.15.
   a) Which three provinces have the greatest number of workers employed in the forest industry?
   b) Which two provinces/territories have the fewest number of workers employed in the forest industry?
   c) Explain this employment pattern.

15 a) Which two provinces dominate the paper and allied products sector? Why do they use their trees for this purpose rather than for lumber and plywood?
   b) Which province dominates the wood industries sector? Why does this province use so much of its wood to produce lumber?

16 Refer to Figure 9.16.
   a) What is the general employment trend in the forest industry? Can you explain why?

   b) Do you think this trend will continue? Why?

17 Construct a **bar map** on an outline map of Canada to illustrate employment in the forest industry (Figure 9.15), the value of forest products shipped (Figure 9.17), or the volume of wood harvested by province (Figure 9.17). For example, if you are mapping employment, use a scale of 1 cm for every 10 000 workers. Begin by plotting the data for British Columbia. Draw a bar beginning in the southern part of the province. The bar should be 0.5 cm wide and 8.9 cm high, since BC has 89 154 workers employed in forestry. (The bars can extend beyond provincial boundaries as long as they begin in the provinces.) Repeat this process for each province and territory. Colour each bar a different colour. Indicate the scale on the map and give it an appropriate title.

18 Using the information in Figures 9.15 to 9.17 and the bar map you created in activity 17, create a display poster illustrating the importance of forests in Canada.

Case study: the Saguenay Valley

One of the most important pulp and paper and logging centres in Canada is the Saguenay River Valley in Quebec. The combination of a large forest resource, many fast-flowing rivers, excellent hydroelectric power sites, and easy access to markets via the lower Saguenay and St. Lawrence rivers makes this an ideal location for pulp and paper mills.

By 1900, logging and sawmill operations were well established in the Saguenay Valley. Logs were easily transported from the boreal forests surrounding the valley along the rivers that flowed into Lac St Jean. By 1920, the technology for producing hydro-generated electricity was available, as was the process for turning softwood trees into newsprint and paper products. Both of these developments led to the growth of the pulp and paper industry along the Saguenay River near Lac St. Jean. The largest power plants and pulp and paper mills are shown in Figure 9.18.

19 Locate the Saguenay Valley on a physical map of Canada.

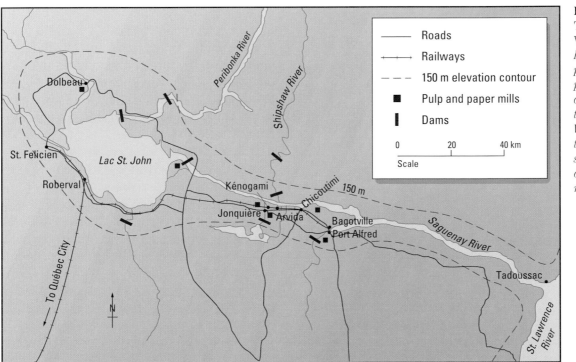

Figure 9.18
The Saguenay Valley *How many pulp and paper mills are located in the Saguenay Valley? Why is this area well suited for pulp and paper mills?*

Figure 9.19
The Shipshaw
power develop-
ment on the
mighty
Saguenay River
*Alcan has six
power houses
on the
Saguenay and
Peribonka
rivers provid-
ing low-cost
electricity to
the company.*

a) In what landform region is this area found?

b) In what forest region is this area found?

c) Draw a sketch to show the pattern of major rivers within the drainage basin of the Saguenay River. Beneath your sketch, write a description of the river pattern.

20 Refer to Figures 9.20 and 9.21.

a) Draw a sketch of the area shown in the air photograph. Mark in the coastline and river, the outline of the town, and the two major highways.

b) Label the following features on your sketch map: the pulp and paper mill; pulp logs; the sawdust pile; Baie des Ha Ha; port facilities; oil tanks; Roberval Saguenay Railway; new residential areas; old residential areas.

c) Why is this an excellent site for the location of a pulp and paper mill?

21 The production of hydroelectric power requires an abundant and steady flow of water falling over rapids or falls and the concentrated runoff of a large drainage basin into a single river. Using climatic data, an atlas, and the sketch map you created in activity 20, explain why the Saguenay River is ideally suited for the production of hydroelectric power.

Managing the forest resource

The greatest threat to Canada's forests comes from human activity. Extensive logging is endangering ecosystems in all forest regions. Over 90 per cent of Canada's forests are publicly owned. Yet in the past, governments issued land leases and logging permits to forestry companies with little study of the environmental impact of these operations and few environmental restrictions or safeguards. Our forests were considered to be limitless.

Extensive logging in Canadian forests began in the late 1800s and early 1900s. Then, many forests were stripped bare. In Ontario and Quebec, for example, so much white pine was cut that the species was unable to regenerate itself in many areas. In response, governments began to regulate logging in publicly owned forests. Companies were required to harvest forests in such a way that they could regenerate themselves in a reasonable period of time. In environmentally sensitive areas logging was barred altogether.

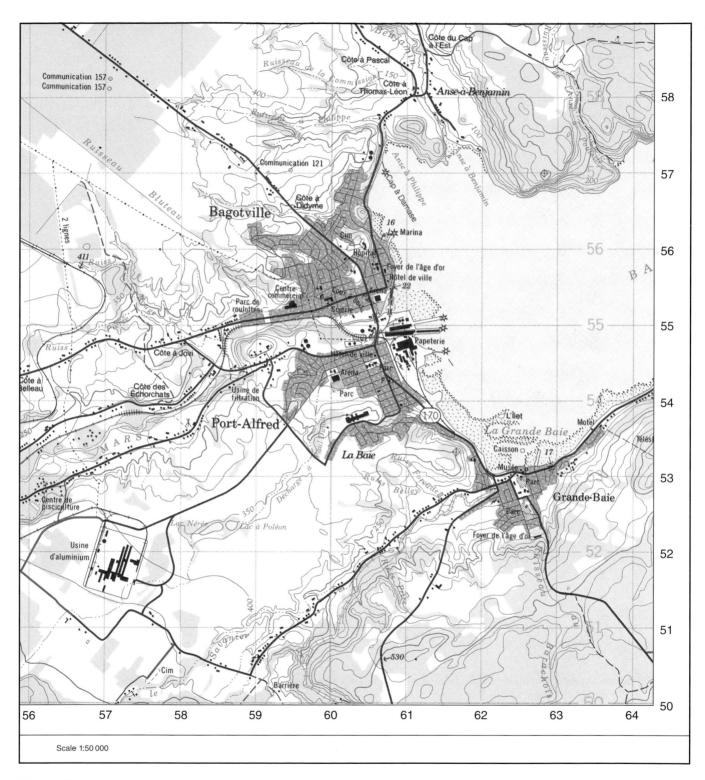

Figure 9.20
Topographic map of Port Alfred

Figure 9.21
Vertical air photo of Port Alfred showing Stone Consolidated's pulp and paper plant in Quebec
Use a six-figure grid reference to identify each location labelled A to H on the photo.

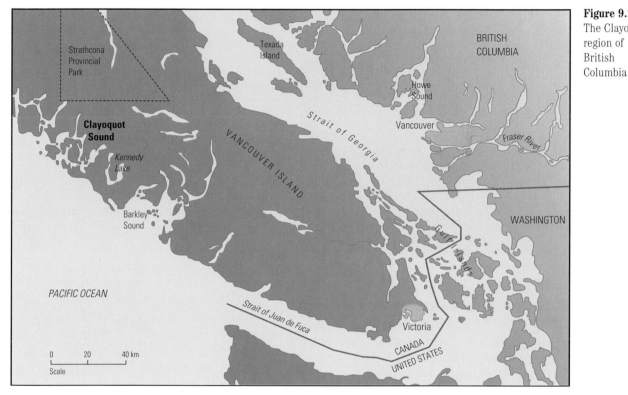

Figure 9.22
The Clayoquot region of British Columbia

By the 1980s, however, these measures were being challenged. Environmentalists charged Canada with a poor record of forest management. By the 1990s, there was a growing dissatisfaction among Canadians with the way in which our forests were being managed. Forestry companies faced public challenges from conservation and environmental groups. In British Columbia in particular, the issue exploded into the national headlines. The controversy even extended beyond Canada's borders. In Europe, conservation groups urged consumers to boycott Canadian forest products in protest against poor forest management practices.

Several factors brought the debate over forest management to the forefront. The environmental movement heightened public awareness of the need to protect all aspects of the environment, including forests. In particular, there was a growing concern over the logging of **old-growth forests**. These areas of mature forests, undisturbed by human activity, have been steadily disappearing. One report predicts that if the present rate of logging continues, by the early twenty-first century few old-growth forests will remain in BC's coastal rainforest outside of provincial and national parks. This issue has raised further questions about the overall manage-

Figure 9.23
A clear-cut mountain slope in British Columbia

22 Summarize the factors that changed Canadians' attitudes towards our forests.

ment of the forest resource. In 1989, a study by the Canadian Forest Service concluded that "Canada does not have the required measures in place to ensure that forestry is sustainable."

Part of the problem is the method of forest harvesting. In 1990, 92 per cent of harvested forests were **clear-cut**. This means that all trees in a block, strip, or patch of forest are removed, leaving barren hills and mountain slopes. (See Figure 9.23.) While this figure dropped to 87 per cent in 1993, those who oppose clear-cutting believe there is still a long way to go towards solving the problem.

All of these factors have joined forces with our changing attitudes. People are beginning to value forests for more than wood and the products it creates. Increasingly, Canadians appreciate wilderness areas for their recreational value and their peace and tranquillity, as well as for their importance in the cycle of nature. We recognize that forests are part of our heritage.

A new management system

In the 1990s, the ways in which Canadian forests were harvested began to change. Today the forest industry is closely monitored to ensure that forests are managed in a sustainable way. New regulations have limited the size of clear-cuts to 40 ha. Tall trees must be left standing around the edges of clear-cut areas to protect seedlings from winds. Forest debris must be left to decay to provide soil nutrients. The amount of land that must be replanted has been increased and forest companies are required to monitor the success of their replanting sites. There is also more investment in **silviculture**—the breeding, developing, and cultivating of trees.

Sustainable development

The best way to ensure the survival of the forest resource is through **sustainable development**. In the past, the Canadian forestry industry did not practice sustained yield management. Trees were cut faster than nature or people could replace them. Today, however, profitable forest resources in many producing areas are becoming scarce. They have been replaced by forests of immature trees or trees of low economic value. In some regions, the distance from cutting areas to mills has increased from 100 km to as much as 600 km as companies scour remote regions for profitable forest stands.

	FOREST A	FOREST B	FOREST C
Maturation period	100 years	50 years	40 years
Forest inventory (usable timber)	1 million trees	1 million trees	1 million trees
Annual allowable cut (number of trees)	1 000 000÷100 = 10 000	1 000 000÷50 = 20 000	1 000 000÷40 = 25 000
Annual replanting and reseeding required (natural and artificial)	10 000 trees	20 000 trees	25 000 trees

Figure 9.24
Sustaining the yield

Under sustainable development, the volume of trees cut in any one year must be equal to, or less than, the volume of trees that are replanted. Figure 9.24 shows how sustainable yield is determined. The annual allowable cut is calculated by dividing the number of trees by the maturation period. In Forest B, for example, it takes fifty years for a tree to mature. There are 1 million usable trees in the forest, so the allowable cut is 20 000 (1 000 000 ÷ 50). To sustain the yield, the forest company must replant this same number—20 000 trees. This will maintain the inventory of Forest B at 1 million trees.

23 a) Why did the forest industry fail to follow the management principles of sustained yield? Why should Canadians be concerned with this failure?
  b) What actions did governments take in the 1990s to support sustainable development?
  c) Why did it take so long for governments to act? What important lessons can we learn from this?

24 Refer to Figure 9.24.
  a) Why might maturation cycles of forests differ?
  b) If a forest had a maturation cycle of fifty-five years and the forest inventory was 750 000 usable trees, what would be the annual allowable cut?
  c) How many trees would need to be replanted or seeded annually to maintain a sustained yield?
  d) Based on your earlier studies of climate and forest growth, suggest which of the maturation cycles would match up with i) the west coast coniferous rainforest; ii) the boreal forest; iii) the Columbian coniferous forest. Give reasons for your decisions.

25 Imagine you are the chief forestry officer in charge of a rich timber area. You must set the quota for the allowable cut based on the principle of sustained yield. List the factors you should consider in determining the annual allowable cut for the next five years.

Alternatives to clear-cutting

There are four alternatives to clear-cutting. **Small-patch clear-cutting** involves clearing 1 or 2 ha of old-growth forest, leaving a border of trees surrounding the cleared patch. The older trees provide shade for the cleared site, which helps the trees to reseed naturally. Logging debris is left to decay, which provides much-needed nutrients for regrowth. **Shelterwood logging** removes up to 70 per cent of the trees at a site. Small patches of old-growth forest are left standing to provide seeds for regeneration. The **seed tree retention** method removes all of a forest stand except for a few seed-bearing trees, usually about twenty-five per hectare. These remain either in small groups or on their own and provide the seeds for new growth. **Selective cutting** harvests only mature trees of certain species. These are removed singly or in small groups. This maintains the uneven age structure of the trees in the forest stand. (See Figure 9.25.)

26 How would each of the four alternatives to clear-cutting help forests recover from logging more quickly?

Silviculture and reforestation

Silviculture is the science of breeding, developing, and cultivating trees. Some of its most important research today is in genetics. This is the development of new varieties of trees that will increase forest productivity. Scientists are working to breed trees that grow faster, resist insects and diseases, and produce a better quality and higher quantity of wood. They are also researching better methods of regenerating forests. Natural regeneration depends on mature trees to supply the seeds for regrowth. Where mature trees have been harvested in clear-cut areas, the forest must be regenerated artificially. Seeds are planted in areas where soils and climatic conditions are well suited to growth. In other areas, seedlings are planted to regenerate a forest more quickly. Tree farms operate in all forest regions to supply seedlings adapted to local temperatures, precipitation, and soil conditions.

Computer-based planning and mapping systems increase the accuracy of forest inventories. Foresters are now able to learn more about the size, composition, age, and quality of forest stands. This information will help them to make better decisions about logging operations.

In the past, reforestation has renewed only a small percentage of harvested forests. In addition, almost half of the forests that are replanted fail to regenerate. Scientists are helping to increase the success of reforestation projects by developing seedlings that have a higher survival rate. The result is that by 1993, more than 4.5 million hectares—34 per cent of the total harvested area—were planted or seeded across Canada. The remaining 66 per cent was left to regenerate naturally.

27 a) Why is silviculture important to the future of Canada's forests?
   b) What accounts for the change in silviculture expenditures shown in Figure 9.26? Why is this encouraging?

Clear-cutting: The forest is completely cleared over an area greater than 40 ha.

Small-patch clear-cutting: The forest is cleared in patches of 1 or 2 ha.

Shelterwood logging: Over 70 per cent of the forest is harvested, leaving patches of old-growth forest.

Seed tree retention: The forest is cleared except for a few seed-bearing trees.

Selective cutting: Only mature trees of certain species are selectively cut from the forest.

Figure 9.25
Methods of cutting forests

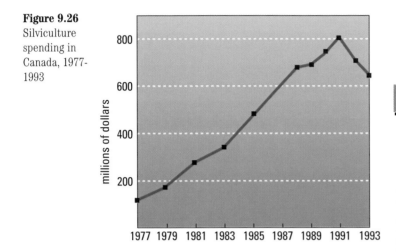

Figure 9.26
Silviculture spending in Canada, 1977-1993

Figure 9.27
Percentage of land protected in Canada, 1970-1994
What is happening to the percentage of protected land in Canada? Why is it important to continue this trend?

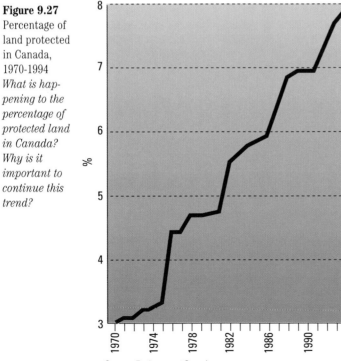

Source: Environment Canada

c) In your opinion, who should bear the greatest financial responsibility for silviculture, governments or private industry? Give reasons for your answer.

28 Identify another resource industry that regenerates its renewable resource. How is this method similar to silviculture? How is it different?

Protected forests

Forest land in protected areas, such as parks and reserves, has increased from 22.1 million hectares in 1960 to 78.8 million hectares in 1994. (See Figure 9.27.) Of these 78.8 million hectares, about 50 million hectares are forest. This represents about 12 per cent of Canada's total forest land. This meets the objectives of the 1990 Green Plan to preserve 12 per cent of the nation as protected land. As the amount of protected land increases, more fragile ecosystems are protected and preserved. This helps to ensure that future generations will be able to enjoy these wilderness areas.

Both federal and provincial governments are continuing to create protected wilderness areas. In 1992, British Columbia announced a plan to double its parks and wilderness areas. Eighty-one new parks will increase the total protected area from 6.5 to 8.5 per cent of the province. This equals 82 000 km^2—an area larger than the entire province of New Brunswick. Ontario proposes to add thirty new parks under its "Keep it Wild" campaign launched in 1994. These parks would protect fourteen old-growth red and white pine forests. Other provinces are also planning to enlarge the protected areas within their boundaries.

29 Investigate the protected areas in your province. Make a list of these areas along with the type of ecosystem of each one. Use tourist guides, road maps, and atlases to help you. Your provincial tourism agency may be able to provide useful information.

Recycling

Recycling is an effective way of reducing the pressure on Canadian forests. One tonne of recycled paper is equal to the amount of paper produced from seventeen to thirty trees! Over half of Canada's paper and paperboard mills now include wastepaper in their production process. Most of these mills are located near urban centres, which provide large amounts of used paper. In 1995, paper company officials estimated that 33 per cent of all newspapers sold in North America were recycled back into newsprint. Within a few years, they expect this figure to exceed 40 per cent. Even so, Canada's recycling record is not as good as it could be. In 1991, for example, the United States and the European Union recycled over 37 per cent of the paper they consumed. Canada recycled only 26 per cent.

As more people recycle, the savings in terms of trees and forests will increase. Some experts suggest that by recycling paper, current levels of paper production can be maintained, while demand for new trees will decline by 30 to 40 per cent. If so,

it will give the forest industry time to restore many cut forests.

30 a) Conduct a class survey to determine how many families recycle their newspapers and magazines.

b) Working with a partner, create a poster encouraging people who don't recycle to do so.

31 Should governments provide subsidies and support for recycling programs? Explain.

Threats to Canada's forests

Forest fires

Fires are part of the normal cycle of forest ecosystems. Some coniferous trees, such as jack and lodgepole pines, depend on fire to release the seeds from their cones. Fire also aids in the regrowth of red and white pine forests by burning competing bushes and trees, clearing the ground, and fertilizing the soil with ash. However, fires may also threaten human settlements, wood supplies, and recreational activities.

The number of fires and the amount of forest they burn varies from year to year, depending largely on climatic conditions. From 1978 to 1992, an average of 1.8 million hectares of all forests, including 680 000 hectares of commercial forests, were burned each year. In the dry, hot summer of 1989, however, 7.5 million hectares of commercial and non-commercial forests were burned across Canada. By comparison, an average 890 000 hectares of commercial forests were harvested by forest companies each year from 1978 to 1992.

Figure 9.28 shows the average area of commercial and non-commercial forests burned each year by province.

On average, human activities cause more than half of all forest fires. Most of these fires occur in accessible areas of commercial forests. Since firefighting crews and equipment are close by and these forests have an economic value, they are a priority for firefighting crews. Yet it is still important for people who use the forest to be aware of the hazards their actions may create. Governments have launched campaigns to increase public awareness of these fire hazards.

While people may cause the greatest number of fires, lightning fires account for the greatest amount of burned forest area.

On average, lightning fires account for between 80 and 90 per cent of all burned forests. This is because most lightning fires occur in remote areas where they are allowed to burn themselves out.

In commercial forests, the detection of forest fires involves the latest technology. This includes automated lightning detection networks and computerized fire and heat-detection equipment. More air and ground patrols and lookout towers have also improved detection and response times. The equipment used to fight fires is among the most advanced in the world. Special Canadair CL-51 water bombers are the only aircraft in the world designed to scoop up water from lakes. Together with helicopters and other aircraft they help

Figure 9.28
Average annual area of commercial and non-commercial forests burned each year, 1970-1993

Manitoba and Saskatchewan, with their drier climates, and the Northwest Territories, where fires are allowed to burn themselves out, have the largest burned areas. Although they have large forested areas, British Columbia, Ontario, and Quebec have lower total burned areas because of their wetter climates.

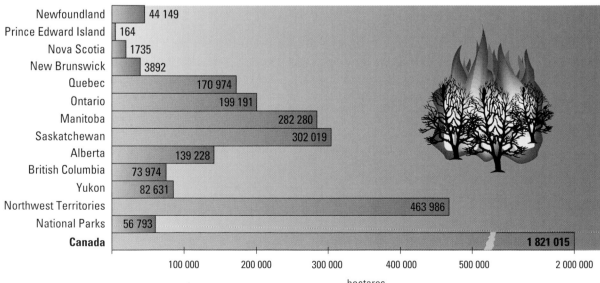

Province	hectares
Newfoundland	44 149
Prince Edward Island	164
Nova Scotia	1735
New Brunswick	3892
Quebec	170 974
Ontario	199 191
Manitoba	282 280
Saskatchewan	302 019
Alberta	139 228
British Columbia	73 974
Yukon	82 631
Northwest Territories	463 986
National Parks	56 793
Canada	1 821 015

fight fires in remote areas. But trained fire-fighting crews remain the most effective weapon against spreading fires.

32 Refer to Figure 9.28.
   a) Calculate the percentage of burned forests in each province from 1970 to 1993. To do this, divide the area burned in each province by the total area burned in Canada and multiply the result by 100.
   b) Present your results in a bar graph, beginning with the highest percentage down to the lowest percentage.
   c) What factors account for the differences in the average area of forests burned in the provinces?

33 a) Explain why more forest fires are caused by human activity while lightning fires burn a much larger area.
   b) How can we reduce the amount of timber lost to fire?

34 The policy of the Canadian Forest Service is to let forest fires in remote areas burn themselves out. Why would the Forest Service adopt such a policy?

these ecosystems. The most compelling evidence of harmful effects is found in eastern North America where acidity levels are high. Here many forests have experienced reduced growth or have died altogether. Many scientists believe acid precipitation is directly responsible. Others believe, however, that acid precipitation harms only those forest stands that are already weakened by other factors, such as disease, insects, or old age.

Acidity levels are also influenced by soil, climate, and tree species. Those species that are most vulnerable to high acidity are sugar maple, red spruce, beech, pine, and ash. In Canada, scientists believe the Great Lakes-St. Lawrence and Acadian forest regions are at greatest risk. This is because they receive high levels of acid precipitation from the smokestacks of the industrial northeast and contain a high proportion of vulnerable species. The southern edge of the boreal forest region east of Ontario also faces a moderate risk.

35 a) What evidence is there that acid precipitation is harmful to forest ecosystems?
   b) Why is there a debate over the effects of acid precipitation on forests?

Acid precipitation

Many scientists consider **acid precipitation** to be another threat to Canadian forests. (The causes of acid precipitation are discussed on page 199.) The effects of acidity on lakes and streams are well known. In forests, however, it has been more difficult to prove how acid precipitation has affected

Insects and disease

Insects and disease are also part of the cycle of forest ecosystems. Insect infestation causes considerable damage to Canadian forests. (See Figure 9.29.) Every year insects destroy an amount equal to 30 per cent of the volume of harvested forest. Insects that are especially threatening are the spruce and

	WOOD LOSS (%)
Insects	
Spruce budworm	38.1
Mountain pine beetle	10.2
Spruce bark beetle	2.0
Aspen defoliators	7.3
Other bark beetles	0.1
Miscellaneous defoliators	1.3
Total insects	**59.0**
Diseases	
Decays (fungi)	22.8
Hypoxylon canker	10.2
Dwarf mistletoes	3.5
Miscellaneous diseases	4.5
Total diseases	**41.0**
Total insects and diseases	**100.0**

Source: *Canada Yearbook.*

Figure 9.29
Annual average forest loss due to insects and diseases

jack pine budworms, the tent caterpillar and gypsy moth in eastern Canada, and the pine bark beetle in British Columbia.

The spruce budworm affects forests across Canada, although it is found mainly in Ontario, Quebec, and the Maritimes. This insect eats the buds and needles of many softwood species. Without buds, the trees cannot produce new foliage. The growth of some trees is stunted; others simply die. The pine bark beetle spreads with incredible speed. In a matter of days a healthy pine tree can be killed by as many as 2000 swarming beetles! Insecticides and herbicides are used to fight these insect infestations.

Diseases cause less damage to forests than insects, but they still take a large toll.

The most serious diseases are fungi and cankers. These weaken the trees and eventually stunt their growth or kill them.

Together, insects and diseases damage larger areas of Canada's forests than are logged by forest companies. As a result, the forest industry places a high priority on controlling and reducing these hazards in commercial forests.

36 a) **Why is such a high priority placed on controlling insects and diseases in our forests?**

b) **Aerial spraying is opposed by many environmental groups. Why do you think this is so?**

Simulation: combatting spruce budworm infestation

A large expanse of forest in Quebec is being ravaged by an infestation of spruce budworm. A three-member committee has been formed to evaluate the options for combatting the outbreak. In a meeting, the committee will hear proposals for solving this problem from representatives of five groups.

37 a) **Form groups of eight. Select three group members to form the evaluation committee. Assign each of the remaining five members a role as described in the briefing notes on pages 185–186. Each group member must present his or her position to the three-panel committee.**

b) **Once the committee has heard all of the presentations, they must decide what action to take to deal with the budworm** outbreak. **Once a consensus is reached, the committee members must present their decision and the reasons for it in a formal one-page report or in a class presentation.**

Briefing notes

A naturalist: Do nothing! Let the budworm eat itself out of house and home. Eventually the infestation will die out. This is a natural pest and natural processes will take care of it. Pesticides will harm the environment and endanger other wildlife. These toxic chemicals may even get into our drinking water and harm us as well. This won't be the first time chemical companies have told us their products are safe, only to find out later they were wrong! In New Brunswick, where these insecticides have been used for over thirty years, studies have linked chemical sprays containing fenitrothion with Reye's syndrome, a sometimes fatal disease that attacks children.

An aerial spraying company representative: Kill the budworm with aerial spraying! Chemical sprays such as fenitrothion and matacil are approved by the federal government. They kill budworms on contact by attacking the central nervous system. These chemicals require only a few applications. They are inexpensive and easily handled, and they produce excellent results. If we sit around and wait it could take ten to twenty years for the budworm to die out naturally. In the meantime the forest will have suffered serious damage. An insecticide like Bacillus thuringiensis (BT) is not the solution, either. This is more expensive than chemical sprays. It is also slower-acting and is affected by the weather. BT has an uneven rate of success—sometimes it works, sometimes it doesn't! The only alternative is a chemical spray.

An insecticide company representative: Kill the budworm using the biological insecticide Bacillus thuringiensis (BT)! This is designed to kill only insects like the budworm. Unlike chemical sprays that kill on contact, BT must be eaten by the insect. It has an extremely low toxic effect on mammals, birds, and fish. It can also be sprayed close to populated areas without danger to human beings. Forest management and reforestation techniques take too long. We have to act now to save the existing forest! The forest industry cannot wait for twenty or thirty years for the damaged forest to regrow. We must apply insecticides like BT to kill the pests as quickly as possible.

A forestry management representative: Solve the insect infestation through silviculture! By regenerating the damaged forest with mixed species rather than large tracts of a single species that is favoured by the budworm, the forest becomes less attractive to this pest. Salvage cutting is not the answer to this problem. Most of the damaged trees are too far from the mill. If they are removed, severe soil erosion may result over large clear-cut areas. There may also be more salvage trees than the mill can handle. You feel that those who want to endanger the environment by using chemicals or insecticides are only endangering human health and the health of the forest ecosystem.

A reforestation company representative: Harvest the trees that have been killed by the budworm and send them to the local paper mill! Salvage cutting recovers some of the commercial value of the timber and helps prevent the build up of secondary pest infestations. The area can then be reforested with tree species that are unattractive to the budworm. In the future, natural regeneration of clear-cut areas will have to be replaced with artificial regeneration in order to discourage the natural growth of balsam fir, a tree that attracts budworms. This avoids the quick-fix solution of pouring toxic chemicals and insecticides into the forest ecosystem through widespread aerial spraying.

We live in the age of metals. Almost every product we use in our daily lives is somehow related to mining. The cars we drive, the cans we open, the cement we walk on, and the stoves we cook on are just a few examples! And then there are the hidden items that come from mining, those things most of us never see—the steel beams in office buildings, the gypsum wallboards in houses, and the wires and cables beneath our city streets! It is easy to see how important the mining industry is to our society.

1 a) **List ten ways in which the products of mining contribute to your life.**
   b) **Describe how Canadian society would be different if we did not have the products of the mining industry.**

Canada's mineral wealth

Canada is a mineral treasure chest. Almost every important mineral used in industrial societies is produced somewhere in this country. There are over 280 mines, producing thirty-four different metals and twenty-six non-metallic minerals, across Canada. With such abundant resources, Canada is able to supply its own domestic needs for all minerals except bauxite, chromium, manganese, and phosphates. This mineral wealth makes mining an important part of the Canadian economy. (See Figure 10.1.)

Employment in mining

Mining creates jobs. There are two types of employment: direct and indirect. **Direct employment** includes jobs where people actually work in the mines. In 1993, 91 000 people—almost 3 per cent of the Canadian labour force—were directly employed in mining. **Indirect employment** includes

MINERAL	VALUE ($ millions)
Gold (5)	2 448
Copper (3)	1 809
Coal (na)	1 798
Zinc (1)	1 289
Potash (1)	1 220
Nickel (2)	1 203
Iron ore (na)	1 111
Cement (na)	842
Sand and gravel (na)	840
Uranium (1)	580
Stone (na)	515
Salt (na)	295
Asbestos (2)	228
Lime (na)	204
Silver (na)	188
Platinum (3)	158
Cobalt (3)	139
Peat (na)	139
Clay (na)	131
Sulphur (2)	128
Lead (5)	124

na = not available
Source: Natural Resources Canada, Minerals and Metals Sector

Figure 10.1
Canada's leading minerals, by value, 1994
Canada's world ranking is indicated in brackets after each mineral.

jobs in supply and service industries that meet the needs of the mining companies and their employees. In 1993, another 2.3 per cent of the labour force was indirectly employed in mining, selling and servicing mining equipment, transporting the minerals to markets, smelting and refining the metal ores, and providing energy for mining companies. Other people find indirect employment in grocery and department stores, medical offices, insurance brokers, travel agencies, and other businesses that provide goods and services to mining communities.

In 1981, almost 245 000 Canadians were directly employed in the **primary industry** of mining, smelting, and refining ore. This was the highest level of mining employment ever reached in Canada. (See Figure 10.2.) Of these, 89 000 people worked in mines producing metals and non-metals. An additional 116 000 were employed in smelters and refineries. Since 1981, however, the number of people directly employed in primary mining has declined. By 1993, the number of mine workers producing metals and non-metals had dropped to 53 000. The number of peo-

Figure 10.2
Employment in the Canadian mining industry, 1961-1992

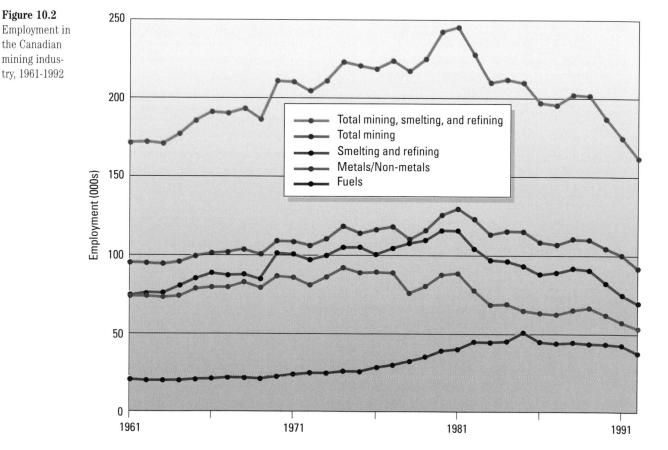

ple working in smelters and refineries had dropped to 68 000. But the value of production has steadily increased.

What factors have led to this trend? Global competition has forced mining companies to become more efficient. Computer technology and more automated and powerful equipment have combined with other labour-saving devices to reduce the number of workers a company needs. In 1961, the average mine worker produced $27 000 worth of minerals a year. By 1992, rising prices and increased production had raised this figure to $382 000. Experts believe that this trend towards higher production values with fewer workers will continue.

Mining also creates employment far beyond the mining towns themselves. The **multiplier effect** is the total impact on the economy that results from the expansion of one of its parts. In the mining industry, for example, the opening of a new mine may create 500 jobs directly and another 1500 jobs indirectly. The indirect jobs may be either in the mining community itself or somewhere else in the country. The multiplier effect in this case would be three— that is, for every job created in mining, three more jobs are created in other parts of the economy (500 × 3 = 1500). The wealth and jobs created by mining in Canada are shown in Figure 10.3.

The multiplier effect also extends beyond our borders. Canada exports 80 per cent of its mineral production each year to over 100 countries. These minerals are then processed into useful products, thereby creating jobs for workers in these countries.

2 **Refer to Figure 10.2.**
   a) **Describe the employment trend in most areas of mining from 1961 to 1980 and from 1981 to 1992.**
   b) **What two factors account for the trend from 1981 to 1992?**
   c) **Which sector of the mining industry did not follow the trend?**

INDUSTRY	ANNUAL WEALTH ($ millions)	JOBS (000s)
Mining	7 974	57.4
Quarrying	727	9.7
Primary metals	6 391	95.2
Metal working	7 691	166.9
Machinery	4 601	85.0
Transportation equipment	14 121	226.8
Total mining-related	**41 505**	**641.0**
Total Canadian economy	**483 018**	**9 394.0**

Figure 10.3
Mining: creating wealth and jobs

Source: Statistics Canada, *Human Activity and the Environment*, 1994.

3   Refer to Figure 10.3.
    a) Calculate the percentages of both wealth and jobs created by each mining-related industry out of the total Canadian economy. For example, to find the percentage of wealth created by mining, divide $7974 by 483 018, then multiply by 100. The result is 1.65 per cent. For jobs, divide 57.4 by 9394, then multiply by 100. The result is 0.6 per cent. Which industry accounts for the highest percentage of wealth? Which industry accounts for the highest percentage of jobs?
    b) Identify the industries that provide direct employment and those that provide indirect employment. Total the value of wealth and employment in each group. Based on these totals, what is the multiplier effect of mining on i) wealth and ii) jobs?

Figure 10.4
Work in an underground mine

4   Write a brief summary of the importance of the mining industry to Canada.

5   Draw a diagram to illustrate how the multiplier effect in the mining industry creates jobs in the mining community and beyond. Include at least ten different jobs that result from a mining operation.

Mineral deposits and locations

Minerals are naturally occurring substances found in rocks, soils, or sediments. Some minerals contain metals or non-metals that people find useful. Mineral deposits that are large enough to be mined profitably are called **ores**.

Minerals are classified into four categories. Each category is generally associated with either metamorphic, sedimentary, or igneous rocks. Knowing the relationship between rock types and mineral deposits is the first step in understanding where minerals are found in Canada.

Metallic minerals

Metallic minerals are most often associated with intrusive igneous rocks. At one time these minerals were dispersed in large volumes of molten rock, or magma, deep in the earth's interior. During periods of mountain building, the magma was forced up towards the earth's surface through **fissures**, or cracks. Super-heated **brines** within the magma dissolved metallic elements from the molten rock, which flowed into some of these cracks. As the brines cooled, they solidified and formed veins of metallic minerals. Today, where these deposits are large enough to be mined profitably, they are called ore bodies. These ores yield many different types of metals, including gold, silver, copper, lead, and zinc.

Fuel minerals

Almost all fuel minerals are found in sedimentary rock. They were formed from the remains of living organisms that were transformed over time by heat and pres-

Figure 10.5 Patterns of Canadian mining

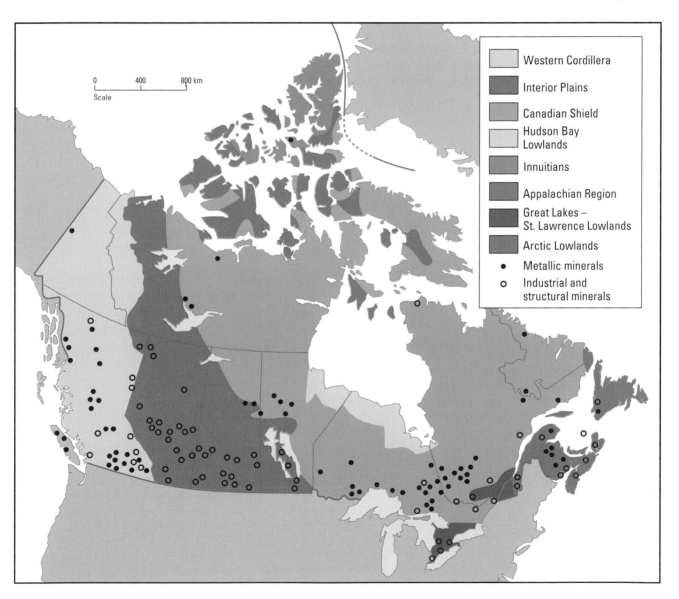

Legend:
- Western Cordillera
- Interior Plains
- Canadian Shield
- Hudson Bay Lowlands
- Innuitians
- Appalachian Region
- Great Lakes – St. Lawrence Lowlands
- Arctic Lowlands
- • Metallic minerals
- ○ Industrial and structural minerals

Scale: 0 400 800 km

sure into coal, oil, or natural gas. These minerals, called **fossil fuels**, release energy when they are burned. (Energy fuels are discussed further in chapter 11.)

Industrial minerals

Industrial minerals are found mainly in sedimentary rock. They were formed in shallow seas located in regions with hot, dry climates. As the water in these seas evaporated, it became more and more salty. Eventually, the salt became so concentrated that it began to build up along the bottom of the sea in layers. In some cases, the seas completely dried up, leaving behind non-metallic mineral deposits of gypsum, potash, or rock salt. This process is evident today in places like the Great Salt Lake in Utah, the Dead Sea in Israel and Jordan, and the Aral Sea in Kazakhstan and Uzbekistan.

Structural minerals

These minerals—sand, gravel, and clay—are the products of river, wind, and glacial deposition. They occur almost everywhere and are associated with all types of rocks.

They are used primarily as construction materials.

6 a) Copy the chart in Figure 10.6 into your notebook. Fill in the information for metallic, fuel, and industrial minerals using Figure 10.5 and Figures 11.12 and 11.23 on pages 218 and 228. (Do not include structural minerals.)
   b) In what physiographic regions are metallic minerals most commonly found? Can you explain why?
   c) In what physiographic regions are industrial minerals most commonly found? Can you explain why?
   d) In what physiographic region are fuel minerals most commonly found? Can you explain why?

7 Refer to Figure 10.7.
   a) List the two largest producers of each mineral by per cent.
   b) Which three provinces produce the greatest variety and quantity of minerals? Give 10 points to the highest producer and 5 points to the second-highest producer of each mineral. For cement, for example, Ontario receives 10 points while Quebec receives 5 points. Total the points for each

Figure 10.6
Mineral locations and relationships

	METALLIC	MINERALS INDUSTRIAL	FUEL
Physiographic regions			
Rock type			
Kinds of minerals			
Provinces with major mines			

PROVINCE	GOLD	COPPER	ZINC	NICKEL	IRON ORE	URANIUM	CEMENT	ASBESTOS*	SAND AND GRAVEL	POTASH	SILVER*	GYPSUM*
Newfoundland	0.0	0.1	0.0	0.0	63.2	0.0	1.1	2.4	1.7	0.0	0.0	0.0
Prince Edward Is.	0.0	0.0	0.0	0.0	0.0	0.0	0.0	0.0	0.1	0.0	0.0	0.0
Nova Scotia	0.0	0.0	0.0	0.0	0.0	0.0	5.7	0.0	2.3	0.0	0.0	80.1
New Brunswick	0.3	1.5	28.4	0.0	0.0	0.0	0.4	0.0	1.1	0.0	25.7	0.0
Quebec	28.2	11.2	14.7	0.0	33.8	0.0	17.4	97.6	11.7	0.0	15.5	0.0
Ontario	47.2	38.5	16.5	78.7	4.7	47.2	34.4	0.0	41.7	0.0	27.5	19.9
Manitoba	1.7	7.0	9.6	21.3	0.0	0.0	4.5	0.0	4.3	0.0	4.7	0.0
Saskatchewan	0.0	0.0	0.0	0.0	0.0	52.8	1.7	0.0	2.0	100.0	0.0	0.0
Alberta	0.0	0.0	0.0	0.0	0.0	0.0	12.2	0.0	15.9	0.0	0.0	0.0
British Columbia	8.4	41.8	11.8	0.0	0.1	0.0	19.6	0.0	17.5	0.0	22.1	0.0
Yukon	2.3	0.0	3.4	0.0	0.0	0.0	0.0	0.0	0.4	0.0	3.3	0.0
Northwest Territories	8.8	0.0	14.6	0.0	0.0	0.0	0.0	0.0	1.4	0.0	1.2	0.0

*1993 data

Totals may not equal 100 due to rounding.

Source: Natural Resources Canada, Mineral and Metals Sector.

province and find the three highest scores.

c) Why do you think these three provinces lead in mineral production?

Methods of mining

After a mineral deposit is discovered, it is explored by geologists to determine its size and shape. Geologists first map the area containing the minerals. They then use diamond drills to sample and determine the size, shape, and depth of mineral-bearing rock hidden underground. These samples are analysed in a laboratory to determine the percentage of useful minerals within the waste rock. With this information, the geologists, mining engineers, and company executives decide if a mineral deposit can be mined profitably. If it can, the company must then decide on a method of mining—**open-pit**, **strip**, or **underground**. (See Figure 10.8 on page 194.) Before the company can begin to set up operations, however, it must conduct an **environmental impact assessment** for the federal and provincial governments. This study, which can take two to three years, must investigate possible effects of the mine on the environment and propose ways to ensure that the project will cause as little damage as possible.

Once a mine has received government approval, the company can begin to prepare the site. This includes building roads and power lines, purchasing equipment, hiring miners, and arranging to market the ore. In remote areas, a whole new town may be built to house the mine employees. Usually, however, this is undertaken by pri-

Figure 10.7
The leading metallic, industrial, and structural minerals, 1994 (% of total value by province)

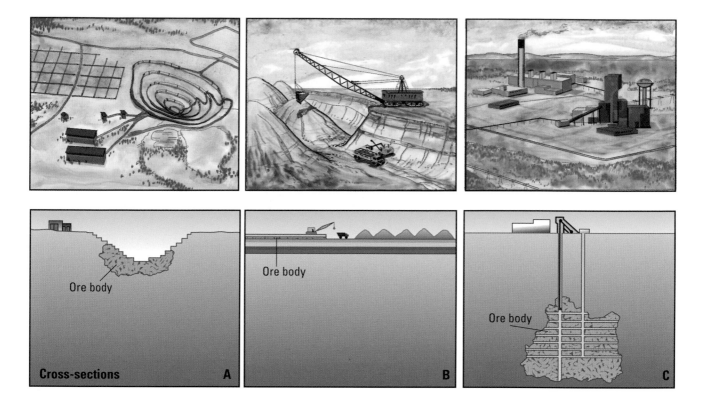

Cross-sections   A   B   C

Figure 10.8
Three types of mining
A Open-pit
B Strip
C Underground

vate developers rather than the mining company itself.

Open-pit mining

Open-pit mining is used when an ore body lies near the earth's surface. A large hole is dug to expose the ore body. The soil and waste rock, called **overburden**, are removed and stockpiled. The mine pit is then excavated in **benches** so that the pit wall looks like a series of giant steps. The benches form a spiral that gradually leads down to the mine floor. They are carefully engineered to prevent the walls from collapsing. Explosives break the rock into pieces. It is then transported by truck to the crusher at the nearby mill. Here the ore is ground down to pebble size, which makes it easier to load and unload from trains and trucks and to melt down at the smelter. A typical open-pit mine is shown in diagram A in Figure 10.8.

One of the problems of open-pit mining is its impact on the environment. Once the ore deposit has been exhausted, the landscape is marred by a huge empty pit and piles of waste rock. Restoring the site requires a lot of time and money. When the pits are located in isolated areas, little restoration takes place because few people see the damage. In settled areas, however, the waste rock may be placed back in the pit, covered with soil, and then planted with grasses or trees.

Strip mining

Strip mines are used when the mineral deposit is within 30 m or so of the ground and is laid down in horizontal layers. After first removing the waste rock and soil, huge excavator shovels scoop up tonnes of the exposed mineral deposit. This is then loaded into trucks for transport to nearby processing facilities. A strip mine is shown in diagram B in Figure 10.8.

Strip mining is most commonly associated with coal, potash, and gypsum deposits. In Canada, however, coal, sand, gravel, and tar sands are usually strip mined. Because strip mining is the least expensive form of mining, it is the preferred method whenever possible.

The biggest problem with strip mining is the destruction caused by the excavators. These huge machines literally eat up the land. The soil is completely destroyed. Environmental protection laws now require companies to restore strip-mining sites. The piles of waste rock must be levelled, covered with soil, and then replanted with grass or trees.

Underground mining

Underground, or shaft, mining recovers ore from deep beneath the earth's surface. These deposits cannot be reached by strip or open-pit mining methods. (See diagram C in Figure 10.8)

An underground mine has one or more vertical shafts leading down to the ore body. (See Figure 10.9.) The shafts are equipped with cages and skips, which are raised and

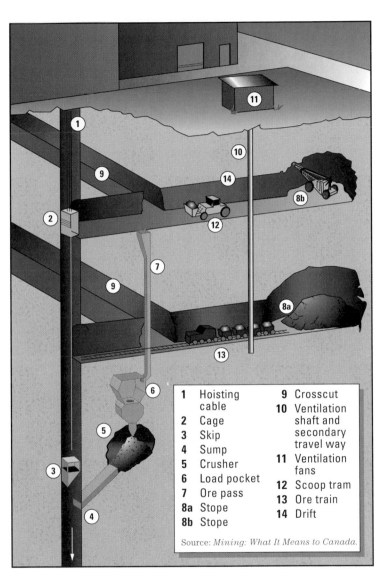

1	Hoisting cable	**9**	Crosscut
2	Cage	**10**	Ventilation shaft and secondary travel way
3	Skip		
4	Sump		
5	Crusher	**11**	Ventilation fans
6	Load pocket		
7	Ore pass	**12**	Scoop tram
8a	Stope	**13**	Ore train
8b	Stope	**14**	Drift

Source: *Mining: What It Means to Canada.*

lowered by hoisting cables. The cages carry miners and their equipment down to the mining site. The skips are filled with ore at the sumps and hoisted to the surface. The shafts also circulate air and transport water, electricity, and other necessities into and out of the mine. From the shafts, horizontal tunnels called drifts are dug into the ore

Figure 10.9
An underground mine

body. These are used to move the ore into underground crushers and then carry it to the surface. Tunnels called crosscuts are used to gain access to ore that lies away from the main drifts. In large mines, small secondary ventilation shafts, marked by large fans, provide additional fresh air. These shafts also serve as a secondary travel way for miners in case of emergency.

Underground mining is the most expensive method of extracting minerals. Except for waste rock left on the surface near the top of the mine shaft, however, it does not have a major impact on the landscape. But when the ores from these mines are smelted and refined, pollutants are released into the air. These contribute to acid precipitation, which is toxic to natural vegetation and aquatic wildlife.

Life in an underground mine

An underground mine is a world of contrasts. Parts of the mine are as quiet as a wilderness lake; the only sound is the steady drip of water trickling down the mine walls. Along the tunnels the voices of the miners can be heard amidst the tap-tap of steel bars gently searching for loose rock. But at the mine site the noise level skyrockets! Explosions blast away the ore. Diesel engines roar as the ore is hauled to the primary crusher. Staccato bursts of the grizzly drill break up the ore around the ore pass chute. The most welcome sound, however, is the hissing of fresh surface air as it rushes through giant ventilation shafts.

Workers are lowered to their work areas in a cage or mine elevator. They change into and out of their work clothes in the underground dry room. Protective clothing includes coveralls, steel-toed boots, hardhats, safety glasses, ear plugs, and gloves. The hardhats have battery-powered headlamps. Mobile equipment comes with headlights and spotlights to illuminate each work site. Fluorescent lighting brightens the most heavily used areas.

There is a variety of work in the mine. Workers blast a stope (resembling a step) into the ore body. Scalers then strike the surrounding rock with long steel rods to pry away any loose pieces. Another crew then secures the ceiling with heavy wire screening held in place by steel rock bolts. Once the ore is blasted, an operator loads the ore chunks, or muck, into a scooptram, or small ore train. The ore is then hauled through the mine to the central ore pass chute. There the ore is broken into smaller pieces by the grizzly drill and sent down the chute to the skip, where it is lifted to ground level. Since there is a lot of mechanical equipment in a mine, a team of mechanics is on call in the underground garages, servicing and repairing the equipment. It is a complex operation!

8 Describe the differences in the shape and depth of the ore bodies in Figure 10.8. How do the characteristics of each ore body make it suitable for each type of mining?

9 a) Strip mining is the least expensive method of mining while underground mining is the most expensive. Suggest reasons why this is so.

   b) In order for an underground mine to be profitable, the mineral deposits must be

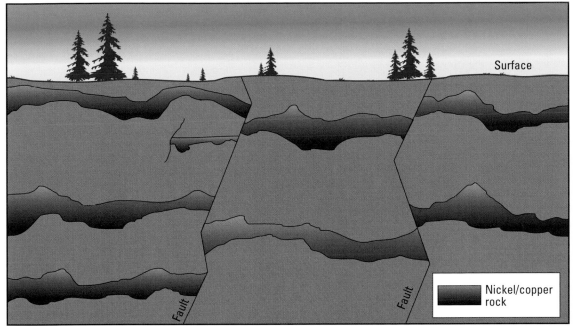

Surface

Fault

Fault

Nickel/copper
rock

Figure 10.10
Geological
cross-section
showing
nickel/copper
deposits

larger and richer than those in open-pit
or strip mines. Explain why.

10 Rank the three mining methods from the
least destructive to the environment to the
most destructive. Give reasons for your
ranking.

11 Refer to Figure 10.10. Sketch a larger ver-
sion of this cross-section on a piece of
paper. Create an underground mining
operation to extract the ore. Include the
following features on your diagram: ore
pass, cage, drift, ventilation shaft, hoisting
cable, stope, crosscut, crusher, skip.

12 Read the description of life in an underground mine and study Figures 10.9.

a) Imagine you are on a tour of this mine.
Write a brief account of your feelings
as you experience this underground
world.

b) Would you like to work in an underground mine? Explain your answer.

13 Study the aerial photograph of the open-
pit mine at Asbestos, Quebec, in Figure
10.11.

a) Give the grid references for i) the deep-
est part of the mine and ii) the waste
rock.

b) On which side of the pit (north, south,
east, or west) is the major ore-
processing complex located?

c) How is the ore brought to the surface?

d) Predict the impact the continued
expansion of the mine will have on the

Figure 10.11
Asbestos: an open-pit mining operation

town, the surrounding farmland, and the environment.

14 Write to a mining company involved in an open-pit mine in your province to find out how it is planning to restore the natural environment of the mine site once the deposit is exhausted.

Processing the ores

Most of the underground and open-pit mines in Canada extract metallic minerals. These ores often contain only a small percentage of metal content. Many copper mines, for example, extract ore with less than 5 per cent metal content; the remaining 95 per cent is waste rock. Gold ore may contain only a fraction of 1 per cent gold and over 99 per cent waste rock.

At the mine site, the ore is processed at concentrating plants to separate it from the waste rock. The concentrated ore may have an increased metal content of as much as 20 or 30 per cent. These concentrates are then shipped to a smelter. There they are heated until they reach the melting point and the metals are separated from the remaining waste rock. Still, the newly formed bars of metal contain impurities of up to 5 per cent. To produce metal with a purity greater than 99 per cent, the bars are sent to a refinery where most of the remaining impurities are removed.

Pollution from smelters

Smelters are located close to the mine sites, which are usually in remote areas away from large populations. (See Figure 10.12.) Copper, lead, and zinc smelters emit sulphur dioxides and nitrous oxides, two of the most serious air pollutants. (In the 1980s, smelters were responsible for 50 per cent of all emissions of sulphur dioxide in Canada; thermal energy plants were responsible for another 20 per cent.) As these gases enter the atmosphere, they are transformed into tiny particles of weak sulphuric acid. These particles dissolve in the water droplets contained in clouds. Eventually this acid precipitation falls to earth as rain or snow. The acid dissolves aluminum in rocks and soils, which then runs off into lakes and streams. The aluminum is highly toxic. It slows the growth of phytoplankton, zooplankton, and other sensitive marine life or kills these species altogether. With the destruction of the base of the food chain, other wildlife that feeds on aquatic life also disappears.

Scientists only became aware of the silent danger of acid precipitation in the late 1970s. Today the environmental damage caused by acid precipitation is widespread in the Canadian Shield and Atlantic Canada. In Ontario, 55 per cent of all lakes in the Shield have already been affected by acid precipitation. Across Canada, it is estimated that of 300 000 vulnerable lakes, 150 000 have already been damaged and another 15 000 are "dead."

To prevent this problem from getting worse, the Canadian government launched the Canadian Acid Rain Control Program. Its goal is to reduce acid precipitation emissions by 50 per cent in eastern Canada by the mid-1990s and in western Canada beginning in the year 2000. The program requires mining companies and other

Figure 10.12
The location pattern of smelters and refineries
Why are concentrating and smelting plants usually located near the mines? Why can refineries be located further away from the mines?

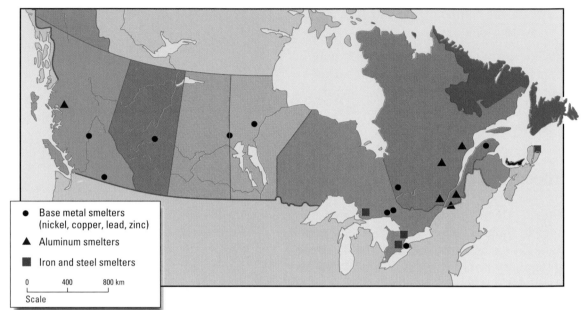

Legend:
● Base metal smelters (nickel, copper, lead, zinc)
▲ Aluminum smelters
■ Iron and steel smelters

Scale: 0   400   800 km

polluters to clean up their operations. At the smelters, for example, sulphur must now be scrubbed from the gases before they are poured into the atmosphere. Other polluters are required to reduce their sulphur emissions by burning fuels with lower sulphur content or switching to natural gas or oil. Canadian government and industry cannot solve the problem alone, however.

This is because over half of the acid precipitation in eastern Canada is caused by emissions from the United States. To resolve this problem, Canada has reached an Air Quality Accord with our southern neighbour in which both countries have agreed to reduce sulphur emissions to environmentally acceptable levels.

Figure 10.13
Sulphur pollutants in Canada

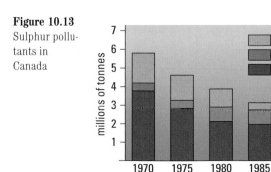

millions of tonnes (y-axis, 1–7)

Legend:
Other sources
Power stations
Smelters

(Estimate)
1970 1975 1980 1985 1990 1995

15 a) Describe the three steps in the processing of metal ores.
b) In a diagram, summarize the approximate concentration of metals from ore to refined metal. Draw four squares of equal size and mark each square in intervals of ten. Label each square as ore, concentrate, smelter metal, and refined metal. In each square, shade in the approximate percentage of the material that is made up of metal.

16 a) What is acid precipitation? Why is it a problem in Canada?

b) What trend in sulphur emissions is shown in Figure 10.13? Why has this trend occurred? Why is this an important change?

c) What can you predict about pollution caused by sulphur emissions in the year 2000 if this trend continues?

Single-industry towns

A **single-industry town** depends on one major industry for its economic survival. That industry usually centres around the development of a nearby natural resource. Canada has many single-industry towns. Some are based on developing renewable resources like forests. Others are centred on nonrenewable resources, like minerals. The prosperity of each community is tied to the demand for the particular resource. But price and demand for natural resources are always changing. This creates a **boom-and-bust economy**. When demand is high, prices are usually high, and the community prospers. But when demand softens, prices fall. Production is scaled back, workers are laid off, and the community is "bust." This cycle is especially evident in the mining communities in Canada's North.

Mining towns are also faced with the prospect of their nonrenewable resource running out. When this happens, the town usually dies. It is too isolated to be attractive to other types of industries, and there are usually no other resources to replace the one that ran out. Many businesses are forced to close their stores and companies.

Jobless workers and their families are forced to leave town in search of work elsewhere. Many families are faced with financial hardship when they cannot sell their homes. Those who remain are left to face a dying town.

17 a) Describe the cycle of a boom-and-bust economy.

b) Why do single-industry towns experience this type of economy?

c) Why would the economy of a single-industry town based on forestry be less risky than one based on mining?

d) If single-industry towns have such uncertain economic futures, why would people still settle there?

18 Research a mine that has shut down in your province. In a report, describe the economic and social consequences of its closure on the community.

Case study: Elliot Lake

In 1955, the town of Elliot Lake in northern Ontario was carved out of the forest, rock, and swamp of the Canadian Shield. It was built to house the miners who worked in the newly opened uranium mines nearby. By 1959, Elliot Lake was the uranium capital of the world. With eleven mines in operation, the town had a population of nearly 25 000. The thriving community had housing subdivisions, schools, paved roads, theatres, churches, hotels, and a hospital.

Uranium from Elliot Lake mines was sold to the United States Atomic Energy Commission for use in producing atomic weapons. In November 1959, however, the

Figure 10.14
Pulling out of boomtown
Identify ways in which this illustration depicts some solutions to the problems of single-industry towns.

US government announced it would not renew its contract with the mines when it expired in 1962. With the demand for uranium in decline, the mines began to close one by one. By 1966, Elliot Lake's population had dropped to an all-time low of 6664. Banks, stores, and businesses shut down. Homes were boarded up and abandoned. Elliot Lake was on the verge of becoming a ghost town.

To keep the town alive, the Canadian government promised to stockpile a limited amount of uranium for an eight-year peri-

od. At the same time, the building of nuclear power plants, which rely on uranium, helped to keep some of the mines open. The economy remained afloat. The population rebounded slightly and hovered between 8000 and 9000 for much of the next decade.

In the late 1970s, however, the fortunes of Elliot Lake took another turn. The mining companies signed long-term contracts with Japan and Britain as well as with Ontario Hydro to deliver uranium for their nuclear power plants. Elliot Lake was on its way to economic recovery! During the first half of the 1980s, the population rebounded to almost 20 000. A boom-like atmosphere returned to the community.

By the end of the decade, however, several factors turned the boom to a bust. New competition from uranium mines in Saskatchewan cut into Elliot Lake's markets. The markets themselves were dwindling. Concerns over safety caused many countries to halt construction of nuclear power plants. The end of the Cold War meant there was little demand for more nuclear weapons. As a result, Elliot Lake's uranium mines were again in a downturn!

YEAR	NO. OF MINE EMPLOYEES	POPULATION OF TOWN
1957	4 275	12 921
1959	9 567	24 316
1961	3 110	15 690
1963	2 591	10 582
1965	1 351	9 020
1967	1 678	7 276
1969	1 836	9 515
1971	1 712	8 769
1973	1 611	8 212
1975	1 853	8 244
1977	2 817	10 729
1979	4 020	14 230
1981	4 687	17 245
1983	5 080	19 619
1985	4 939	19 650
1987	3 860	16 229
1989	3 590	13 825
1991	1 478	14 089
1993	564	12 387
1995	565	14 400

19 Refer to Figure 10.15.
  a) Construct a multiple line graph showing changes in the number of mine employees and in the population of Elliot Lake from 1957 to 1995. Mark the number of people in intervals of 1000 on the vertical axis of the graph and the years at two-year intervals along the horizontal axis. Plot the population of Elliot Lake and join the dots with a continuous line. Using another colour, plot the number of mine employees and connect these dots. Label the boom and bust period(s).
  b) Describe and explain the pattern of boom-and-bust cycles your graph reveals.

Economic diversification

How do communities protect themselves from the negative effects of a boom-and-bust economy? The most successful strategy for a city's survival is economic diversification. This means that a community must expand its economic base by developing other industries instead of relying on just one. The more diversified the economy, the less impact a downturn in mining fortunes has.

Case study: Sudbury

Sudbury, Ontario, is a single-industry city that has learned to cope with a boom-and-bust economy. The Sudbury basin contains one of the world's largest and richest deposits of copper-nickel ore. Today, Sudbury

Figure 10.15
The boom-and-bust cycles of Elliot Lake

produces about 30 per cent of the world's nickel. In 1971, nickel and copper mines employed 37 per cent of Sudbury's labour force. By the 1990s, however, the mines employed only 15 per cent—about 11 000 people. The reason? Low nickel prices. With high unemployment and limited opportunities in other industries, the people of Sudbury were facing economic disaster.

Sudbury officials decided the solution to their dilemma was economic diversification. The first step was to encourage the growth of local businesses that specialized in mining and to market their products and services to other countries. The second step was to develop a plan with the federal and provincial governments to relocate a variety of service industries to the city. These included Laurentian University, several hospitals, a federal income-tax centre, and Science North, northern Ontario's most popular tourist attraction. The influx of these and other government services to Sudbury created a more inviting atmosphere for other new industries. This reduced unemployment and increased new residential and commercial construction projects.

Such economic diversification may not be possible for all communities, however. Sudbury has a number of advantages. It has a population of over 150 000. It is located on the Trans-Canada Highway and has major rail and communication lines with the large markets of southern Ontario. Such solutions are not always possible for isolated towns in the far North.

20 a) Define *economic diversification*. Why is this one solution to the problem of boom-and-bust cycles in single-industry towns?

b) Why were the types of new industries attracted to Sudbury ideal for overcoming boom-and-bust cycles?

Economic diversification in Elliot Lake

Like Sudbury, Elliot Lake realized that it needed to diversify to offset its boom-and-bust economy. Apart from its mineral wealth, one of the area's greatest attributes is its scenic location. With its abundance of lakes, forests, and wildlife, Elliot Lake began to develop and promote tourism. The attractions of the community include the following places of human and natural interest. (The numbers correspond to the numbered locations in Figure 10.16.)

1 Timber Village museum: This museum is the only one of its kind in northern Ontario. It offers hands-on exhibits of the area's pioneer past and early logging years.

2 Tourist Information Centre: Staffed by the Blind River Chamber of Commerce, the centre provides visitors with details of local and regional tourist information.

3 Murray Fault: Over 2000 million years ago, a major fracture created this interesting and unusual rock outcropping. It extends from here to Sudbury and the site of Science North.

4 Black Creek: This preserve gives photographers and nature enthusiasts the opportunity to observe a variety of marshland wildlife and northern wildflowers.

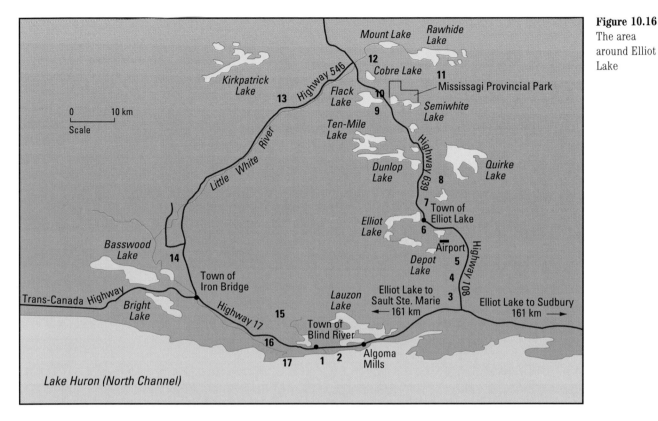

Figure 10.16
The area
around Elliot
Lake

5 Elliot/Depot canoe route: The scenery along this 320 km canoe route (one of seventeen routes in the area) is ideal for campers and hikers. It also offers excellent lake and speckled trout fishing.

6 Nuclear Museum and tourist information: Located in Elliot Lake, this museum depicts the local mining history, the nuclear resource story, and an impressive wildlife display. Accommodations and shopping facilities are located nearby. Tourist information is available year-round at the Elliot Lake and area Chamber of Commerce.

7 Tillite outcrops: These world-renowned outcrops were formed by glaciers thousands of years ago.

8 Ancient lake bottom: The bottom of this preglacial lake is fascinating to visit.

9 Flack Lake: A paradise for trout fishing, Flack Lake is located in the centre of the Laurentian Plateau. Accommodations, cross-country ski trails, and boat rentals are available.

10 Nature trail: Fascinating examples of ripple rock and fossils are found along this nature trail around the edges of Flack

Lake. Picnic areas and a boat launch are provided. Trail guides are available nearby at Mississagi Park.

11 Mississagi Provincial Park: This provincial park features 101 campsites, a boat launch, nature trails, canoeing, a lake and speckled trout fishery, and a logging museum. During the winter, visitors can take advantage of the many cross-country ski trails.

12 Cobre Lake: This lake is the site of an abandoned copper mine as well as the remains of the "Algoma Family Robinson" homestead.

13 White River Road: Canoeing, accommodations, and roadside picnic areas are available along this scenic route through Algoma's boreal forest.

14 Red Rock Dam: Situated in the heart of the district's deer wintering yards, Red Rock Dam is one in a series of hydroelectric generating stations on the Mississagi River.

15 White Falls: Visitors can camp in this area, explore the abandoned ruins of an early power plant, and see the stunning waterfalls cascade 90 m down a limestone hill.

16 Eldorado Resources Limited: Tours of this plant are offered during the summer months. Reservations are required.

17 Dr. Hamill Park: This park leads into the Mississagi Delta where visitors can canoe through the shaded delta islands; canoe rentals are available in the town of Blind River. The area is home to heron and cormorant colonies, as well as several species of semi-rare wildflowers. The area is historically interesting as well. A century ago, it was the centre of the Hudson Bay fur trade.

21 Design a brochure to attract tourists to Elliot Lake. Include information highlighting the physical setting (landforms, forests, wildlife, and bodies of water), human and natural points of interest, and recreational activities.

Canadians are among the highest energy consumers in the world. (See Figure 11.1.) This is because Canada is a large, industrialized country, with a scattered population, cold climate, and large resource base. We consume huge amounts of energy in transportation, heating, and industrial and agricultural processes. Our high standard of living, with our cars, appliances, computers, and other energy-consuming devices, also contributes to our high energy use. Because we have an abundance of low-cost energy, we tend to take our energy use for granted. All of these factors contribute to Canadians' high energy consumption.

1 **Refer to Figure 11.1.**
   a) **Rank energy consumption per person by country, in descending order from greatest to least.**
   b) **Suggest why energy consumption per capita is i) highest in the United Arab Emirates; ii) high in Canada and the United States; iii) lower in Europe than in Canada and the United States.**

2 **Using Figure 11.1, construct a bar graph to show energy consumption per person.**
   a) **List the developed countries in order from highest energy consumption to lowest. Do the same for the developing countries.**
   b) **Draw a vertical scale using intervals of 200 kg. Be sure the scale extends to the highest value in your list. Label the names of the countries along the horizontal axis.**

DEVELOPED COUNTRIES	KILOGRAMS OF OIL EQUIVALENT
Australia	5 316
Belgium	4 989
Canada	7 821
Finland	5 635
Germany	4 170
Japan	3 642
Kazakstan	4 435
The Netherlands	4 533
Norway	5 096
Russia	4 438
Saudi Arabia	4 552
Singapore	5 563
Sweden	5 385
Trinidad and Tobago	4 696
United Arab Emirates	16 878
United States	7 918

DEVELOPING COUNTRIES	
Chad	16
Burkina Faso	16
India	242
China	623
Indonesia	321
Brazil	666
Nigeria	141
Egypt	539
Bolivia	310
Mexico	1 439

Source: *World Development Report*, 1995.

Figure 11.1
Leading energy-consuming countries per person, 1993
Developed countries include those with a high standard of living and a democratic government as well as the former communist countries of Europe. Developing countries are those nations in Latin America, Africa, and Asia that have not attained full industrialization.

JANUARY		JULY	
ACTIVITY	ENERGY SOURCE	ACTIVITY	ENERGY SOURCE
Taking a hot shower	Electricity from a hot-water heater		

Figure 11.2
Energy and its uses

c) Draw a bar for each country based on its energy consumption level. Give your graph a title.

d) What does your graph reveal about energy consumption per person in the developed and developing world? Why is there such a difference?

3 Copy Figure 11.2 into your notebook.
a) List five major activities in a typical day in January. Identify the major energy source that makes each of these activities possible. For example, taking a hot

Figure 11.3
Oil workers at an Alberta oilfield

shower requires electricity from a hot-water heater. Repeat this process for a typical day in July.
b) What two sources of energy do you use most often?
c) Describe how you would cope without these energy sources in January and in July.
d) What have you learned about your energy habits?

4 Much of the energy consumed in our society is *hidden energy*—that is, it is not visible. When we cannot see energy at work, we tend to forget that we are using it. Look around your home and school for hidden energy uses. List six to eight of these and identify the type of energy required for each one.

Energy and the economy

Energy production is important to the Canadian economy. The value of all energy-related production in 1993 was $49 billion. That is 7 per cent of the **Gross Domestic Product** (GDP), the value of all goods and services produced in the country. The sale of natural gas, electricity, oil, and coal make up 11 per cent of Canada's total exports. In 1993, 17 per cent of all investment capital in Canada went into energy projects.

Energy production also provides over 200 000 jobs for Canadians. These include finding, transporting, processing, and distributing energy sources. Finding energy deposits requires experts in aerial and satellite photography, geology, physics, chemistry, and engineering. Drilling crews establish the size of the reserves. Geologists work with engineers and accountants to determine if the deposit is large enough to be mined profitably. If it is, crews dig shafts or drill wells to extract the oil, gas, or coal. Trucks, trains, or pipelines then transport the energy to processing facilities and markets.

Energy is also important to the general labour force. It enables us to perform our work more easily and more productively. This relationship is evident if we compare the growth of GDP and energy consumption. From 1958 to 1971, energy consumption grew as the GDP grew. After 1972, however, the link became weaker as a rapid rise in energy prices forced companies to conserve energy while increasing efficiency. The result was a

decline in the amount of energy needed for each dollar of production. (See Figure 11.5.)

Energy prices also have an impact on the number of jobs in Canada. When oil prices rise, as they did in the 1970s and 1980s, many jobs disappear. When energy prices fall, new jobs may be created. So an abundant, reliable, and low-cost energy supply is important to the Canadian economy in a variety of ways.

5 Refer to Figure 11.4.
   a) Which categories are directly related to the energy industry? Which are indirectly related?
   b) What percentage of the value of energy products are direct? What percentage of all energy-related jobs are indirect?

Figure 11.4 Value of energy products and the number of jobs, 1993

INDUSTRY	VALUE OF ENERGY PRODUCTION ($ billion)	NUMBER OF JOBS (000)
Crude oil	12	
Natural gas	11	
Coal	2	
Total energy production	**25**	**35.7**
Plastic products	3	51.9
Refined petroleum products	2	14.1
Chemicals	10	92.8
Pipeline transportation	3	6.1
Other	7	
Total energy-related production	**50**	**201**
Canadian Gross Domestic Product	**712**	**9 394**
% of Canadian total from energy-related industries	**7.0%**	**2.1%**

Source: Statistics Canada.

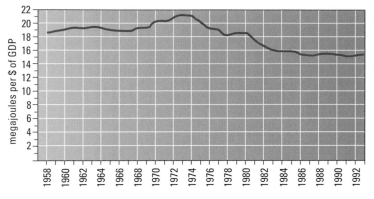

Source: Statistics Canada, *Human Activity and the Environment* 1994.

Figure 11.5
Energy consumption per dollar of production, 1958-1993

c) **What is the multiplier effect of energy production in the Canadian economy based on value? (Divide the value of total energy-related production by total energy production.)**

6 **Refer to Figure 11.5. Describe the trend in energy use per dollar of Gross Domestic Product from 1958 to 1973 and from 1973 to 1993. What factors explain the trend since 1973?**

7 **Refer to Figure 10.2 on page 188.**
a) **Follow the line graph showing the change in employment in fuel production from 1961 to 1992.**
b) **Describe this trend, then compare it to the price of oil in Figure 11.7 on page 212. What connection is there between energy prices and employment? How would you explain this?**

Canadian energy use

Canadians are the sixth highest energy users in the world on a per capita basis. This means that every Canadian uses a lot of energy! In 1993, Canada consumed 2.6 per cent of total world energy. This is a slight drop from 2.8 per cent in 1982. While our energy use has increased by 16 per cent in the last decade, world energy consumption has risen at a rate of 25 per cent. These figures reflect increased energy consumption by developing countries as well as the efforts of Canadians to use energy more efficiently.

There are many reasons for Canada's high energy use. Many of our major industries are energy intensive. Industry consumes 31 per cent of all energy in Canada. The vast size of our country means that long-distance transportation costs are high. The frequent use of cars rather than mass transit to commute also contributes to high energy use. As a result, transportation is the second-largest energy consumer at 30 per cent. The Canadian climate, with its long, dark, cold winters, means we consume large amounts of energy for light and heat. Residential users consume 19 per cent of all energy. Commercial businesses consume another 15 per cent. Together these factors explain why Canada uses more energy per capita than warmer industrial countries like the United States and Australia and smaller northern countries like Sweden and Germany.

The differences in energy demand across Canada are shown in Figure 11.6. It is not surprising that Ontario consumes the greatest amount of energy. It has the largest population and the greatest industrial base of the ten provinces. What may be surprising, however, is that Alberta ranks second, even though Quebec and British Columbia have larger populations. In fact, on the basis of energy use per person, Alberta and

Saskatchewan rank first and second in Canada! This is because energy production is centred in these two provinces. It takes a great deal of energy to produce energy. In addition, these provinces can provide energy at lower prices, which contributes to greater energy use. Yukon and the Northwest Territories are the third highest energy consumers per person. This reflects the need for energy for heat and light during the long, cold, dark winters as well as transportation costs in a vast region with scattered pockets of population. Lower energy consumption per person in Ontario and Quebec is the result of a warmer climate with longer summers and more daylight hours, energy-efficient industries, and higher energy costs.

8 Refer to Figure 11.6.
   a) Calculate the number of squares 1 cm x 1 cm needed to show total energy use

by region. Each square should represent 100 petajoules of energy. For example, the number of squares for Atlantic Canada would be 697.3 ÷ 100 = 6.973 (7 squares after rounding).

b) On an outline map of Canada, draw the correct number of squares for each region.

c) Consider the Ontario-Manitoba border as the dividing line between western and eastern Canada. What percentage of total energy demand originates in eastern Canada? What percentage originates in western Canada? Draw a thick line to show the division between east and west, then label the percentages on your map.

d) What does your map reveal about energy consumption in Canada?

9 Refer to Figure 11.6.
   a) Draw a bar graph to show energy use per person for each region. Arrange the

Figure 11.6
Energy use in Canada, by region, 1993

REGION	ENERGY USE	
	TOTAL (petajoules)	PER PERSON (gigajoules/person)
Atlantic Canada	697.3	300
Quebec	1 655.8	240
Ontario	2 867.3	284
Manitoba	272.5	250
Saskatchewan	492.3	498
Alberta	1 790.6	703
British Columbia	1 063.1	324
Yukon and Northwest Territories	33.7	392
Total	**8 872.7**	**325**

Source: Statistics Canada.

regions in order from highest use to lowest. Mark the consumption values along the vertical scale. Label the regions along the horizontal axis. Plot the bars for each region. Give your graph a title.

b) Which two provinces have the highest energy use per person? Why?

c) Which two provinces have the lowest energy use per person? Why?

Fluctuating energy prices

Oil is the world's dominant energy source. The price of oil is the major influence on the price of natural gas, thermal electricity, and coal. It is also a major influence on the development of new energy supplies. If prices rise, new oilfields may be opened up to take advantage of higher prices. If prices fall, some oilfields may shut down because production is no longer profitable. High prices also encourage greater energy efficiency and the development of alternative energy sources. Lower prices, on the other hand, encourage more wasteful consumption.

Oil prices have changed dramatically since 1970. (See Figure 11.7.) Rising prices in the late 1970s and early 1980s encouraged energy conservation and the development of alternative energy sources. As a result, world demand for oil decreased. In response, the major oil-exporting countries increased their production in order to maintain their share of the market. This caused oil prices to fall to a low of $14 a barrel in 1988. Since then, oil prices have continued to rise and fall with supply and demand. Most experts expect the average price for a barrel of oil to hover between $15 and $20 into the twenty-first century.

Figure 11.7
The ups and downs of oil prices, 1961-1994
Why does the price of oil have a major influence on the prices of other energy sources? How does the price of energy influence production? How would this affect employment in the energy industry?

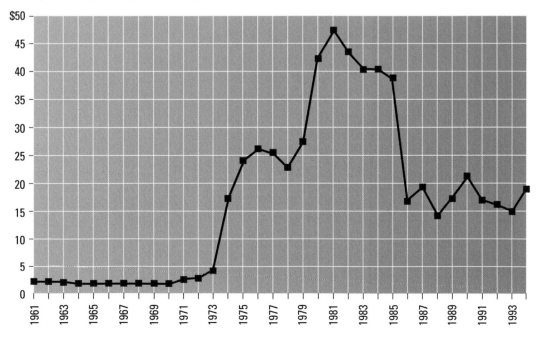

10 Refer to Figure 11.7. Describe the pattern of oil prices from 1961 to 1994. Why did prices fluctuate so much during this period? What events might cause oil prices to rise above $15 to $20 a barrel?

Sources of energy

At the turn of the century, coal was the dominant energy source in Canada. It supplied over 70 per cent of our fuel needs. Coal was abundant and inexpensive. It could be easily transported to the large Ontario and Quebec markets via Great Lakes freighters from mines in Pennsylvania, Ohio, and Illinois. Coal was well-suited to the steam-based technology of the Industrial Revolution. By the middle of the twentieth century, however, coal's popularity began to decline. As the most accessible coal beds were exhausted, it became more expensive to mine deposits in remote regions. As a result, coal prices rose. At the same time, petroleum (oil) and natural gas came onto the market as alternative energy fuels. They were less expensive and cleaner-burning than coal, which produced smoke, soot, and ash in home heating and serious air pollution at coal-powered thermal electric plants. By 1950, coal had declined to only 50 per cent of total Canadian energy use.

In the last half of the century, oil became the dominant energy source. Petroleum supplied the type of fuel needed for the internal combustion engines used in automobiles, ships, and thermal-generating stations. By 1975, Canadians derived 44 per cent of their energy from oil. By the 1990s, however, oil's position as the energy leader began to decline. Dwindling reserves and the high cost of extracting new supplies from oil sands and frontier exploration threatened to increase costs. Natural gas, a low-cost, clean-burning fuel that is ideally suited for home heating and thermal electricity, became a popular alternative.

Another important source of energy is hydroelectric power. In the 1970s, Canada's large, accessible rivers provided many opportunities for hydroelectric power generation. Today, however, these power projects are in decline. Most of the best hydro sites in southern Canada have already been harnessed. Transmitting power from remote hydro sites to southern markets is costly. There is also growing concern over the impact these huge power projects have on the environment.

In the 1980s, nuclear energy emerged as a possible energy source for the future. This form of energy has been particularly important in Ontario and Quebec, where existing sources are unable to meet growing demand. However, the high cost of constructing nuclear power plants, along with safety concerns, have limited the use of nuclear energy. Canada's primary energy sources since 1900 are shown in Figure 11.8.

11 Refer to Figure 11.8.
   a) Classify each energy source as renewable or nonrenewable.
   b) Estimate the percentage of Canada's energy supply that came from nonrenewable resources for each year on the graph. For example, in 1900 approximately 72 per cent came from nonrenewable sources (70 per cent from coal

Figure 11.8 Canada's primary energy sources, 1900-2010

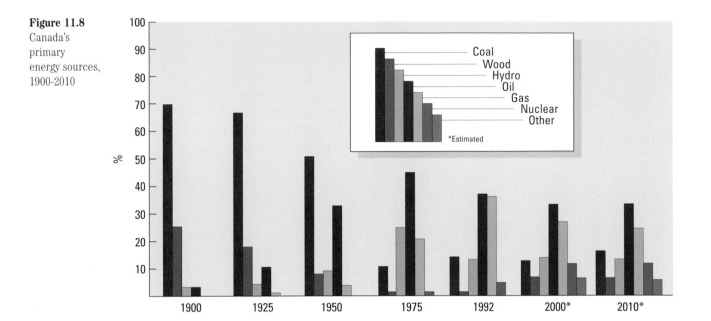

c) What was the peak year of renewable energy use in Canada? What information in Figure 11.7 might explain this?

d) What has happened to renewable energy use since this peak? Why?

e) If energy prices were to increase in the future, what might happen to these percentages? Explain why.

Nonrenewable conventional energy sources

Fossil fuels—petroleum, natural gas, and coal—are composed of hydrocarbons (materials made up of atoms of hydrogen and carbon) formed from the remains of plants and animals that once lived in tropical swamps and shallow seas. The carbon compounds that made up their bodies became storehouses of energy from the sun. As their remains fell to the bottom of the seas or swamps, they were buried in soft muds and preserved from decay. These muds were buried by other sediments. Where this process repeated itself over millions of years, huge basins filled with layer upon layer of carbon-rich sediments were formed. Pressure from above turned these sediments into sedimentary rock layers. Today, these basins are the world's major reservoirs of fossil fuels, especially petroleum and natural gas.

The major sedimentary basins in Canada are shown in Figure 11.9. They cover a large part of the country, except the Canadian Shield, an area of ancient igneous and metamorphic rocks, and the two mountain systems of the west and east

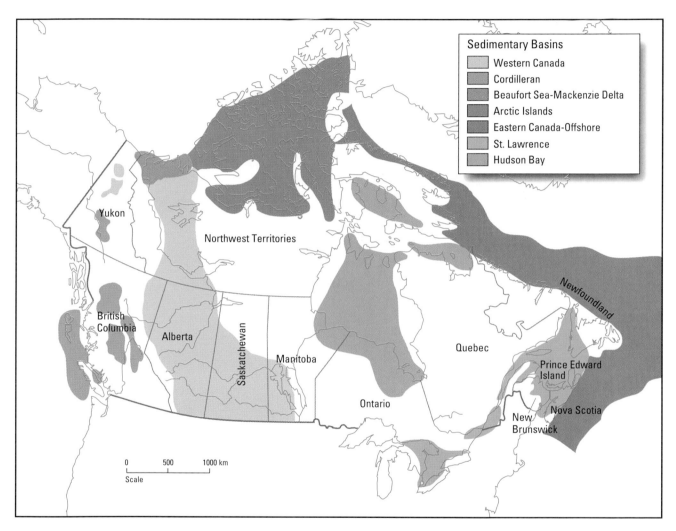

Figure 11.9 Canada's sedimentary basins
Estimate the amount of land area covered by sedimentary basins to the nearest 10 per cent. Why is it an advantage to have these large sedimentary basins?

coasts. The Western Canada Sedimentary Basin is the largest on land. The Eastern Canada Offshore Basin on the continental shelf along the east coast is the largest offshore basin. Fossil fuels have been discovered in all of these areas.

Petroleum

Oil was formed from the decomposed bodies of plankton (microscopic marine animals and plants) buried in the muds of

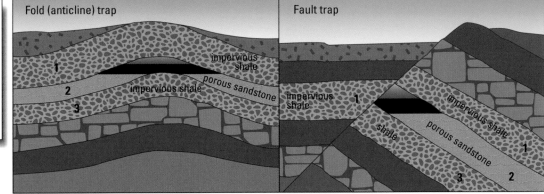

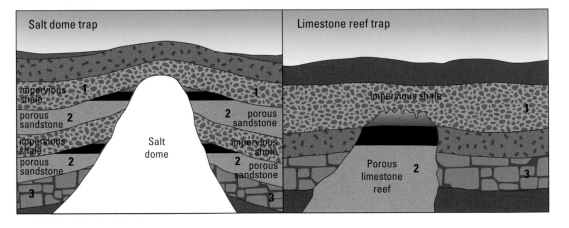

Figure 11.10

Four common oil and natural gas traps

shallow seas. Over millions of years, these organic liquids were transformed by pressure and chemical reactions into small drops of petroleum liquid within shale and siltstone rock. In some cases, these widely dispersed drops were squeezed out of their source rocks into more porous **reservoir rocks**, such as limestone and sandstone. Here the petroleum liquid mixed with the groundwater that flowed through the porous rock. As these liquids accumulated in the reservoir rock, the lighter oil floated above the water, where it concentrated in petroleum **traps**. (See Figure 11.10.) An

impervious **cap rock** prevented the oil from flowing out of the traps. The oil floated on top of the water into the highest part of the reservoir rock. An abundance of these oil traps have been discovered in the Western Canada Sedimentary Basin.

In other situations, the oil may have flowed upwards through sloping reservoir rocks to ground level, where it was soaked up by sand. The Athabasca oil sands of northeastern Alberta were formed in this way. (See Figure 11.14.) In this case, gently tilted beds of older, porous limestone were overlain by layers of younger sands.

As the oil moved upwards through the limestone, it seeped into the sand layers, creating an oil sand deposit.

Discovering oil

In the early 1900s, small oilfields in south-western Ontario and the Turner Valley in Alberta were discovered simply by drilling wells at sites where oil and tar were seeping out of the ground! As the field of geology developed, scientists discovered that oilfields occurred where sedimentary rocks were gently folded and faulted and where salt domes or porous reefs were buried beneath sedimentary rock. In western Canada, these formations were uncovered by studying rock outcrops and geological surveys. Once a potential site was identified, exploration wells were drilled. But they were not always successful. Often, the wells came up dry, as the oil may have escaped from the trap, or may never have been there in the first place!

Today, oil exploration is much more sophisticated. Seismic waves transmitted beneath the earth's surface reveal the structure of the rock layers. These waves bounce off different rock layers beneath the ground and return to the surface. They are recorded by highly sensitive instruments called geophones and plotted on reflection seismograms. Computers use the different travel times of the waves to produce cross-sections of the rock layers. These enable geologists to identify possible oil traps. Even with modern technology, however, drilling a wildcat well into an unexplored trap formation is still the only way to find out if oil is present. But even if the wildcat comes up dry, rock samples recovered during drilling reveal information about the age, porosity, depth, and type of rock at the site. This information may lead to oil discoveries in nearby rock beds.

When an oilfield is discovered, exploration wells are drilled outwards from the wildcat well to determine the size and extent of the find. Once exploration is complete, development wells are carefully placed and drilled to maximize the oil recovery.

Canadian oil supplies

The discovery of oil at Leduc, Alberta, in 1947 sparked an oil boom in western Canada. Over the next six years Canada became an oil-rich country as new oilfields were added to the map. Since then, the bulk of Canada's oil has come from **conventional oilfields**. These are fields that produce oil in a liquid form that is capable of flowing naturally or being pumped without processing. Most of these fields are in Alberta, Saskatchewan, British Columbia, and the Northwest Territories. Small amounts of oil are also produced in southwestern Ontario, at the Bent Horn field in the Arctic Islands, and at the Cohasset/Panuke field in the Atlantic Ocean off the coast of Nova Scotia.

The percentage of Canada's total energy supplied by oil reached its peak in the 1970s. Today, its position is being challenged by natural gas. The major reason for this is a decline in Canadian supplies of conventional oil. No large, new oilfields have been discovered in the Western

Figure 11.11
Crude oil production and movement, 1992

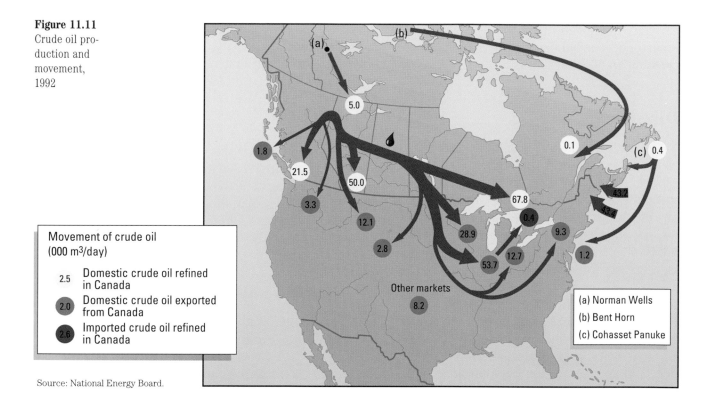

Movement of crude oil
(000 m3/day)

2.5   Domestic crude oil refined in Canada

2.0   Domestic crude oil exported from Canada

2.6   Imported crude oil refined in Canada

Other markets

(a) Norman Wells
(b) Bent Horn
(c) Cohasset Panuke

Source: National Energy Board.

Canada Sedimentary Basin in the past twenty years. This has meant a steady decline in conventional oil reserves while production and consumption has continued at high rates. (See Figure 11.12.)

In the 1970s, there were dire predictions about the impending exhaustion of older, conventional oilfields. Today, however, many of these fields continue to produce large amounts of oil. Technological improvements have made it possible to extract greater amounts of oil from old wells. Once the oil no longer flows under natural pressure, it can be pumped artificially. This allows a much higher proportion of oil to be recovered and has extended the life of older fields by a decade

or more. Even with technology, however, only about 30 per cent of the oil in a conventional field is recovered. The other 70 per cent remains in the reservoir rock, a challenge and opportunity for new technologies to recover in the future.

12 When more oil is produced than is consumed, there is a surplus. When more oil is consumed than is produced, there is a deficit.
  a) Refer to Figure 11.11. Add the export figures on the map to obtain Canada's total oil exports. Do the same for the import figures.
  b) Compare the two figures. Does Canada have an oil deficit or a surplus? Write

YEAR	RESERVES (millions m^3)
1961	710
1962	744
1963	786
1964	1120
1965	1170
1966	1295
1967	1348
1968	1429
1969	1429
1970	1411
1971	1369
1972	1306
1973	1226
1974	1175
1975	1105
1976	1012
1977	967
1978	942
1979	902
1980	859
1981	827
1982	779
1983	792
1984	776
1985	790
1986	774
1987	753
1988	738
1989	707
1990	657
1991	614
1992	590

Source: Statistics Canada.

Figure 11.12
Canadian conventional crude oil reserves, 1961–1992

a brief statement describing your findings.

13 Refer to Figures 11.11 and 11.13. On an outline map of Canada, shade in the provinces that are largely supplied by Canadian oil. Use another colour to shade those provinces that rely on imported oil.

14 Currently, Atlantic Canada must rely on imported oil supplies. What problems might dependence on foreign oil present?

Future oil supplies

The Athabasca oil sands

In future, oil supplies in Canada must come from **unconventional oilfields**. These are deposits in oil, or tar, sands and other heavy deposits. Unable to flow naturally, this oil must first be heated or liquefied. Unconventional oilfields are less accessible and more costly to extract. The first of these to be developed is the Athabasca oil sands in Alberta. These are Canada's largest petroleum deposits, and the second largest deposits in the world. They cover an area almost as large as New Brunswick and contain up to 160 billion cubic metres of crude oil. (See Figure 11.15 on page 221.)

Oil sands are a thick, black, sticky mixture of sand, clay, water, and oil. Unfortunately, it is extremely difficult and costly to separate the oil from the sand. In the past, oil companies found it much less expensive, and therefore more profitable, to produce oil from conventional fields. In the 1960s and 1970s, however, renewed interest in the oil sands was sparked by

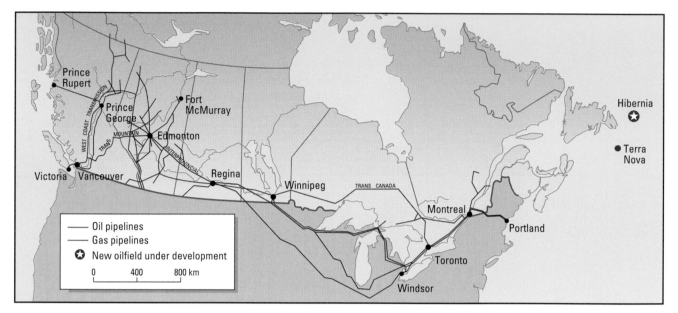

Figure 11.13

Canada's oil and gas pipeline connections

Pipelines are the most economical method of moving oil and natural gas over land. Pipelines link the oil and gas fields of western Canada with the energy-consuming regions in the east. The small market in Atlantic Canada and its distance from the producing provinces make it unprofitable to supply this region with Canadian-produced oil and gas.

Figure 11.14
Profile of the
Athabasca oil
sands deposits

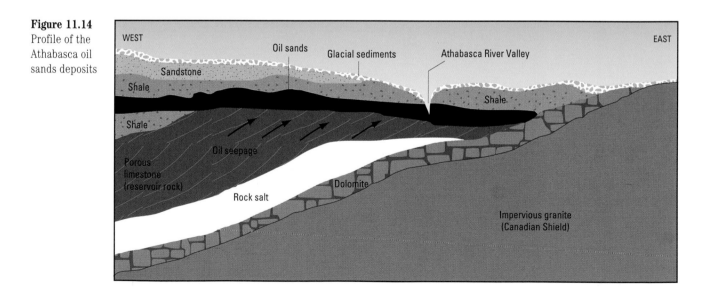

rising energy prices and declining reserves of conventional oil. In addition, instability in the Middle East threatened oil supplies from this oil-rich region. As a result, major oil companies invested millions of dollars in oil sands research and development. They discovered that these deposits contain potential reserves equal to more than 30 per cent of the world's actual conventional oil reserves. (**Potential reserves** are known deposits that cannot be recovered profitably under existing technology and prices. **Actual reserves** are known reserves that can be developed profitably.) Based on current consumption, the oil sands could supply Canada's oil requirements for the next 300 years!

Two plants are in operation in the Athabasca oil sands. In 1967, Suncor opened the world's first commercial oil sands plant. Syncrude opened a second plant in 1978. The construction of these facilities cost billions of dollars and employed thousands of engineers, technicians, tradespeople, and other workers. Both plants have invested millions of dollars to limit the environmental impact of their operations. Protective measures ensure that oil, chemicals, and other toxic wastes do not seep into the Athabasca River. Together, the Suncor and Syncrude operations supply 10 to 15 per cent of Canada's domestic oil production. As deposits of conventional oil are depleted, this figure will increase. For now, however, future oil sands plants have been postponed due to low oil prices and environmental concerns.

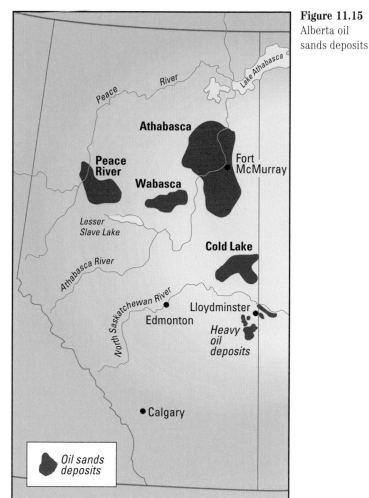

Figure 11.15
Alberta oil sands deposits

15 Refer to Figure 11.15. Draw a sketch map to show the location of the four major oil sands deposits. Include Calgary and Edmonton on your map.

16 a) Most of the workers employed in the construction of the oil sands plants lived in Fort McMurray. In what years would this centre have been a boom town?
b) What happened to growth here in the 1990s? Explain why.

17 Environmentalists are concerned about the impact of oil sands development on

Figure 11.16
Canadian oil
sands reserves
*As prices rise
or fall and
new technology
is developed,
the amount of
potential and
actual reserves
in a given oil
deposit can
change. In
what years
were there
sudden
increases in
Canadian oil
sands reserves?
Why did these
increases
occur?*

YEAR	RESERVES (millions m³)
1970	172
1971	169
1972	165
1973	161
1974	158
1975	154
1976	151
1977	111
1978	322
1979	353
1980	334
1981	325
1982	316
1983	310
1984	329
1985	343
1986	574
1987	572
1988	565
1989	542
1990	524
1991	502
1992	482
1993	460
1994	440

Source: Statistics Canada.

ecosystems downstream on the
Athabasca River. Research to find out
more about these concerns. Do you think
the risks to the environment should prevent the construction of new plants in the
future? Give reasons for your opinion.

Arctic exploration

Exploration in the Arctic reached its peak in the early 1980s when several oilfields were discovered in the Beaufort-Mackenzie and Arctic basins. Since 1985, the Bent Horn oilfield in the Arctic Islands has produced a small amount of oil annually. This is shipped to east coast refineries by tankers during the short summer season. When oil prices dropped below $20 a barrel in the late 1980s, however, new exploration in the Arctic came to a halt. (See Figure 11.7 on page 212.) To pay for the high cost of exploration and development in this region, oil prices must be between $25 and $30 a barrel.

18 a) **Explain the boom-and-bust cycle in Arctic oil exploration in the 1970s and 1980s. Refer to Figure 11.7 in your answer.**
   b) **Why would oil and gas deposits in the North have to be much larger than the deposits in Alberta and Saskatchewan before they are developed?**
   c) **Under what conditions might a new boom occur in oil exploration in the North?**

Offshore oil: Hibernia

Oil exploration off Canada's east coast began in the early 1960s. At the peak of activity, seven oil companies were drilling on the continental shelf, creating jobs for 3000 people in Nova Scotia and 2000 people in Newfoundland. They made four major discoveries: the Hibernia and Terra Nova oilfields on the Grand Banks off Newfoundland, and the Panuke and Cohasset oilfields on the Scotian Shelf, 250 km off Nova Scotia.

The Hibernia oilfield is estimated to contain 100 million cubic metres of oil—enough to produce 20 000 m³ of oil a day for twenty years. The Terra Nova field is about two-thirds this size. It is expected to produce 14 000 m³ of oil a day for twelve years. The Panuke and Cohasset fields are much smaller. The location of these sites close to large markets in Atlantic Canada, Quebec, and the United States makes these deposits profitable. The oil can also be transported year-round to refineries along the eastern seaboard by the cheapest form of transportation, tanker.

In the early 1980s, a **consortium** of oil companies joined forces with the federal and provincial governments to develop the Hibernia and Terra Nova fields. Although oil prices began to fall after 1985, it was impossible to stop the project because of the huge financial investment already made. But the pace of development was slowed considerably to wait for a rebound in oil prices.

In 1994, construction began on the giant Hibernia drilling and production platform. (See Figure 11.18.) When completed in 1997, the fully assembled platform will

Figure 11.17
Four types of offshore drilling rigs

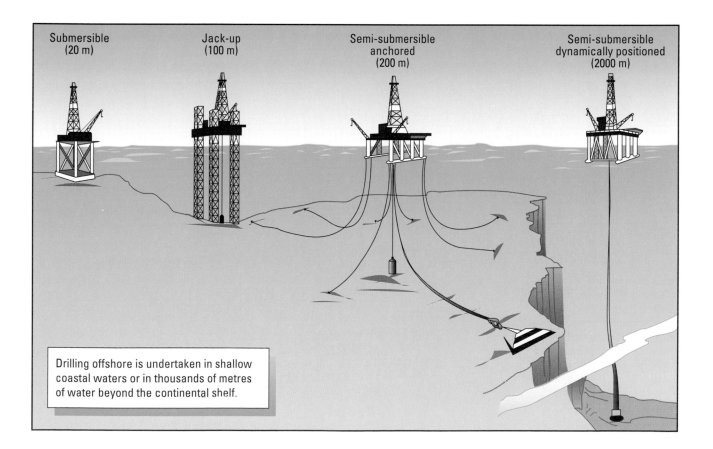

Submersible (20 m)

Jack-up (100 m)

Semi-submersible anchored (200 m)

Semi-submersible dynamically positioned (2000 m)

Drilling offshore is undertaken in shallow coastal waters or in thousands of metres of water beyond the continental shelf.

be towed to the drilling site 300 km east of St. John's and anchored to the seabed. Oil will be moving to markets by 1998. The price tag for this huge venture is expected to reach $6 billion. The Terra Nova project gained final approval in December 1995. Oil production is expected to start in 2001. Unlike the Hibernia platform, the Terra Nova site will use floating oil-rig technology at a cost of $2 billion.

The Hibernia production platform is designed to withstand the huge icebergs that drift through the North Atlantic. These icebergs are extremely dangerous— and deceptive! The ice that lies hidden under water can reach depths of 200 m or more. The part that is visible above water, however, is usually only a third this size.

These immense blocks of ice break away from glaciers in Greenland and travel south with the cold Labrador Current. On average, over 2600 icebergs reach the Grand Banks each year!

Other dangers in the North Atlantic include fog and storms. One fierce gale toppled the giant floating drill rig *Ocean Ranger* in February 1982, killing eighty-four crew members. Workers must also contend with the cold. On the Grand Banks, the temperature is below freezing for more than half the year. The lessons learned from past disasters and the knowledge of weather conditions were taken into account in the designing of the Hibernia platform.

Figure 11.18
The topsides (front) and gigantic gravity base structure of the Hibernia offshore oil drilling and production platform at the Bull Arm construction site

19 Refer to Figures 11.9 on page 215 and 11.13 on page 220.
   a) On an outline map of eastern Canada, indicate:
      i)   the Eastern Canada Offshore Basin;
      ii) the Hibernia and Terra Nova oil-fields;
      iii) the provinces that would most likely be supplied with Hibernia oil.
   b) What are the advantages of the location of the Hibernia field?
   c) Compare your map with Figure 11.13 on page 220. Will Hibernia and Terra Nova oil compete for markets with oil from western Canada? Explain your answer.

20 a) List the risks facing oil companies and their crews as they develop Hibernia. Classify these as human or economic risks.
   b) Why are icebergs the greatest risk in developing Hibernia?
   c) Why did development go ahead despite these risks?

Simulation: playing the oil risk game

Drilling for oil is a risky business! The objective of this oil risk game is for your oil exploration company to make as much money as possible from your investment of **risk capital**. The game controller (your teacher) will establish the number of rounds to be played. Once all the rounds are completed, the company with the greatest *percentage increase* on its initial risk capital is the winner.

21 a) Divide the class into six groups. Each group will represent one of the oil exploration companies in Figure 11.19. Your company is determined by the roll of a die. The first group to roll a 1 represents Astrol Oil Limited, the first group to roll a 2 represents Flamingo Petroleum Limited, and so on. Each company has a fixed amount of risk capital to invest. For example, Astrol Oil can spend up to $200 million. Each member of your group sits on the oil company's board of directors. Appoint a chief executive officer (CEO) to co-ordinate your group and an accountant to record the company investments on a balance sheet similar to the one in Figure 11.22.
   b) Working with your group, use an atlas and Figure 11.20 to study the possible locations where your company might drill. Plot these on an outline map of Canada. Each company is allowed to drill at up to three sites per round. Choose the locations and number of wells you intend to drill based on the amount of risk capital your company has. Companies are allowed to pool resources with one another to increase the total risk capital and the number of sites available. (In real-life situations companies often work together to create a consortium to share costs.) *Only two companies are allowed to pool resources in one round.* Once your company has decided where to drill and how much to spend, the accountant must record this information on the balance sheet.

Figure 11.19
Exploration
companies

COMPANY NAME	RISK CAPITAL FOR EXPLORATION
Astrol Oil Ltd.	$200 million
Flamingo Petroleum Ltd.	$100 million
Grace-Tex Drilling	$ 50 million
Nordic Exploration	$ 30 million
Oranco International	$ 30 million
Zetco Exploration	$ 30 million

c) The risk factor at each drilling site is determined by the roll of the dice. The game controller will roll the dice. The return on your company's investment will be determined by the impact on investment description in Figure 11.21 that corresponds to the number rolled.

Figure 11.20
Drilling sites

LOCATION	NATURAL ENVIRONMENT	ACCESSIBILITY	DRILL METHOD	AVERAGE CONSUMPTION COST PER WELL	RETURN ON INVESTMENT
Beaufort Sea Arctic	Offshore drilling Extreme cold, heavy ice Two-month summer thaw Winter darkness	Remote contact by air and sea Serviced from Tuktoyaktuk	Artificial island	$62 000 000	5 x $ invested
Southern Alberta Medicine Hat	Prairie grassland Cold winter, warm summer	Conventional oil area serviced from Calgary by road year-round	Conventional land drill rig	$300 000	2 x $ invested
Hibernia Grand Banks off Newfoundland	Offshore drilling Frequent storms Threat of icebergs Year-round drilling	Contact by air and sea only from St. John's	Offshore semi-submersible, dynamically positioned drill rig	$63 000 000	5 x $ invested
Northwest Territories Alberta border	Northern prairie Long, cold winter Warm summer	Contact by land and air year-round	Conventional land drill rig	$1 300 000	3 x $ invested
Banquereau Bank off Nova Scotia	Offshore drilling South of iceberg zone Continental shelf Year-round drilling	Contact by air and sea only from Halifax	Offshore jack-up drill rig	$42 000 000	4 x $ invested

DICE ROLL	IMPACT ON INVESTMENT
2	Good news! Oil strike! Bad news! OPEC fails to reach agreement; world oil prices collapse. Potential return on your investment is reduced by 50 per cent.
3	Oil strike! Claim maximum return on investment.
4	Too bad, your company hit a dry well; no return on your investment.
5	Locations in eastern Canada hit dry well; locations in western Canada and Arctic strike oil.
6	Storms and late spring ice damage drill island in the Beaufort Sea. Reconstruction and loss of valuable equipment reduce potential return by 50 per cent. Oil strike at all other sites!
7	World oil prices rise due to increased conflict in the Middle East. Oil strike! Return on investment doubles.
8	Bad luck! Another dry well means no return on your investment.
9	Spectacular blow-out produces massive oil slick that threatens east coast fisheries. All east coast exploration halted for six months until new environmental regulations are established. Oil strike! But east coast profits are reduced by 50 per cent.
10	All wells are dry; zero return on investment.
11	Dry wells in western Canada and Arctic gives zero return on investment. Oil strike in eastern Canada! Maximum return on investment.
12	Talks among OPEC nations break down. World oil prices collapse. Potential return on investment is reduced by 25 per cent. Oil strike!

COMPANY BALANCE SHEET

Company name _____

Round _____

Bank balance _____
(risk capital)

OIL RISK

Drilling sites	Cost
1 _____	1 _____
2 _____	2 _____
3 _____	3 _____
Total drilling costs	_____
New bank balance (balance at start of round minus total drilling costs)	_____

DICE ROLL RESULTS

Gain	
1 _____	
2 _____	
3 _____	
Total gain	_____
New company bank balance	_____

Figure 11.21 (left)
Impact on investments

Figure 11.22 (right)
Balance sheet

For example, a roll of 4 is bad news since no one finds oil. When the roll indicates a strike, the company's investment is increased by the amount shown in the "Return on investment" column in Figure 11.21. A roll of 3, for example, is good news for a company drilling in the Beaufort Sea/Arctic area. It produces a return of five times the $62 million investment—$310 million. The accountant must enter the results for each round on the balance sheet.

d) Once all the rounds have been played, the accountant must return the completed balance sheet to the controller, who determines the winner. To calculate the company's percentage gain, use the following formula: profit or loss ÷ initial risk capital x 100 per cent.

22a) Why is this called the oil *risk* game?
   b) Justify the cost difference between drilling in the Beaufort Sea and in southern Alberta.
   c) What have you learned about oil investment as a result of playing this game?

Natural gas

Like crude oil, natural gas is formed from the remains of plankton (microscopic marine organisms) that fell to the sea bottom and were covered by fine muds and

Figure 11.23
Natural gas production and movement in Canada, 1992
Natural gas exports to the United States have grown considerably in volume and value in recent years.

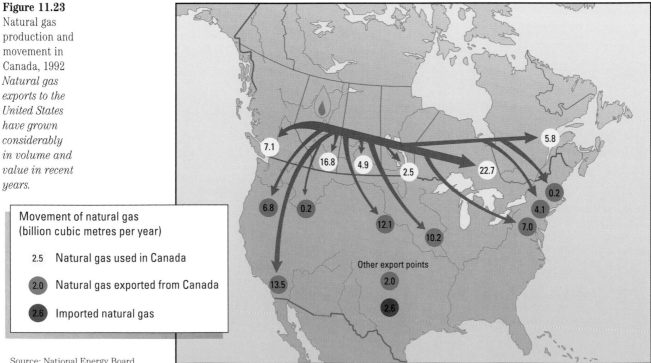

Movement of natural gas
(billion cubic metres per year)

2.5 Natural gas used in Canada

2.0 Natural gas exported from Canada

2.6 Imported natural gas

Source: National Energy Board.

silts. These remains were altered over millions of years into gases. They accumulated in the same traps as those that contain oil. (See Figure 11.10 on page 216.) Since the gases were lighter than both the oil and groundwater, they rose to the top. Drilling rigs often tapped into these gas layers before reaching the oil below. For decades, natural gas was regarded as a useless by-product of oil discoveries and was burned off. It did not gain prominence as an energy source until the 1950s.

Today pipelines transport natural gas from Alberta gas fields to markets in the other Prairie provinces, eastern Canada, and southern British Columbia. (See Figure 11.13 on page 220.) Pipelines are the only method of moving natural gas. While it is possible to transport super-cooled methane, known as liquefied natural gas (LNG), in special tankers, this is more expensive than pipelines. As a result, Canadian gas sales are limited to markets in Canada and the United States served by these pipelines.

By the mid-1990s, natural gas was one of Canada's most important sources of energy. The main reason for its popularity is its low price. While the cost of most fuels increased during the 1980s, the cost of natural gas declined. New discoveries between 1960 and 1981 expanded the supply. Since then reserves have levelled off or declined slightly as the pace of exploration has slowed. In the early 1990s, 83 per cent of Canada's actual natural gas reserves were found in Alberta, 12.5 per cent in British Columbia, 4 per cent in Saskatchewan, and 0.5 per cent in southern Yukon and the Northwest Territories. Large gas reserves were found in the Arctic Islands, Beaufort

YEAR	RESERVES (millions m³)
1963	1160
1964	1213
1965	1282
1966	1308
1967	1370
1968	1469
1969	1530
1970	1561
1971	1561
1972	1563
1973	1685
1974	1751
1975	1676
1976	1738
1977	1790
1978	1911
1979	1977
1980	2028
1981	2085
1982	2148
1983	2126
1984	2106
1985	2080
1986	2032
1987	1956
1988	1932
1989	1958
1990	1978
1991	1965
1992	1929
1993	1919
1994	1930

Source: Statistics Canada.

Figure 11.24
Canadian natural gas reserves, 1963-1994

Sea-Mackenzie Delta, and Eastern Canada Offshore Basin during the exploration boom of the 1970s and early 1980s. However, because of low energy prices and abundant supplies from more accessible sources, these deposits have not been developed. As potential reserves, they may supply Canadian needs in the next century, but at a higher cost than present gas resources.

Another reason for the popularity of natural gas is that it is a clean-burning fuel, so it does not pollute the environment as much as coal and oil. Many cars, buses, and other vehicles are converting from gasoline to natural gas to reduce pollution and to save money.

23 Refer to Figure 11.23.
  a) **Identify the five provinces/territories that produce natural gas.**
  b) **Total the natural gas production in Canada and the amount of natural gas exported to the United States. Calculate the export figure as a percentage of total production.**

24a)On an outline map of Canada, shade the provinces that are supplied by Canadian natural gas, as indicated in Figure 11.23. Use a different colour to shade those provinces that are not supplied with Canadian natural gas.
  b) **What form of transportation is used to move natural gas to its markets? Why?**
  c) **What factors explain why some areas are served by Canadian natural gas while others are not?**

25a) Why have the large gas fields in the Arctic Islands, Beaufort-Mackenzie, and Eastern Canada Offshore Basin not been developed?
  b) **Which sedimentary basin would most likely be developed first? Give reasons for your answer.**

Coal

Coal is the third nonrenewable fossil fuel. It was formed from the remains of ancient forests and swamps. As trees and other plants died, their leaves, branches, and trunks fell into the swamps. Unable to decay in these waters, they accumulated to form thick layers of vegetal remains. These were buried over millions of years by sediments and the remains of other swamps. Pressure and chemical changes turned the sediments into sedimentary rocks, such as sandstone and shale, and the vegetal remains into coal.

Areas under high pressure produced a hard, carbon-rich coal known as **anthracite**. This coal became an important home-heating fuel. **Bituminous coal**, which is softer than anthracite and contains more impurities, formed where pressure was not as great. It is used primarily in iron ore smelters and thermal electric plants. **Lignite**, a soft, low-value coal with many impurities, formed close to ground level where pressure was greatly reduced. It is used to power thermal electric plants that are located directly beside the huge, low-cost strip mines where it is produced.

For the first half of the century, coal was Canada's most important source of energy. After 1950, however, coal's popularity gave way to oil, natural gas, and hydroelectric power. (See page 213.) In the 1970s, however, there was a revival in coal production. All of this activity took place in British Columbia, Alberta, and Saskatchewan, where there are vast reserves of bituminous and lignite coal. (See Figure 11.25.) The growth in coal production was a result of two factors: increased demand for thermal electricity in western Canada and the opening of large export markets for coal in Asia. Lignite coal in Alberta and Saskatchewan is used to power huge thermal electric plants that supply the growing energy demands of cities like Edmonton, Calgary, Regina, and Saskatoon. Most of the bituminous coal mined in British Columbia and western Alberta is destined for Japan and South Korea. Small amounts of coking coal are also exported from Nova Scotia to European markets. Between 40

and 45 per cent of all coal mined in Canada is exported. Ontario, however, must import coal to supply its steel mills and thermal electric plants. This is because it costs less to import coal from the United States by train and Great Lakes freighter than to ship it from western Canada.

26 Refer to Figure 11.32.
   a) Draw a bar graph to show the percentage of Canadian coal produced by each of the five coal-producing provinces.
   b) Describe the location of the coal-producing areas. Why is this pattern an advantage for shipping coal to Asia and Europe? Why is it a disadvantage for southern Ontario and Quebec?

27 a) What are the disadvantages of coal as an energy source? Why has Canadian coal production increased in spite of these disadvantages?

Figure 11.25
Coal production, by province, 1994

PROVINCE/TERRITORY	PRODUCTION (000 t)	% OF CANADA'S TOTAL COAL PRODUCTION
Newfoundland	0	0
Prince Edward Island	0	0
Nova Scotia	3 509	4.8
New Brunswick	332	0.5
Quebec	0	0
Ontario	0	0
Manitoba	0	0
Saskatchewan	10 685	14.7
Alberta	35 674	49.0
British Columbia	22 608	31.1
Yukon and Northwest Territories	0	0
Total	**72 808**	**100.0**

Source: Statistics Canada.

Thermal power

Thermal electric power is a secondary energy source produced using primary energy sources such as coal, oil, and natural gas. Today, coal generates over 75 per cent of thermal electricity. Most of the rest is produced by oil and natural gas.

To create thermal energy, fossil fuels are burned to heat water to create jets of hot steam under high pressure. The steam is directed against turbine blades, which then turn generators to produce electricity. (See Figure 11.26.) Thermal electric plants are built where there is a shortage of electricity from hydroelectric power and where there are abundant, inexpensive supplies of fossil fuels. In some areas, thermal plants are used to supplement power sources during peak demand periods.

The amount of electricity produced by thermal energy varies, from 1 per cent in Quebec to 100 per cent in Prince Edward Island. (See Figure 11.27.) The cost and availability of other forms of energy are the major factors that determine the use of thermal power. It is most commonly used in provinces where coal and natural gas are in great supply.

Thermal power has many advantages. It can be produced from a variety of fuels. Electricity from thermal plants is usually cheaper than other sources, except hydro. Thermal plants can be located close to high-demand areas or next to power transmission lines that can move the electricity to these areas. Boilers can be closed down when demand is low and restarted when it increases. In some cases, the hot water left over after power is generated can be used to heat nearby factories, houses, and offices in a process called **co-generation**. Yet there are also disadvantages. Thermal plants emit large amounts of carbon dioxide, sulphur dioxide, and nitrous oxides into the atmosphere. These contribute to global

Figure 11.26
A thermal electric power plant

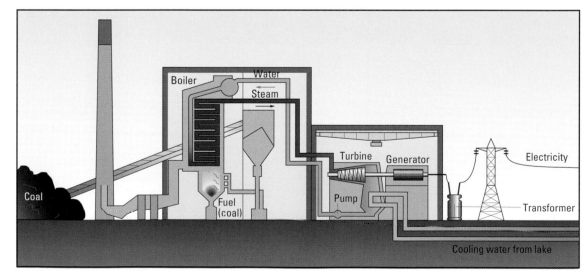

warming and acid precipitation. To reduce these emissions, the plants must install expensive scrubbers in their smokestacks or use coal with a lower sulphur content. Both of these measures raise the cost of electricity. In addition, thermal plants rely on nonrenewable energy, so they are not the solution to future energy shortages.

Nuclear thermal energy

Thermal energy can also be generated using nuclear power. The methods used to generate electricity in both nuclear and conventional thermal plants are similar. The main difference is the heat source. Nuclear power plants use the heat generated by splitting atoms of radioactive materials, such as uranium-235, in a process called **nuclear fission**. The rate of decay, and thus the amount of heat produced, is controlled in complex nuclear reactors. Long fuel rods in the reactor core heat up as the number of atoms being split increases. The heat is absorbed by heavy water that is continuously cycled through a series of pipes that pass through the reactor and a steam generator. In the steam generator, the heat is transferred to a second system of pipes, which turns water into steam. From this point the process is identical to that in conventional thermal plants. The steam is directed against the blades of the turbine, which turns the generator and produces electricity. (See Figure 11.28.)

Nuclear power is an important source of electricity in Ontario and New Brunswick. In Ontario, the high energy demand cannot

Figure 11.27
Percentage of electrical energy production by principal fuel type

PROVINCE/TERRITORY	COAL	NATURAL GAS	PETROLEUM	HYDRO	NUCLEAR	% OF CANADA'S TOTAL GENERATION
Newfoundland	0.0	0.0	6.1	93.9	0.0	7.3
Prince Edward Island	0.0	0.0	100.0	0.0	0.0	0.0
Nova Scotia	61.0	0.0	28.4	10.6	0.0	1.9
New Brunswick	10.8	0.0	44.9	13.8	30.5	3.6
Quebec	0.0	0.0	1.1	95.6	3.3	30.3
Ontario	24.1	1.0	1.1	27.5	46.3	29.3
Manitoba	1.9	0.0	0.3	97.8	0.0	3.9
Saskatchewan	74.0	4.6	0.0	21.3	0.0	2.8
Alberta	79.6	16.7	0.0	3.7	0.0	8.9
British Columbia	0.0	8.1	1.5	90.4	0.0	11.8
Yukon/NT	0.0	9.0	24.5	66.5	0.0	0.2
Canada	**17.8**	**2.9**	**3.5**	**60.1**	**15.7**	**100.0**

Source: Statistics Canada.

Figure 11.28
A nuclear-
generating
station
*Heavy water is
cycled through
a series of
pipes (A). A
second system
of pipes turns
the water into
steam (B).*

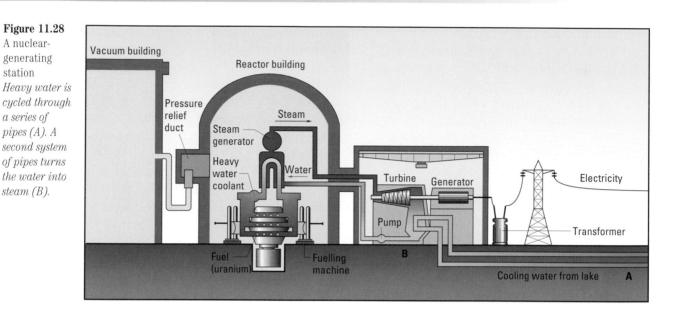

be met by hydroelectric power or by its small supplies of oil and natural gas. High levels of air pollution and the cost of importing coal from the United States and western Canada make the use of coal-burning thermal plants unacceptable. The only option is nuclear energy, which produces almost 50 per cent of Ontario's electricity. New Brunswick has a similar situation. Greater use of coal increases pollution and the threat of acid precipitation to the province's valuable forest resource. Tidal power is still too expensive and is unlikely to be developed for many years.

Nuclear energy was once considered to be the fuel of the future. Scientists believed it was a low-cost and pollution-free energy source. Operating on only small amounts of uranium, these power plants were considered to be sources of abundant energy. However, the promise of nuclear power has faded. The complex safety and backup systems needed to guard against accidents

and breakdowns in the reactors have made the cost of building nuclear plants extremely high. As a result, power from nuclear plants is as expensive as that from other sources. In addition, there has been concern over safety in the wake of disasters such as Chernobyl in Ukraine in 1986. These factors have largely halted construction on new nuclear plants in many countries, including Canada.

28 Refer to Figure 11.27.
   a) Calculate the total percentage of thermal electricity generated in each province. Rank the provinces from highest to lowest. Plot these figures on a bar graph using a scale of 10 cm to represent 100 per cent. Design a legend for your graph.
   b) Identify the four provinces that are the most dependent on thermal electricity and the four provinces that are the least dependent. Choose two provinces

from each group and explain their level of dependence.

29 Refer to Figure 11.27. If the price of oil were to increase rapidly, which provinces or territories would likely experience the greatest increase in power rates?

30 Your home town has been chosen as the site of a new thermal power plant. Which type of plant, conventional or nuclear, do you think should be built? List the pros and cons for your community in an organizer, then explain the reasons for your decision.

Renewable energy sources

Hydroelectric power

Hydroelectric power is a clean and safe energy resource. It harnesses the power of falling water and requires no other forms of energy. Hydro power is Canada's only major renewable energy source.

Canada is the world's largest producer of hydroelectric power, with almost 14 per cent of total world output. Physical geography is the main reason for our vast hydroelectric resources. Abundant precipitation is channelled into large drainage basins and river systems. (See Figure 7.10 on page 113.) Many rivers originate in well-watered uplands, mountains, and plateaus. From there they flow down steep, narrow valleys that make ideal sites for hydroelectric dams. On plains and lowlands, dams are constructed to raise water levels and create an artificial drop. The falling water turns the turbines, which in turn drive the generators that convert the mechanical energy of moving water into electrical energy. Where river flow varies from season to season, a reservoir may be created behind a dam to store water.

The availability of hydroelectric power varies. Some provinces may lack suitable rivers or the rivers they have may be located too far from the markets. Today, almost all of the large hydro sites in southern Canada have been developed. The cost of building dams, plants, and transmission lines from northern sites to southern markets will cause electricity prices to jump. In addition, there is concern over the environmental effects of dams and reservoirs. Rapid changes in river flow below dams disrupts wildlife habitats. Reservoirs often flood wilderness areas and destroy wetlands. Forest ecosystems and the traditional way of life of aboriginal peoples are disrupted. Opposition to large power dams has grown in recent years. In 1995, the Quebec government postponed indefinitely the start of the final phase of the James Bay Power Project, in part in response to environmental concerns.

31 Refer to Figure 11.27. Which four provinces are the most dependent on hydroelectric power? Which two provinces are the least dependent?

32 a) Why is hydroelectricity the preferred power source in Canada?
   b) Figure 11.8 on page 214 suggests that hydroelectric power will account for a decreasing percentage of Canada's total energy supply by 2010. Why?

33 Some hydroelectric power projects have built dams that create artificial lakes in

Figure 11.29
Hydroelectric dam and generating station

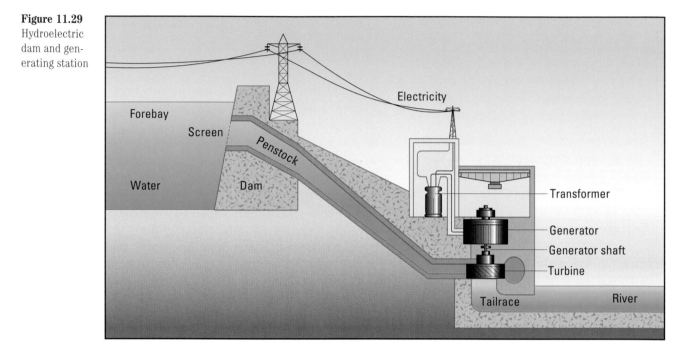

Forebay

Screen

Penstock

Water

Dam

Electricity

Transformer

Generator

Generator shaft

Turbine

Tailrace

River

former river valleys. Three examples can be found in Canada—in southern Ontario along the St. Lawrence River, on the Columbia and Peace rivers in British Columbia, and in northern Quebec on La Grande Rivière. Research one of these projects to discover the advantages and disadvantages it created for the region. Consider the benefits in terms of energy and employment versus the negative impact in terms of the environment and the people living in the region. When you have completed your research, decide whether or not the benefits of the project exceeded the costs. Give reasons for your decision.

Alternative energy sources

Tidal power

Tides are created by the gravitational pull of the moon and the sun on the oceans. On the open sea, tides cause the surface water to rise or fall by about 1 m. This level changes, however, when tides enter a funnel-shaped body of water like a bay. Here the water is squeezed by the bay's narrow sides to create tides. In New Brunswick, the Bay of Fundy has the highest tides in the world. The **tidal range**—that is, the difference in the water height between the highest and lowest tides—reaches almost 12 m! (See Figure 11.30.) Hydroelectric power could be produced here by damming the tidal basin and harnessing the tidal flow through gates and turbines. Of the 100 sites in the world considered suitable for tidal power, the Bay of Fundy has the greatest potential.

In 1984, North America's first tidal-power generating station was completed on the Bay of Fundy near the mouth of the Annapolis River. It had an electric generating capacity of 20 MW. This is enough electricity to supply 2500 homes a year. The success of the Annapolis project may open the way for the full-scale development of tidal power plants at three potential sites in the Bay of Fundy, at the mouths of Cobequid Bay, Cumberland Basin, and Shepody Bay. The three sites have a combined power potential of 7500 MW.

The development of the Bay of Fundy sites would enable Nova Scotia and New Brunswick to become producers and exporters of reliable, renewable power. There would be no pollution since this is a clean source of energy. Once built, fuel and main-

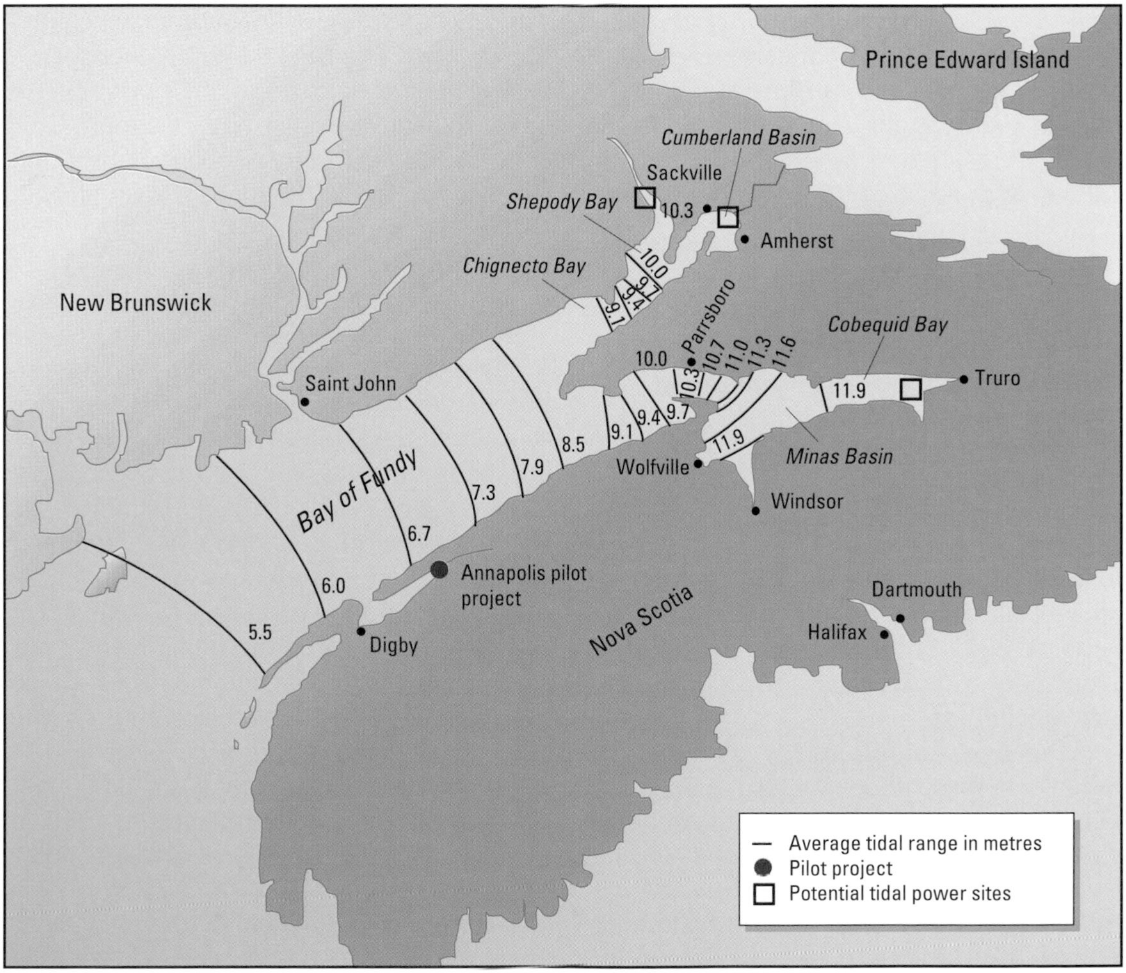

Figure 11.30 Tidal ranges and potential tidal power sites

tenance costs would be minimal. The power generated could be plugged into the existing energy grid of the Atlantic region, thereby eliminating the cost of building new transmission lines. The power could then be sold across the Atlantic region and exported to the United States. On the negative side, however, construction costs would be high. Present estimates suggest that tidal power would be more expensive than thermal electricity produced with local coal. Since power must be generated at low tide, the plant would be less flexible in when it produces power. Environmental concerns are also a factor. Scientists are still investigating the damage dams might cause to ecosystems and how erosion and deposition patterns in the Bay of Fundy might be affected.

34 Why are the tidal ranges between the open ocean, the Bay of Fundy, and Cobequid Bay and Shepody Bay so different? What factors determined the location of these three potential tidal power sites?

Solar energy

Solar energy may be the most widely recognized alternative energy source. It can be harnessed in one of three ways: passive solar energy, active solar energy, and photovoltaic energy.

Passive solar energy involves the design of homes, offices, factories, and other buildings to capture the maximum benefits of solar heat. The careful placement of windows lets in more sunlight. The use of thermal windows and insulation in outside walls reduces heat loss. Better air circulation distributes heat more evenly. Today, solar energy provides about 4 per cent of heat requirements in Canada. This figure could increase to 10 per cent by the year 2010 through the use of high-performance windows, underground heat storage facilities, and better ventilation and insulation.

Active solar energy uses the sun to heat fluids or air and to drive turbines to generate electricity. In Canada, researchers believe this energy could be used to heat industrial buildings, outdoor pools, and water heaters. Active solar energy accounts for less than 1 per cent of total energy use. Saskatchewan has the greatest potential to increase its active solar energy supply. This is because of its high electricity costs and the fact that it has the highest level of solar radiation in Canada.

Photovoltaic energy produces electricity directly from the sun. Photovoltaics are used to supply small amounts of power for lighting, telecommunications, and monitoring devices in remote locations. This source of energy accounts for less than 0.1 per cent of total generating capacity in Canada. Until photovoltaic technologies become more efficient and costs decline, it will have a limited role as an energy source.

Solar energy is clean, inexhaustible, and renewable. After the initial investment in equipment, there are limited maintenance costs and no other fuels are required. On the other hand, the price of solar electricity is much higher than conventional power. Because of its northern latitude, Canada receives less solar radiation than many other countries, and it varies from season to season. During the peak demand period in winter, solar energy potential is at its lowest. On the east and west coasts and in the Great Lakes region, frequent cloud cover further reduces the availability of solar energy. Since these are the most highly populated areas in Canada, this is a major limitation for the potential of this energy source.

35 a) Why is solar energy less likely to be developed in Canada than in other countries?
b) Of the three types of solar energy, which one is most likely to become the most widely used? Explain.

Geothermal energy

The heat of the earth's interior can be used to generate geothermal energy. Just 30 km below ground level, rock temperatures reach 900°C! These temperatures occur where magma has moved close to the earth's surface as a result of volcanic activity. Geothermal energy develops where groundwater comes close enough to the hot rock to heat it to temperatures of 200°C or more. This superheated water flows under high pressure through cracks leading towards the earth's surface. Geothermal power plants are built where wells can be drilled into these fractures. When this superheated water is brought to the surface, it instantly turns into steam, which is used to drive turbines and generate electricity.

Although there are no commercial geothermal plants in Canada, several test sites are now being investigated. One is in the Meager Creek area, 160 km north of Vancouver in the Coast Range Mountains. The Meager Creek site has an estimated potential of 260 MW of electricity, enough power for a community of 350 000 people. In eastern Canada, a different source of geothermal energy is being tapped. Carleton University in Ottawa pumps warm groundwater from limestone aquifers to heat its buildings. A similar project in Springhill, Nova Scotia, uses warm water from abandoned underground coal mines. Experts believe large amounts of potential geothermal energy also lie within the sedimentary rocks beneath the Canadian prairies. They estimate the usable heat contained here is large enough to supply all of Canada's energy needs well into the future.

Geothermal power is a clean, renewable, and sustainable energy source. Its cost should be competitive with that of conventional thermal plants. However, Canada's lack of experience in finding and evaluating potential geothermal sites makes it hard to estimate future potential accurately.

36 a) What physical conditions are needed for the development of geothermal energy?
b) Why might Meager Creek be only the first of many geothermal energy projects in this part of Canada?

Wind power

Wind power is a clean, non-polluting, renewable source of energy. It is most economical in areas where winds are strong and steady throughout the year. The best locations are where mountains or hills funnel air into narrow passes, thereby increasing wind speeds. Under ideal conditions, energy produced from wind power is competitive with most conventional energy sources. Only natural gas and hydroelectricity are cheaper.

One problem with wind power in Canada is the limited number of sites with reliable winds year-round. Currently wind power is used at only two test sites. Near Pincher Creek, Alberta, wind-powered water pumps are irrigating fields and raising water from wells on cattle ranches. At Cap Chat, Quebec, the world's largest vertical axis wind turbine is being tested.

37 What are the site requirements for a successful wind farm?

Biomass energy

Biomass energy is derived from organic waste products from forests, paper and lumber mills, farms, and municipal garbage. Most industrialized countries produce so much waste that the supply of material to generate biomass energy is enormous! Where low-cost waste materials are abundant, biomass energy is competitive with conventional fuels. The energy potential from biomass is believed to exceed Canada's total energy needs many times over.

Unfortunately, burning biomass fuels adds to carbon dioxide levels in the atmosphere. When municipal waste is used as the energy source, toxic smoke and liquids are produced. Other processes involve growing crops specifically for their biomass energy. This has led to concern that this could reduce the amount of land available for food crops. Development of biomass processing facilities will also require large amounts of money as well as ongoing technological improvements. More research is needed before we can fully benefit from this untapped energy source.

38 a) List some examples of biomass materials that could be used to produce energy.

b) What waste materials from your home could be used to create biomass energy? Explain why.

Energy conservation

Conservation is one of the most effective methods of reducing demand on our energy resources. It is possible to increase the efficiency of the energy we use and make it do more work with less waste. The rapid increase in energy prices in the 1970s launched our energy conservation drive. As we began to pay more for energy, we looked for ways to use energy more efficiently. Cars became smaller, lighter, and more fuel efficient. Appliances were designed to use less energy. Public utilities showed customers how to reduce their energy consumption. Governments encouraged homeowners and industries to upgrade insulation. Building codes were revised to increase insulation standards. Canadians soon recognized the financial benefits of using less energy.

A study by the federal government has suggested that savings through energy conservation may be as high as 30 per cent of total energy demand. But there has been a declining interest in conservation and a reduction in investment in renewable resources since energy prices dropped in the mid-1980s. It may take another round of price increases to get Canadians back on the conservation track.

39 Explain why energy conservation can be an important source of energy in Canada.

40 a) Working with a group, brainstorm a list of twenty ways in which we can conserve energy.

b) Select several ways in which your school in particular could conserve energy. Create a poster to promote these conservation ideas.

Energy and the environment

Many environmental issues today involve energy resources. One of the most serious is the burning of fossil fuels and the air pollution this creates. Coal, oil, and natural gas produce gases like carbon dioxide, nitrous oxide, and sulphur dioxide. These gases are closely linked to global warming, acid precipitation, and urban smog and pollution.

Carbon dioxide is a leading greenhouse gas and a major contributor to global warming. The amount of CO_2 in the atmosphere has increased steadily throughout the twentieth century. Because Canadians are among the highest energy users in the world, we are major contributors to this problem.

Environmentalists are urging us to reduce our use of fossil fuels for the good of the earth. At the Environmental Summit in Rio de Janeiro in 1992, the industrialized countries, including Canada, pledged to reduce their CO_2 emissions to 1990 levels by the year 2000. To meet this goal, the federal government introduced emission-control guidelines for automobiles. It also established the Efficiency and Alternative Energy program to promote greater energy efficiency and alternative energy sources. Yet despite these measures, Canada has increased its reliance on fossil fuels. By the mid-1990s, carbon dioxide emissions were not declining, but were in fact slowly rising.

Nitrous oxide and sulphur dioxide, produced in the burning of coal in thermal electric plants and gasoline in cars and trucks, produce acid precipitation. (See pages 183 and 199.) In the last two decades, Canada has reduced its sulphur dioxide emissions considerably. (See Figure 10.13 on page 200.) But the case of nitrous oxide has not been as encouraging. The rapid increase in the number of cars and trucks on our roads has offset reductions in nitrous oxide emissions that resulted from pollution-control devices. Greater reliance on burning coal for thermal electricity has also added to nitrous oxide emissions. The only real solution to this problem is to switch from fossil fuel energy sources to renewable sources.

41 a) What important energy choices must Canadians make over the next fifty years?

b) Why is it important to make these choices as soon as possible?

42 Working with a group, research to find out what the following groups can do to promote the use of alternative energy sources: i) governments; ii) energy companies; iii) manufacturers of energy-consuming equipment; iv) you, your family, and your friends.

Unit 4

CULTURAL DIVERSITY

Compared to some other parts of the globe...perhaps Canada is a more suitable place for building another new home on a relatively more solid ground. This harsh and beautiful land has never ceased to accommodate what can further enhance its beauty. And the Canadian cultural mosaic, symbolizing unity in diversity, has a charm of its own.

W.A. Shaheen, Ottawa-based Urdu poet and editor, in "Another Home?", *Across Continents: A Review of Urdu Language and Literature in Canada* (1988), edited by Wali Alam Shaheen, Anwar Nasim, and Izhar Mirza.

A Hot Day in Kensington Market by William Kurelek/Courtesy of the estate of William Kurelek and the Isaacs Gallery, Toronto

Canada's population

Canada is the second largest country in the world by size. Our total land area is 9 970 600 km². But in terms of population, Canada is a relatively small country, with only 29 million people. Some people would say that Canada is underpopulated. If we were to compare Canada with China, they would be right! In area, China is almost as large as Canada. But its population is more than 1.2 billion! This means there are forty-three Chinese for every one Canadian.

In reality, however, much of Canada's land area is inhospitable. The vast majority of our population hovers along the southern fringe of the country where the climate is more moderate. In addition, three out of every four Canadians live in cities and towns. So even though we have lots of space, it doesn't always seem as if we do!

During the early days of settlement, Canada's population was extremely small and population growth was slow. Since the late nineteenth century, however, Canada has become one of the most popular countries for people seeking a new life. **Migration** has produced the diverse and growing population we have today. In fact, if Canada had to rely on its population to grow naturally—that is, through more births than deaths—our population would actually be getting smaller. So continued migration is important to our future prosperity.

The age of the population is also changing. Older Canadians are living longer. Fewer Canadian babies are being born. As a result, the number of young people is becoming smaller while the number of older Canadians is increasing.

The study of population—its numbers, distribution, trends, and issues—is called **demography**. It is important that we understand demography because changes in our population affect us in many ways. Figure 12.2 provides a population databank for Canada and the provinces since 1881.

1 a) **Construct a line graph to show the growth in Canada's population between 1881 and 1994. The vertical axis should be 20 cm long, with each centimetre representing 2 million people. Label the line "Total population." The horizontal axis should be 20 cm long, with each 2 cm interval representing twenty years beginning in 1881; include the year 2021. Be sure to label the 1994 popula-**

Figure 12.1
Canada's
bustling cities

tion in the appropriate location along the time line. Label the axis "Years."

b) Draw a continuous line to show Canada's population at each time period.

c) In your notebook, describe the rate of Canada's population growth at different periods between 1881 and 1995.

d) Based on the most recent trends, estimate Canada's population in 2011 and 2021. Graph your predictions using a dotted line from 1995 to 2021.

POPULATION OF CANADA (000s)	1881	1901	1921	1941	1961	1981	1994
	4 325	5 371	8 788	11 507	18 238	24 343	29 248

PROVINCE	% OF CANADA'S TOTAL POPULATION						ACTUAL POPULATION 1994 (000s)
Atlantic Canada							
Newfoundland	—	—	—	—	2.5	2.3	582
Prince Edward Island	2.5	1.9	1.0	0.8	0.6	0.5	135
New Brunswick	7.4	6.2	4.4	4.0	3.3	2.9	759
Nova Scotia	10.2	8.6	6.0	5.0	4.0	3.5	937
Central Canada							
Ontario	44.6	40.6	33.4	32.9	34.2	35.4	10 928
Quebec	31.5	30.7	26.9	29.0	28.8	26.4	7 281
Western Canada							
Manitoba	1.4	4.8	6.9	6.3	5.1	4.2	1 131
Saskatchewan	0.6	1.7	8.6	7.8	5.1	4.0	1 016
Alberta	0.6	1.4	6.7	6.9	7.3	9.2	2 716
British Columbia	1.1	3.3	6.0	7.1	8.9	11.3	3 668
Yukon and Northwest Territories	—	0.9	0.1	0.1	0.1	0.3	94

RURAL-URBAN POPULATION (%)							
Urban	26	38	49	54	70	76	77
Rural	74	62	51	46	30	24	23

Source: Statistics Canada, Cat. No. 11.001E, 1995.

Figure 12.2
Population databank, 1881-1994

Population growth

In Canada, the number of births has been increasing steadily over the last ten years. In 1994, for example, there were 388 496 births, compared with 377 031 births in 1984. This means that over 1000 babies are born every day of the year in Canada. We have a population problem! But it is not the problem you might expect based on what you have just read. Canada's problem is that our population is in danger of *shrinking*. Confused? Read on!

Birth and death rates

Population growth is the result of two factors: **natural increase** and **immigration**.

Figure 12.3
Birth and death rates in Canada, 1925-1994
Birth and death rates are per 1000 population.

YEAR	BIRTH RATE	DEATH RATE
1925	26.1	10.7
1930	23.9	10.8
1935	20.5	9.9
1940	21.6	9.8
1945	24.3	9.5
1950	27.1	9.1
1955	28.2	8.2
1960	26.8	7.8
1965	21.3	7.6
1970	17.5	7.3
1975	15.8	7.3
1980	15.5	7.2
1985	14.9	7.0
1990	14.3	6.9
1994	13.4	7.2

Source: Statistics Canada, Cat. No. 11-001E, 1995.

Natural increase occurs when the birth rate is greater than the death rate. The **birth rate** is the number of births per 1000 population. It is calculated by dividing the total number of births in one year by the total population, then multiplying the result by 1000. The **death rate** is the number of deaths per 1000 population. It is calculated the same way, using the number of deaths. When the number of births is greater than the number of deaths, the population is increasing naturally. Let's see what is happening to the natural population increase in Canada.

2 The total population of Canada in 1994 was 29 248 000. There were 388 496 births and 209 515 deaths. Calculate the birth and death rates for 1994. (Remember: Divide the total number of births/deaths by the total population, then multiply by 1000.)

3 Refer to Figure 12.3.
   a) Create a **continuous line graph** to show this data. The vertical axis represents birth and death rates per 1000. It should be 15 cm long, with each centimetre representing a birth or death rate of two. The horizontal axis should be 15 cm long, with each centimetre representing a period of five years beginning with 1925. Be careful to plot the 1994 data at the appropriate place. Label each axis.
   b) Plot the birth rate for each year on the graph. Connect the dots with a continuous line. Using another colour, repeat the process for the death rate. Label your lines, or use a legend.

c) In your notebook, describe what has happened to birth rates and death rates in Canada since 1925.

d) A sharp upward turn in the birth rate line indicates a significant increase in the number of births. This is known as the **baby boom**. A baby boom occurred in Canada following the Second World War. During the 1950s, the Western industrial economies were rapidly improving as they switched from producing arms to producing consumer goods. Wages were on the rise and couples were raising families. Locate this period of high birth rate on your graph and label it the "Baby Boom."

4 Now let's determine the rate of natural increase in Canada between 1925 and 1994. On the graph you created in activity 3, shade in the area between the birth rate and death rate lines. This is the rate of natural increase. Which year had the largest rate of natural increase? What trend can you identify?

1.4 births per woman.) In Malawi in Africa, the fertility rate is 7.7—the highest in the world. What explains such differences?

Malawi has an extremely high **infant mortality rate**. For every 1000 births, 93 infants die before reaching the age of one. Because of this, parents have many children so that some of them will survive. Children also contribute to the workforce. In Malawi, 80 per cent of the population relies on **subsistence farming**—that is, they farm to provide their own food. Parents also look to their children to support them in their later years.

In industrialized countries like Canada and Germany, infant mortality rates are low. In Canada, the rate is 6.8 deaths per 1000 births. Advanced health-care facilities ensure that most infants survive. Many couples also choose to have smaller families, or not to have children at all. These factors contribute to low fertility rates. Germany's low fertility rate has resulted in a shrinking population. Canada, too, has a low fertility rate, so our population is also in danger of shrinking.

Fertility rates

The **fertility rate** is the average number of live births each year for every woman of childbearing age. (Childbearing age is generally considered to be between fifteen and forty-five.) Fertility rates vary from country to country. This is the result of a variety of factors, including levels of health care and economic development and social and cultural traditions. In Canada, the fertility rate is 1.7 births per woman, which is low. (The lowest fertility rate is in Germany, at

The growth rate

The population growth rate is calculated as a percentage increase over the previous population total. Figure 12.4 shows the growth rate between 1981 and 1994. Although Canada's population continues to increase, its percentage growth is actually slowing down. This trend is evident in other industrialized countries as well. In the United States and Australia, the percentage growth is only 1 per cent; in many European countries and in Japan, the growth rate is less than 0.5 per

Figure 12.4
Population
growth in
Canada,
1981–1994

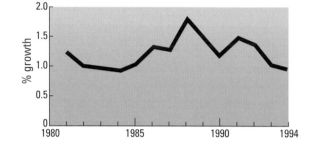

cent. All of these industrialized countries face the prospect of shrinking populations. Eventually, the size of their domestic markets—that is, the number of consumers available to buy the products they make—will begin to shrink as well. If these economies are to continue to prosper, they will have to rely increasingly on trade with other countries.

5 If there is an increasing number of births in Canada each year, how can we have a declining birth rate? One way to shed light

Figure 12.5
Creating a
population
pyramid

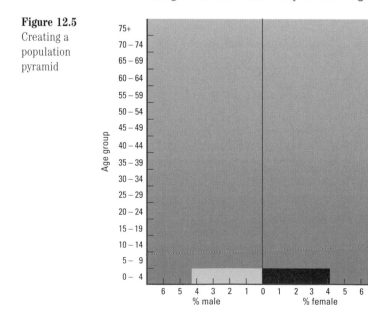

on this puzzle is to construct a **population pyramid** using Figure 12.5 as a guide.
a) Draw a horizontal line 14 cm long. Draw a vertical line 14 cm long, beginning at the midpoint (7 cm) on the horizontal base line. Indicate the intervals for the male/female percentages along the horizontal axis and the age categories along the vertical axis. Label both lines.
b) Using the 1971 age and sex figures for Canada in Figure 12.6, draw horizontal bars to the left of the vertical line to represent the male totals in each age category. Do the same for the female data on the other side of the line. The bars for age 0-4 have been completed for you. Do not shade the bars.

You are probably familiar with the shape of a pyramid. The widest part is at the bottom, with the pyramid gradually narrowing towards the top. Ideally, this should be the shape of a population pyramid, too. The greater number of young people is at the bottom and the pyramid gradually narrows as the population ages. But the shape of your population pyramid for Canada is quite different. What does this tell us about Canada's population in 1971 and what trends we might expect to see in the future?

6 Describe the shape of the 1971 population pyramid you created in activity 5. How would you explain the narrow base? HINT: If you need help, refer to the line graph for birth and death rates you created in activity 3.

7 a) Using the data for 1993 in Figure 12.6, create a second population pyramid following the steps in activity 5.
   b) Compare the two pyramids. Between 1971 and 1993, what has happened to the "bulge" of the pyramid that represents the baby boom?

A population pyramid can also provide information about certain age categories. The active working age is between 15 and 65. Those people under 15 and over 65 are usually not active income earners. They are often supported by family members, pensions, or retirement savings. People in these categories are referred to as the population's **dependency load**.

8 a) Use two colours to shade the bars of your population pyramids. Use one colour for the working population and another colour for the dependency load.
   b) What was the dependency load in 1971?
   c) What was the dependency load in 1993?
   d) Predict what will happen to the dependency load as the baby boom generation reaches the retirement age of 65.

AGE CATEGORY	1971		1993	
	MALE	FEMALE	MALE	FEMALE
75+	1.3	1.8	1.7	3.0
70-74	1.0	1.2	1.3	1.7
65-69	1.4	1.5	1.8	2.1
60-64	1.8	1.8	2.1	2.2
55-59	2.2	2.2	2.2	2.2
50-54	2.4	2.4	2.5	2.4
45-49	3.0	2.9	3.2	3.1
40-44	2.8	2.8	3.8	3.8
35-39	3.0	2.9	4.2	4.2
30-34	3.0	3.0	4.6	4.6
25-29	3.7	3.6	4.4	4.2
20-24	4.4	4.4	3.7	3.6
15-19	5.0	4.8	3.5	3.3
10-14	5.5	5.2	3.5	3.3
5-9	5.3	5.1	3.5	3.4
0-4	4.3	4.1	3.5	3.4

Source: Statistics Canada, Cat. No. 91-213, 1995.

Figure 12.6 Percentage of population by age group

9 In 1991, the percentage of Canada's population over the age of 65 was 11.6 per cent. By 2006, this figure is expected to be almost 15 per cent. By 2030, it will exceed 25 per cent. This increase in the number of Canadians over 65 is called the **greying of the population**.

a) In groups, discuss the impact of this phenomenon on such things as social services (hospitals, nursing homes, etc.); the amount of income tax paid by the working population; advertising target groups; types of housing and construction starts; the travel industry; and job opportunities.

b) Share your findings in an open discussion with the class.

Migration

Population is affected by more than birth and death rates. It is also affected by migra-tion. The term **migration** means to leave one place to settle in another. One aspect of migration is **immigration**. This is the movement of a person into a foreign country as a permanent resident. The other aspect is **emigration**. This is when people leave a country to live elsewhere. In the early 1990s, it was estimated that Canada had 4.3 million immigrants. This means that one out of every seven Canadians was born in another country. (Only Switzerland and Australia have more foreign-born residents.) This creates a great cultural diversity in the Canadian lifestyle.

When the total number of people immigrating to a country is compared to the total number of people emigrating from it, the result is the **net migration**. This figure can be a surplus, which indicates a gain in population. It can also be a deficit, which indicates a loss. In 1984, for example, Canada received 88 200 immigrants, but lost 46 300 emigrants. Therefore the net migration was a surplus of 41 900.

YEAR	IMMIGRATION	EMIGRATION
1984	88 200	46 300
1985	84 300	44 800
1986	97 500	51 400
1987	152 000	40 500
1988	161 900	37 400
1989	192 000	37 900
1990	214 200	39 200
1991	230 800	43 100
1992	248 200	44 300
1993	254 321	44 700
1994	219 268	45 051

Source: Statistics Canada and the Department of Employment and Immigration, *Overview of Immigration*, 1994.

10 Refer to Figure 12.7.

a) **Calculate the net migration for Canada for each year between 1984 and 1994.**

b) **In which year was the net migration the highest? In which year was it the lowest?**

c) **What trend in the net migration can you observe between 1984 and 1994?**

d) **Calculate i) the total number of immigrants, ii) the total number of emigrants, and iii) the total net migration over this period.**

Figure 12.7
Canada's migration totals, 1984-1994

Components of population growth

Population growth is a result of both natural and migration factors. Populations increase (or decrease) when the number of births in a country is greater than (or less than) the number of deaths, thereby creating natural change. Populations also increase (or decrease) when the number of people immigrating to a country is greater than (or less than) the number of people emigrating from it; this creates the net migration. Thus population growth or decline can be summarized as *natural change + net migration = actual population change.* Figure 12.8 shows how these factors have affected Canada's population since 1971.

11 Copy Figure 12.8 into your notebook.
  a) Calculate the natural change, net migration, actual population change, and new total population from 1976 to 1994. The period 1971 to 1976 has been completed for you.

b) Summarize the trend in i) the rate of natural change, ii) net migration, and iii) total population change between 1971 and 1994. Based on your findings, how important is net migration to maintaining future population growth in Canada?

Current trends

Canada's population in 1994 was 29 248 000. If present trends in birth and death rates continue *without* migration, Canada will reach **zero growth**—that is, no natural increase—in the early twentieth century. To maintain Canada's current population, the fertility rate must be 2.1 births. But we have seen that the present fertility rate is only 1.7. Some population experts predict that if this trend continues, by the year 2050 Canada's population will have dropped to 18 000 000!

12 a) Working in a small group, consider the impact that a shrinking population would have on employment, goods and

Figure 12.8
Population components of growth, 1971-1994

PERIOD	BIRTHS	– DEATHS	= NATURAL CHANGE	+ IMMIG.	– EMIG.	= NET MIG.	ACTUAL POP. CHANGE	TOTAL POP.
				(000)				
1971-76	1758	823	935	841	352	489	1971–76 = +1424	1976 = 22 993
1976-81	1820	842		588	217			
1981-86	1873	885		500	477			
1986-91	2328	1142		2396	1640			
1991-94	1592	805		996	177			

services, government, transportation, and schools. Create a chart highlighting the advantages and disadvantages of a declining population. Display your chart and compare it with those of other groups.

b) What recommendations would your group make to help Canada overcome the problem of a shrinking population?

Population patterns

The number of people within a measured land area is called the **population density**. This is calculated by dividing the number of people by the land area in which they live. High population density occurs in places in which a large number of people live in a small land area. Low population density occurs where few people live in a large land area.

13 Each of the diagrams in Figure 12.9 represents an area of 1 km². Each dot represents 100 people.
   a) What is the density of each area?
   b) Which diagram represents a high-density area?
   c) Which diagram represents a low-density area?

d) In which diagram is the population dispersed, or spread out? In which diagram is the population concentrated, or clustered together?

e) A geography student in Europe may read that Canada has a population density of two people per square kilometre. Why is this figure misleading? Refer to diagram B in your answer.

14 Refer to Figure 12.10. Calculate the population density for each province and territory, then rank them from highest to lowest. The population density for Newfoundland has been completed as an example.

Canada's population is not evenly distributed. In some places, like the Greater Toronto Area, millions of people live in a relatively small area. In other places, like the far North, few people live in a vast area. Canada's **population distribution** is illustrated in Figure 12.11 on page 254.

15 Refer to Figure 12.11.
   a) Describe Canada's population distribution.
   b) Which provinces have the highest population density?
   c) Use the line scale on the map to determine how many Canadian cities are

Figure 12.9
Population density patterns

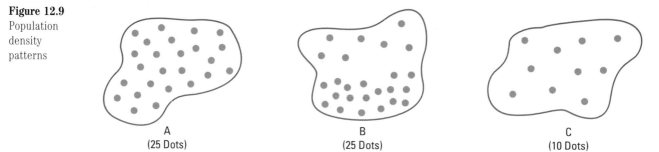

A
(25 Dots)

B
(25 Dots)

C
(10 Dots)

PROVINCE/TERRITORY	LAND AREA (km^2)	POPULATION (1994)	DENSITY
Newfoundland	371 690	582 000	1.56/km^2
Prince Edward Island	5 660	135 000	
Nova Scotia	52 840	937 000	
New Brunswick	72 090	759 000	
Quebec	1 356 790	7 281 000	
Ontario	891 190	10 928 000	
Manitoba	548 360	1 131 000	
Saskatchewan	570 700	1 016 000	
Alberta	644 390	2 716 000	
British Columbia	929 730	3 668 000	
Yukon and Northwest Territories	3 771 990	94 000	

within 400 km of the United States border. How many cities are more than 400 km from the US border?

d) How does Canada's population distribution help trade between industries and services in Canadian cities and potential customers in the United States?

Factors influencing population patterns

Why is Canada's population stretched from east to west along the southern border with the United States? There are many historic reasons why settlement patterns develop. Most of these, however, have their roots in physical geography.

Which areas would support Canada's early settlements? Obviously, places with good soils, a moderate climate, and accessible water transportation were attractive to settlers. Southern Ontario and southern Quebec along the Great Lakes-St. Lawrence waterway offered an abundance of quality soils. In addition, the climate produced a lengthy growing season between April and October. Further north, the unforgiving rocks of the Canadian Shield and the short growing season made the land inhospitable; isolated settlements were established here only to harvest mineral and forest resources. Settlements in the south, on the other hand, flourished as industries developed to meet the needs of a growing population. Eventually trade links developed with the heavily populated northeastern United States. This resulted in the development of a rail, road, and water network that allowed for easy transportation of both goods and people.

Once settlements were established, **industrial inertia** took over. Large towns and cities became magnets for new businesses seeking markets. Immigrants flocked to these thriving centres where they could

Figure 12.10
Population densities

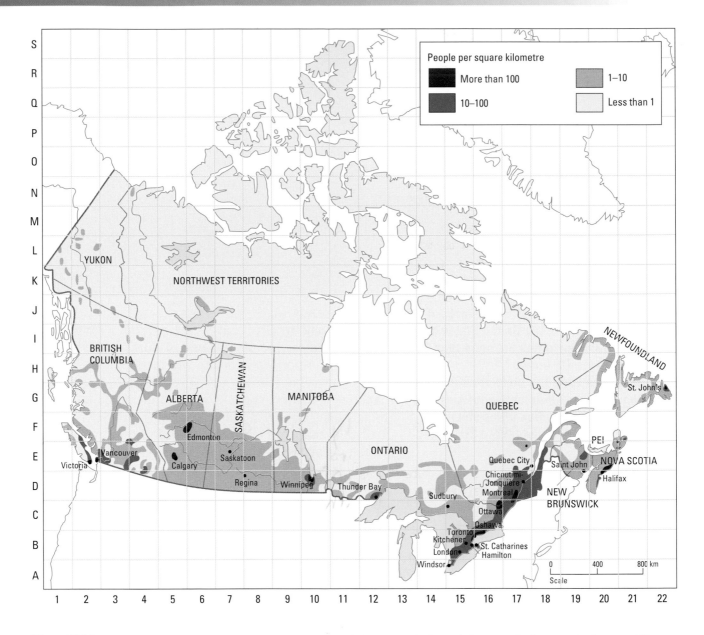

Figure 12.11
Population distribution in Canada

find work and have access to services. Today, the area stretching from Windsor to Quebec City, known as the **Windsor-Quebec City Axis**, dominates the population map of Canada. Here we find 60 per cent of Canada's population and almost 75 per cent of its industry. Called the **industrial heartland**, the area contains six of Canada's ten largest cities, including Toronto and Montreal.

Population distribution outside the heartland was also influenced by climate, soils, and resources. Settlements emerged in southern coastal regions to exploit ocean resources and inland forests. Some cities, like Vancouver, Halifax, and St. John's, became important ports and major trading centres. In the Prairie provinces, settlements sprung up across the plains as service and trade centres for the agricultural operations of the region. Many communities clustered around the rail lines that linked Canadians from coast to coast and provided transport for prairie grains. However, nowhere in this **hinterland** is there a concentration of population that can compare with that of the heartland.

16 **Using the appropriate maps of Canada in an atlas, determine how each of the following factors have influenced population distribution in Canada: i) landforms; ii) soils and vegetation; iii) climate; iv) resources. Describe your findings in point form.**

The population databank in Figure 12.2 on page 245 shows the regional percentage of Canada's population for twenty-year periods since 1881. This helps us to see how central Canada has maintained the greatest share of population, even though the western and Atlantic regions have become more populous over time.

17 Refer to Figure 12.2.
 a) Calculate the percentage of total population for each province and the territories for 1994.
 b) Find the regional population percentages for Atlantic Canada, Central

Canada, and Western Canada for each year. To do this, add the provincial totals in each region. For example, Atlantic Canada had 20.1 per cent of Canada's population in 1881 (2.5 + 7.4 + 10.2).

c) Copy the divided bar graph in Figure 12.12 into your notebook. Graph all of the population percentages you calculated in part b). Be sure to keep the regions in the same order when you plot your graph. The population percentages for 1881 have been done for you.

d) Describe the changes that have taken place in the population percentages of Western Canada and Atlantic Canada. How would you describe the regional distribution of Canada's population in 1994?

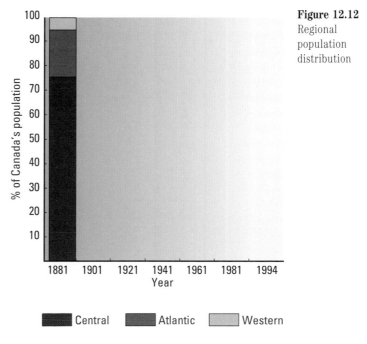

Figure 12.12
Regional population distribution

Destinations of immigrants

Although Canada receives many immigrants each year, not all provinces and cities receive an equal number of these new residents. In recent years, Ontario has attracted more immigrants than any other province, followed by British Columbia, Quebec, and Alberta. It is estimated that 55 per cent of all Canadian immigrants settle in Ontario.

Today immigrants are likely to locate in large cities rather than rural areas. This is in stark contrast to the early days of immigration. Then, most immigrants settled in less populated regions like Manitoba, Saskatchewan, and Alberta. In 1911, for example, 50 per cent of Saskatchewan's population were immigrants. Most of these were farmers, attracted by offers of inexpensive farmland.

Today, 57 per cent of all immigrants live in the largest cities of Toronto, Montreal, and Vancouver. Toronto has the largest immigrant population—about 1.7 million. This is 40 per cent of the city's total population. There are many reasons for this trend towards urban settlement. Cities offer more job opportunities and a greater variety of services. They also have established ethnic communities that help to ease the transition for immigrants into their new environment. More than 50 per cent of all immigrants are reuniting with and/or are sponsored by family members. This also tends to support immigration to large urban centres. Figures 12.13 and 12.14 show the destinations of immigrants in 1993.

Figure 12.13
Immigration by province, 1993

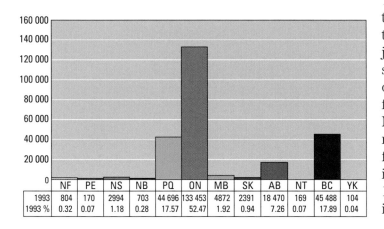

	NF	PE	NS	NB	PQ	ON	MB	SK	AB	NT	BC	YK
1993	804	170	2994	703	44 696	133 453	4872	2391	18 470	169	45 488	104
1993 %	0.32	0.07	1.18	0.28	17.57	52.47	1.92	0.94	7.26	0.07	17.89	0.04

Figure 12.14
Immigration by metropolitan area

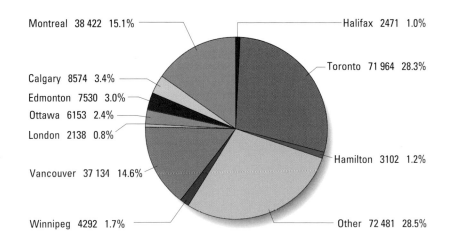

Montreal 38 422 15.1%

Halifax 2471 1.0%

Calgary 8574 3.4%

Edmonton 7530 3.0%

Ottawa 6153 2.4%

London 2138 0.8%

Vancouver 37 134 14.6%

Winnipeg 4292 1.7%

Toronto 71 964 28.3%

Hamilton 3102 1.2%

Other 72 481 28.5%

YEAR	TOTAL	USA	ASIA	EUROPE
1978	86 313	9 945	24 007	30 075
1983	89 157	7 381	36 906	24 312
1988	161 929	6 537	81 136	40 689
1993	254 670	15 718	146 672	46 343
	CARIBBEAN	S. AMERICA	AFRICA	OCEANIA
1978	9 240	6 782	4 261	1 233
1983	9 706	4 085	3 552	1 151
1988	15 108	7 255	9 380	1 822
1993	16 515	9 562	16 852	3 053

Source: Citizenship and Immigration Canada.

Figure 12.15
Sources of immigrants to Canada, 1978-1993

18 a) **Study the data in Figures 12.13 and 12.14. Write a summary outlining where the majority of immigrants settle in Canada.**

b) **Some people suggest that immigrants should be required to live in the Canadian centres where they are most needed for employment or to enhance population growth. What do you think? Give reasons for your answer.**

19 a) **Figure 12.15 shows the source of Canada's immigrants for selected years between 1978 and 1993. For each year, calculate the percentage of immigrants from each region. To do this, divide the regional total by the year's total, then multiply by 100. For example, in 1978 the percentage of immigrants from the Caribbean was 10.7 (9240 ÷ 86 313 x 100).**

b) **Which region contributed the greatest increase to the number of immigrants between 1978 and 1993? Which region contributed the least?**

Figure 12.16
Chinatown in Toronto

Figure 12.17
Top five source
countries for
immigrants,
1980 and 1993

1980		1993	
1 Vietnam	25 541	1 Hong Kong	36 485
2 Britain	18 245	2 India	20 298
3 United States	9 926	3 Philippines	19 640
4 India	8 483	4 Taiwan	9 845
5 Hong Kong	6 309	5 China	9 440

Interprovincial migration

Natural increase and migration also affect the growth or decline of provincial populations. Each province in Canada is experiencing a natural increase in population. But in some provinces the overall population growth is very slow. This is a result of migration out of the province.

The most important reason why people move from one province to another is economic. Sometimes prosperous times in another province attract people seeking greater economic opportunities. Similarly, when there is a downturn in the economy, people may be forced to seek job opportunities elsewhere. Consider Alberta during the oil boom between 1976 and 1981. This oil-producing province became a magnet for migrants. But when oil prices collapsed in the early 1980s, so did the good times in Alberta. Jobs disappeared. Many people moved east to get in on the renewed prosperity of the manufacturing industries of Ontario. In turn, by the 1990s, the boom in the east had screeched to a halt. But British Columbia was flourishing as international economic activity centred on the Pacific Rim. As a result, many people migrated to that province.

20 Figure 12.18 shows the population change by province and territory for four periods, 1977–81, 1982–86, 1987–91, and 1992–94.
a) Which provinces had a large decrease or a large increase in population during these periods?
b) Which provinces reversed their migration trend from one period to the next?
c) Calculate the total decrease or increase for each province during the period 1977 to 1994. How might these statistics influence provincial governments' recommendations to the federal government concerning the level of immigration to Canada?

21 Working with a group, develop a list of the advantages of living in your province. Use this list as the basis for creating strategies that would promote your province as a destination for migrants from other provinces.

22 Your family is thinking about moving to another province in the hope of finding better job opportunities and more financial security.
a) Using your library resource centre, create an economic and social profile of one destination in Canada in which you would like to live. Include such criteria

PROVINCE/TERRITORY	1977-81	1982-86	1987-91	1992–94
Newfoundland	–21 086	–14 117	–11 357	–11 427
Prince Edward Island	–1 451	+811	–66	+1 812
Nova Scotia	–8 185	+7 442	–607	–1 567
New Brunswick	–13 680	+835	–2 063	–917
Quebec	–156 817	–67 235	–45 406	–30 313
Ontario	–60 890	+165 460	+28 876	–28 675
Manitoba	–42 115	–2 395	–39 533	–13 501
Saskatchewan	–11 729	–7 057	–69 396	–12 368
Alberta	+190 719	–82 737	–13 199	–10 713
British Columbia	+131 176	+3 226	+154 126	+109 807
Yukon	–2 363	–2 393	+872	–916
Northwest Territories	–3 579	–1 840	–2 247	–2 315

Source: Statistics Canada, 1995.

Figure 12.18 Net inter-provincial migration

as employment levels, areas of employment opportunities, income levels, housing costs, quality of life, etc.

b) Compare what you have discovered about your destination with your present situation. Determine whether there would be more advantages or disadvantages to making this move.

Immigrating to Canada

Case study: Chi Chung Lo

Chi Chung Lo is a resident of Canada. He is a member of an ethnic group whose origins are many thousands of kilometres away in Hong Kong. Chi Chung Lo considers himself Chinese because his first language is Cantonese, a Chinese dialect. He also speaks fluent English.

In his homeland, Chung, as he prefers to be called, worked in a factory that manufactured hi-tech computers. He is well educated. After thirteen years of school, he attended university, where he obtained a four-year degree in electronics and computer science. After he graduated from university at the age of twenty-two, Chung got a job as a supervisor of a computer-chip installation unit after completing a one-year training program. Chung worked for the computer company for eight years. During that time he married, but he and his wife do not yet have children.

In 1992, at the age of thirty, Chung emigrated from Hong Kong to Canada. What prompted Chung to uproot his life in his homeland to move to a foreign country?

Hong Kong is one of the most densely populated places in the world. With over 5200 people per square kilometre, land is very expensive. While Chung worked long hours he earned only moderate pay. It seemed unlikely that he and his wife would ever be able to afford their own home in Hong Kong.

In 1898, Great Britain signed a ninety-nine-year lease on Hong Kong with China. When the lease expires in 1997, control of Hong Kong reverts to the People's Republic of China, which is now a communist state. Many residents, including Chung, worried that a communist government might impose sweeping changes on their economic system and way of life. So economic and political considerations were the **push factors** that influenced Chung's decision to leave Hong Kong. But where would he go?

Chung had heard many good things about Canada. His uncle, who lives in Vancouver, offered to sponsor him as a Canadian immigrant. Chung discovered that there were many high-paying jobs for someone with his qualifications. He also felt there were greater opportunities for advancement. He applied to a Canadian-owned company in Hong Kong and was offered a job at company headquarters in Calgary.

Chung was pleased that there were ethnic neighbourhoods in many Canadian cities. This meant he could share his background and experiences with people of his own heritage. There were Cantonese newspapers and social groups. These would be particularly helpful for his wife, whose English was not as fluent as Chung's. Chung also heard many good things about the quality of education in Canada. This was an important consideration because of the family he and his wife hoped to have. These were some of the **pull factors** that made Canada an attractive choice.

Once Chung decided to immigrate to Canada, he had to contact Canadian immigration officials. He discovered that he had to apply to become a Canadian resident at the Canadian High Commission in Hong Kong. He could not move to Canada first and then apply to immigrate once he was there. Chung completed all of the necessary documents. He was screened as an assisted relative under the independent class.

The classification system

Hundreds of thousands of people from all over the world apply to live in Canada each year. Whether or not they are accepted depends on many factors. These are established in the federal government's immigration policy. All applicants are processed under the federal classification system.

There are three classifications for immigrants: independent class, family class, and refugee class. Independent class applies to those people who can contribute to the country's economic prosperity through their skills and ambitions. Family class serves mainly to reunite family members; under this plan, any Canadian citizen over the age of nineteen may sponsor close relatives who wish to immigrate to Canada. Refugee class applies to displaced people from countries around the world who are being driven from their homes for political or cultural reasons.

Each applicant in the independent class is assessed on a **points system**. (This system does not apply to applicants in the family and refugee classes.) This screening process was established to ensure that everyone is evaluated fairly

CLASS	DESCRIPTION	ASSESSMENT
FAMILY	• Spouse and his/her unmarried children under nineteen • Parents, grandparents • Orphaned brothers, sisters, nephews, nieces, grandchildren under nineteen • Fiancé • Any other relative if the sponsor does not have any of the above or any family in Canada	• No points necessary • Sponsoring relative must prove s/he has the finances to support the applicant
INDEPENDENT a) Assisted b) Investors c) Entrepreneurs d) Self-employed e) Others f) Retired	• Any relative not included under the family class • Those having a personal net worth of $500 000 and willing to invest at least $250 000 in Canada for five years • Those who will establish a business in Canada and employ one or more Canadians • Those who have proven their ability to support themselves • Those who have job skills to establish employment • Those over fifty-five who are financially self-supporting	• All applicants are assessed by a points system • Exempt from points system assessment
REFUGEES	• Those who fear persecution if they return to their former country	• No points necessary

NOTE: All applicants are subject to medical and background checks. This is to determine if there are any health or legal reasons for denying the applicant entry into Canada.

Source: Department of Employment and Immigration Canada.

Figure 12.19
Immigrant classes, 1994

Figure 12.20
Immigration
points system

FACTOR	MAXIMUM	NUMBER OF POSSIBLE POINTS
Education	16	One for each year of formal education
Vocational preparation	18	1-3 months training = 3 points 1-2 years = 9 points 10+ years = 18 points (0 points is an automatic refusal)
Experience	8	Usually 1 point for each year of experience related to vocation
Occupation	10	Determined by the demand for vocation. NOTE: If there is no demand for a particular job the applicant will be refused immigrant status. (Does not apply to entrepreneurs and investors)
Arranged employment	10	10 points if there is an arranged job. (Does not apply to entrepreneurs and investors)
Demographic factor	8	Established by the Minister
Age	10	10 points if 21 to 44 years of age 2 points subtracted for each year either over 44 or under 21
Knowledge of French or English	15	10 points for fluency in one language 15 points for fluency in both languages
Personal suitability	10	Points given on the basis of a personal interview
Bonus for assisted relative	5	
Bonus for self-employed immigrants	30	

The pass mark for each category is as follows:
Entrepreneur	25
Investor	25
Self-employed	70 (includes 30 bonus points)
Skilled worker	70
Assisted relative	70 (includes 5 bonus points)

Source: Revised Selection Criteria for Independent Immigrants. Department of Employment and Immigration Canada.

and that successful applicants do not become a burden to Canadian taxpayers. Each year the Canadian government sets an immigration **quota** for each classification. These quotas are only guidelines. In some years, the number of immigrants may exceed the quota; in other years, the number may be less than the quota. The purpose of the quota is to serve as a guide for future policy decisions. In establishing the quota, several factors are considered: the number of refugees; the demand for family reunification; the economy; and the rate of population increase.

23 a) In chart form, outline the push and pull factors that influenced Chung's decision to immigrate to Canada.
   b) List the reasons why Chung would qualify for immigrant status under the independent class.
   c) Using the points system in Figure 12.20, calculate the number of points you think Chung would have received. NOTE: You will not have adequate information to complete some sections. Assume that i) under Occupation, Chung received 4 points for occupational demand; ii) that under Personal Suitability Chung received 7 points out of 10 for his personal interview; and iii) that for the Demographic Factor Chung scored 6 points because of Canada's declining birth rate. Don't forget to check the bonus points!

Immigration policy

Canada's immigration policy reflects the economic needs of the country. After Con-federation in 1867, Canada wanted immigrants to develop the West; Europeans were lured to the new country with offers of free land. During the economic depression of the 1930s, however, unemployment was at an all-time peak. As a result, the door was almost closed to immigration. There have been similar shifts between open- and closed-door immigration policies in recent years. Figure 12.21 shows immigration patterns since 1867.

24 Refer to Figure 12.21.
   a) What factors have led to an influx of immigrants to Canada?
   b) What factors have led to a decrease in the number of immigrants admitted to Canada?

25 Refer to Figure 12.22.
   a) Calculate the percentage of the annual total for each immigrant class. Percentages for 1975 have been calculated as an example.

   Family: $\dfrac{64\ 124}{197\ 881} \times 100 = 32.4\%$

   Refugee: $\dfrac{5\ 566}{197\ 881} \times 100 = 2.8\%$

   Independent: $\dfrac{128\ 191}{197\ 881} \times 100 = 64.8\%$

   b) Using your results from part a), draw a **divided circle graph** for each year. To determine the number of degrees for each portion of the graph, multiply the percentage for each category by 3.6. For example, for 1975 Family is 32.4% x 3.6 = 117°; Refugee is 2.8% x 3.6 = 10°; Independent is 64.8% x 3.6 = 233°.

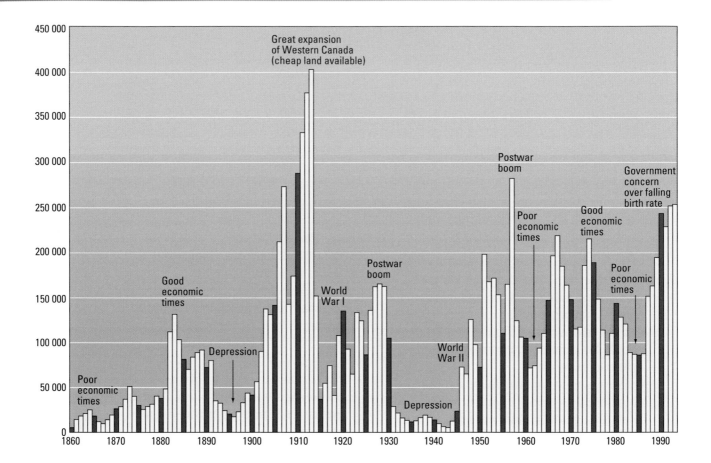

Figure 12.21
Immigration
to Canada,
1860-1994

c) **Using different colours to represent each of the three classes, colour each graph.**

d) **Describe what has happened to the percentage of immigrants in each class since 1975.**

e) **Describe the trend in the total number of immigrants to Canada from 1975 to 1993.**

CLASS	1975	1986	1993
Family	64 124	41 610	111 670
Refugee	5 566	6 403	22 219
Independent	128 191	49 461	120 432
Total	**197 881**	**97 479**	**254 321**

Figure 12.22
Immigrants
admitted by
class, 1975,
1986, and 1993

Source: Statistics Canada and Department of Employment and Immigration, 1995.

Simulation: creating an immigration policy

You are a member of the federal government's immigration committee. You are responsible for establishing Canada's immigration policy for the next five years. Working in groups, select a chairperson to keep the group on task and another member to record your committee's recommendations.

26 a) Evaluate the present classification system and the reasons for it. Discuss any changes you would like to see and why. Form your own classification system.

b) Make a list of entry requirements for each class you have established. Be specific! Consider the present points system. Identify any elements you believe are unfair. Propose changes that you think would make the system more equitable. If you wish to retain a revised points system, indicate how the applicants should be screened. Include a breakdown of the points structure.

c) Determine your quotas for the next five years and indicate the basis for your decision. You will have to consider the advantages and disadvantages for Canada in having a large or small population increase.

d) Present your results on large chart paper and share your ideas with the class.

Canada is a multicultural society. Over 4.3 million people living in Canada were born in another country. That is over 16 per cent of the population. Today immigrants to Canada come from all parts of the globe. They bring with them a rich variety of customs and traditions. In Canada, immigrants are encouraged to maintain their cultural identities. As a result, many Canadians describe themselves in terms of both their native homeland and their adopted homeland. And so our society is a mix of Pakistani-Canadians, Italian-Canadians, Chinese-Canadians, and so on.

Immigrants who become Canadian citizens are **first-generation Canadians**. Their children born in Canada are **second-generation Canadians**. In our multicultural society, it is common for second- and even third-generation Canadians to maintain their cultural heritage.

Figure 13.1
Canada's multi-cultural society
Events like Folklorama in Winnipeg celebrate Canada's ethnic diversity.

1 **a) Survey your class to discover the number of first-, second-, and third-generation Canadians.**
b) List all of the different cultural groups that are represented in your class.

Culture

In your survey, you may have discovered that Canada's population has links to many parts of the world. This creates a unique Canadian lifestyle in which diverse languages, customs, and traditions are brought together in a fascinating and rich cultural mix. But what does the term **culture** really mean?

If you were corresponding with a pen pal in another country, your letters would probably describe your life in Canada—where you live, what your hobbies are, and where you go to school. This would give your pen pal a mental picture of your culture, and would perhaps provide at least one snapshot of Canadian culture. Culture includes everything about us. Nothing can be left out. Culture includes the present, but it is also influenced by the past. Language, attitudes, values, family structure, and entertainment are only some of the elements of culture.

2 **Figure 13.2 is a cultural organizer. Copy this organizer into your notebook. Write a description of your culture for each of the headings. For example, for Language, describe the languages you speak at home,**

at school, and with your friends. Include as many details as possible.

Cultural snapshots

How do cultures vary within Canadian society? The following case studies illustrate how two families from different parts of the world have adapted to life in Canada while maintaining their unique cultural values.

Case study: Mohammed Mirza

In 1971, Mohammed Mirza left Pakistan to study mathematics at the University of Winnipeg. He was awarded a scholarship, which helped him to complete a postgraduate degree. Mohammed considered studying abroad a great opportunity to learn about a country that was quite different from his own. He had been raised on a farm outside the city of Quetta in western Pakistan. Living in a Western city like Winnipeg was a unique and exciting experience.

Following his studies, Mohammed was offered a job with a Vancouver-based engineering company. He accepted the position and applied to become a permanent resident of Canada. In 1978, Mohammed returned to Pakistan to marry Sabira. The marriage had been arranged by their families—a tradition in Pakistan. Today the couple have two children. Their son Ebad is eighteen. He'll be enrolling at Simon Fraser University in Burnaby, BC, where he eventually plans to study medicine. Their daughter Anjum is sixteen. She attends grade 10 at the local high school. Like many young students, she has not yet decided what career she will pursue.

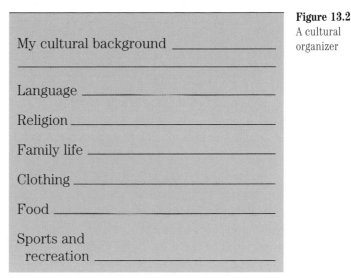

My cultural background _____
_____
Language _____
Religion _____
Family life _____
Clothing _____
Food _____
Sports and
 recreation _____

Figure 13.2
A cultural organizer

At home, Mohammed and Sabira speak in their native language of Urdu. At work and in the community at large, however, they speak English. Ebad and Anjum speak both Urdu and English fluently. Although they are proud of their ability to speak Urdu, they prefer to speak English.

The Mirza home is filled with mementoes of their culture. Mohammed and Sabira value their culture, which is deeply rooted in the religion of Islam. Islamic law governs the lives of the Mirza family. There is evidence of this throughout their home. On the dining room wall is a photograph of the Kaaba in Mecca, the shrine that is the centre of Islam. Above the fireplace in the family room is a copy of the Islamic holy book, the Koran. The Mirza family joins in all Islamic holy observances, including the month-long Ramadan in which strict fasting is observed from sunrise to sunset each day, and the Eid, a week-long festival that celebrates the end of the fast.

The Mirzas enjoy traditional Pakistani foods and spices, and they are able to buy these at specialty stores. They eat a variety of foods, however, including steak, chicken, and pasta. While Mohammed and Sabira's favourite place to eat out is an Indonesian restaurant in downtown Vancouver, the children prefer pizza and hamburgers from the local fast-food outlets.

On special occasions, the family wears traditional Pakistani clothing. These are hand-embroidered *Shalwar* and *Qameez*—silk pants and tunic. Most of the time, however, both parents and children enjoy relaxing in casual clothes.

Mohammed subscribes to a Pakistani newspaper to learn about events in Pakistan. He is also able to keep up with his favourite sports, cricket and field hockey, which are popular in Pakistan. Mohammed's son Ebad has never played cricket, even though his father has tried to teach him the game. Like many young Canadians, Ebad likes playing baseball and basketball. His sister Anjum also enjoys basketball, but she especially likes field hockey and is a member of her school's team.

Mohammed Mirza enjoys living in Canada. He is proud that he has maintained his cultural heritage and that this contributes to the richness of Canada's multicultural society. He believes that the blending of ethnic cultures offers the best of both worlds and makes Canada a wonderful country in which to live.

3 a) What generation are Mohammed and Sabira Mirza?

b) What generation are Ebad and Anjum Mirza?

c) What generation would Ebad or Anjum's children be?

Case study: Michelle Rapponi

Michelle Rapponi lived in Rossano in southern Italy, where she was a school teacher at the local elementary school. She first came to Canada in 1982 to visit her uncle, who lives in Woodbridge, Ontario. There she met her future husband, Tony. Tony was born in Canada, although his family had emigrated from Milan, Italy, many years earlier. In 1983, Tony visited Michelle in Rossano. They decided to marry and live in Canada.

With her family's blessing, Michelle became a permanent resident of Canada in 1984. She and Tony were married in a huge family reunion and celebration. Today Michelle teaches grade 6 in Woodbridge. She and Tony have one son, Mario. He is in grade 5 at the same school. He is not looking forward to being in his mother's class next year!

At home, the Rapponis speak mostly Italian, but Mario prefers to speak English with his friends. He also speaks only English at school. He enjoys taking French and hopes to be able to speak it fluently one day.

The Rapponi home is full of Italian cultural influences. On the front verandah Michelle creates miniature gardens in an array of planters. Italian paintings and needlepoints adorn the walls. A crucifix is a prominent feature in the family room. Photographs of family members living in Canada and in Italy are displayed throughout the house.

The Rapponis enjoy a wide variety of foods. Michelle and Tony's favourite dishes are traditional Italian pastas; pizza is Mario's favourite. Michelle particularly enjoys small Italian cakes, which she buys at a local bakery. On Friday evenings, the Rapponis frequently drive to downtown Toronto to have dinner in one of their favourite restaurants. They enjoy all kinds of foods, from Thai to Swiss!

Tony has a passion for soccer and helps coach Mario's team in the local soccer league. They both enjoy watching soccer matches from the Italian professional league every Sunday morning on the Toronto-based Italian-language television station. During the winter, their interest turns to hockey. Both Tony and Mario play in local leagues and are avid fans of the Toronto Maple Leafs. Mario sometimes goes to the local bocce courts to watch his father play this traditional Italian game that is similar to lawn bowling.

The family attends the local Catholic church at least once a week. During the major religious holidays of Christmas and Easter, they attend services more frequently. For these occasions, the family wears formal clothing. But like many people, Michelle, Tony, and Mario are most comfortable in casual clothes.

The Rapponis' religion extends to their son's education. Mario's school is a Catholic separate school. Michelle and Tony support this system as a means of ensuring that their religious values play a role in their son's life.

As an Italian-Canadian, Michelle Rapponi is pleased that she has been able to enjoy the advantages of life in Canada while maintaining her cultural values and traditions.

	MIRZA FAMILY	RAPPONI FAMILY	MY FAMILY
Language			
Religion			
Family life			
Clothing			
Food			
Sports and recreation			

Figure 13.3 A cultural comparison organizer

4 a) **What generation is Michelle Rapponi?**
   b) **What generation is Tony Rapponi?**
   c) **Would Mario Rapponi be a second-generation or third-generation Canadian? Give reasons for your answer.**

5 a) **Figure 13.3 is a cultural comparison organizer. Copy this organizer into your notebook and compare the cultures of the Mirza and Rapponi families with your own.**
   b) **What are the similarities and differences among the Mirza culture, the Rapponi culture, and your own family's culture?**

Cultural imprints

When people from around the world join together in one place, the result is a rich mixture of ideas and values. Just as different styles and sizes of shoes leave unique footprints, different ethnic groups leave unique **cultural imprints** on the Canadian landscape.

There are two kinds of cultural imprints: social imprints and physical imprints. **Social imprints** are the ways in which people behave. They include such things as customs, language, and religion. **Physical imprints** are the ways in which people affect their surroundings. They include such things as architecture, restaurants, and specialty shops. In Canada, cultural imprints are all around us.

6   a) **Identify three social imprints and three physical imprints in each of the cultural case studies you read on pages 267–269.**
    b) **Identify and describe any cultural imprints in your community.**

Social imprints

One of the most important social imprints in any culture is language. Canada has always had a diversity of languages. Long before European settlement, aboriginal peoples had their own distinct languages. European settlers introduced other languages, particularly French and English. As a result of immigration, Canada today is home to a rich diversity of languages from around the world.

Although Canada is officially a bilingual country, it is rapidly becoming a multilingual society. In 1991, Statistics Canada estimated that almost 25 per cent of all new immigrants spoke a first language other than English or French. The term **first language** refers to the language a person learns to speak first and continues to understand. This may be true even though the person may use a different **primary language** within the larger community. The primary language (sometimes called the official language) is the language most commonly spoken in a country. For example, Portuguese may be the first language in the home, while English is the primary language used at school and work and in the general community.

Figure 13.5
Physical imprints

Figure 13.4
Social imprints

7 a) Use the terms *first language* and *primary language* to describe the languages spoken by each person in the cultural case studies on pages 267–269.

b) What is the likely language pattern of the next generation in the Mirza and Rapponi families?

8 Use the information in Figure 13.6 to create a **divided bar graph** to highlight language patterns in Canada.

a) Draw twelve vertical bars, each 10 cm high and 1 cm wide. Each bar represents 100 per cent of the population in each province or territory. Indicate percentage intervals in measurements of ten along the side of the bar.

b) Beginning with the Atlantic provinces, label the province or territory beneath each bar.

c) Choose a colour to represent each language group, English, French, Bilingual, and Other. Prepare a corresponding legend.

d) Subdivide each bar according to the percentages in the table. Begin with English at the top, followed by French, Bilingual, and Other. What language patterns does your graph reveal?

Figure 13.6
Provincial distribution of population by primary language

PROVINCE/TERRITORY	ENGLISH	LANGUAGE (%) FRENCH	BILINGUAL	OTHER
Newfoundland	96.5	0.4	3.0	0.1
Prince Edward Island	89.6	0.2	10.1	0.1
Nova Scotia	91.1	0.2	8.6	0.1
New Brunswick	57.9	12.5	29.5	0.1
Quebec	5.5	58.0	35.4	1.1
Ontario	86.1	0.5	11.4	2.0
Manitoba	89.4	0.2	5.2	5.2
Saskatchewan	94.2	0.1	5.2	0.5
Alberta	92.1	0.1	6.6	1.2
British Columbia	91.6	0.1	6.4	1.9
Yukon	90.5	0.1	9.3	0.1
Northwest Territories	85.1	0.1	6.1	8.7
Canada	**67.1**	**15.2**	**16.3**	**1.4**

Source: Adapted from Statistics Canada, Cat. No. 96-311, 1993.

9 You are planning a vacation in a foreign country. You would like to learn how to say a few key phrases in the language of the country you'll be visiting.
a) Make a list of simple phrases you will need to know on your vacation, such as "hello," "good morning," and "thank you."
b) Find out the language spoken in the country you plan to visit. With the help of a bilingual dictionary, find the translations of the key phrases you listed in a). Write your phrases and their translations in a handy pocket guide.

10 Divide into groups of four. Select one cultural group in Canada for your group to represent. Using your school's library resource centre, research the social imprints this cultural group has had on Canadian society. Assign one of the following topics to each member of the group: religious holidays and observances; marriage and family customs; clothing and personal styles; and traditional foods. When your research is complete, prepare a visual presentation of your findings.

Figure 13.7
The five most widely spoken languages in Canada, 1971-1991
How might the first languages of new immigrants affect language rankings in the future?

1971			1991		
RANK	LANGUAGE	%	RANK	LANGUAGE	%
1	English	60.2	1	English	60.0
2	French	26.9	2	French	24.1
3	German	2.6	3	Italian	1.9
4	Italian	2.4	4	Chinese	1.8
5	Ukrainian	1.4	5	German	1.7

Source: Statistics Canada, Cat. No. 96-311E, 1995.

Figure 13.8
The most common languages of immigrants to Canada in the last 10 years

LANGUAGE	%
1 English	23
2 Chinese	18
3 Spanish	7
4 Polish	6
5 Arabic	5
6 Punjabi	4
7 French	3

Source: Statistics Canada, Cat. No. 96-311E, 1995.

Physical imprints

Most immigrants arriving in Canada are attracted to the major urban centres. One of the main reasons for this is the opportunity to live in ethnic neighbourhoods among people of a similar cultural background. Many immigrants prefer living among people of their own ethnic heritage to avoid **culture clash**. This is the feeling of isolation that people experience when they move to a new environment where things are different and unfamiliar. Living among people with a similar background makes the adjustment to a new life easier.

Canada's urban centres are sprinkled with **ethnic neighbourhoods**. These are areas within the larger community that share common cultural and ethnic characteristics. Ethnic neighbourhoods leave a significant physical imprint on the community at large.

Figure 13.9 shows an Italian neighbourhood in Toronto. We can see the cultural imprints. But we can't tell how far this neighbourhood extends or how the community has changed over time. To learn more, we need to gather more data.

The **census** is the means by which the federal government counts and collects information about Canada's population. Every five years, Statistics Canada conducts a survey of every person living in the country. The census reveals information about age, ethnicity, language, and other facts about Canadians. This information helps governments plan their social policies and businesses create their marketing strategies.

The census is divided into geographic regions called **census subdivisions**. Large urban centres are further divided into smaller areas called **census tracts**. This makes it possible to gain information about an entire city as well as only specific areas within the city. Figure 13.10 shows the census tract divisions for Metropolitan Toronto.

Figure 13.9
Toronto's Little Italy
What evidence is there that this is an Italian neighbourhood?

11 During the 1991 census, Statistics Canada surveyed ethnic origins. Figure 13.11 indicates the census tracts in Metropolitan Toronto in which at least 750 people stated they were of Italian background. Using this information, we may be able to determine where the Italian-Canadian neighbourhood in Figure 13.9 is located.

a) Place a piece of tracing paper on the map showing Toronto's census tracts. Using the **graded shading** method, shade the census tracts according to the following scale: greater than 1500—purple; 1250-1499—dark blue; 1000-1249—medium blue; 750-999—light blue; less than 750—unshaded.

b) Once you have shaded the areas, draw a thick line around the census tracts that you believe make up the Italian-Canadian community in Toronto.

c) Using street names as a guide, describe the extent of the Italian-Canadian neighbourhood.

12 a) To what extent does the data in Figure 13.12 support the idea that Canada has two dominant ethnic groups?

b) What has happened to these groups individually and in combination between 1911 and 1991?

c) Which is Canada's third largest ethnic group?

d) Which ethnic groups are increasing in percentage?

e) What does the increase in the "Other" category suggest?

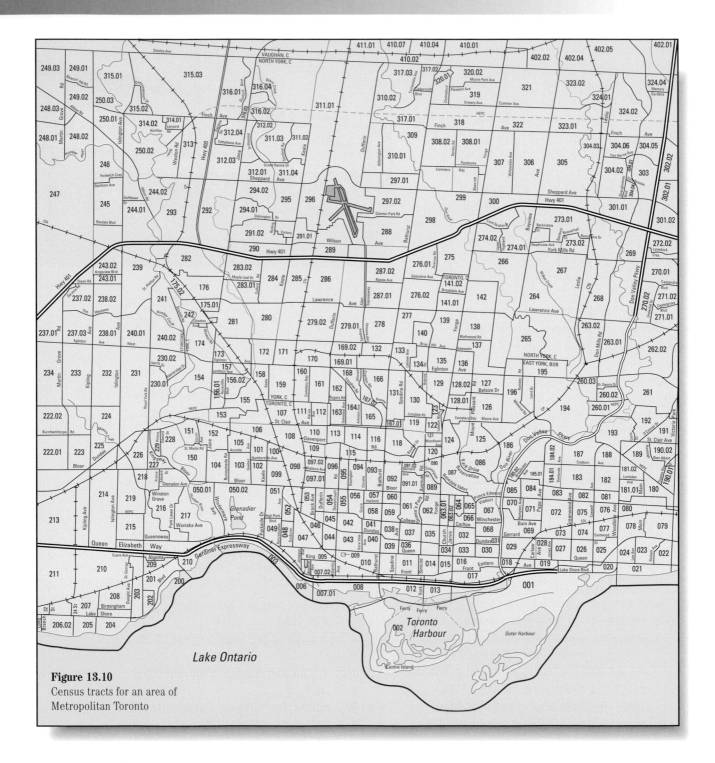

Figure 13.10

Census tracts for an area of
Metropolitan Toronto

NUMBER OF ITALIANS	CENSUS TRACTS
Over 1500	112, 159, 161, 279.01, 279.02, 280, 283.02, 284, 285, 289, 291.02, 293, 294.02, 295, 311.02, 311.04, 312.01,312.03, 313, 314.02, 315.01, 315.03, 316.01
1250-1499	107, 110, 162, 163, 164, 170, 240.02, 243.02, 250.02, 282, 283.01, 286, 291.01, 292, 294.01, 311.03, 312.04, 315.02
1000-1249	056, 108, 111, 168, 240.01, 247, 290
750-999	042, 081, 094, 160, 169.01, 169.02, 176, 230.02, 244.02, 245, 250.01, 281, 297.02, 311.01, 316.02.

Source: Statistics Canada, Cat. No. 95.354, 1995.

Figure 13.11
Census tracts showing Italian ethnic background, 1991

13 Create a **divided circle graph** to show the 1991 data in Figure 13.12.

a) Multiply each percentage figure by 3.6. This will give you the number of degrees in the circle for each ethnic group.

Figure 13.12
Canada's population by ethnic group

ETHNIC GROUP	1911	1951	1981	1991*
		(%)		
British	55.5	47.9	43.5	42.0
French	28.6	30.8	28.9	27.4
Chinese	0.4	0.2	1.3	2.2
Dutch	0.8	1.4	1.8	1.3
German	5.6	4.4	5.1	3.4
Italian	0.6	1.1	3.4	2.8
Jewish	1.1	1.3	1.1	0.9
Aboriginal	1.5	1.2	1.9	1.7
Polish	0.5	1.6	1.2	1.0
Scandinavian	1.6	2.0	1.3	0.6
Ukrainian	1.0	2.8	2.4	1.5
East Indian	0.3	0.8	0.9	1.2
Other	2.8	5.3	8.1	14.0

*The question asked in 1991 was "To which ethnic or cultural group(s) did this person's ancestors belong?" There were 2.8 per cent who responded "Canadian." These are included in the "Other" category.

Source: Statistics Canada, Cat. No.93-315, 1994.

b) **Using separate colours to represent each ethnic group, create your divided circle graph.**

14 a) **Survey the ethnic origins of your class. (Some students may have to trace their families through several generations to find their country of origin.)**
   b) **Create a circle graph following the same procedure and using the same colours as in activity 13.**
   c) **Compare the ethnic backgrounds in your class with those of the country as a whole. What are the similarities and differences? What might account for these?**

15 **"Canada contains people from a variety of cultures who have added a significant flavour to the Canadian lifestyle." As a class, discuss the different ways in which ethnic groups have imprinted Canadian society.**

Multiculturalism

In 1973, Canada officially introduced the policy of **multiculturalism**. This encourages Canadians of all backgrounds to retain their cultural heritage while at the same time respecting the differences among us. The federal government supports multiculturalism through funding for the arts and other cultural events. Governments at all levels, together with businesses and community organizations, sponsor a variety of ethnic celebrations. These range from neighbourhood parades to huge festivals like Toronto's annual Caravan, with its shows, exhibits, and restaurants representing cities and countries from around the world. The result of multiculturalism is that Canada has become a **cultural mosaic**.

The opposite of multiculturalism is **assimilation**. This occurs when all ethnic groups are encouraged to blend into the single dominant culture of their adopted homeland. The result is a shared cultural imprint, usually with a single dominant language. Also called the **melting pot**, Canadians can observe assimilation in action by looking to our southern neighbour, the United States.

16 a) **Describe three positive and three negative aspects of a multicultural society.**
   b) **Which type of society do you prefer, a cultural mosaic or a melting pot? Explain why.**

17 **Prepare a case study of one ethnic group *other* than Pakistani or Italian. Use your library resource centre to obtain background information. Then interview an immigrant who is a member of the ethnic group you have chosen. From your research and interview you should discover:**
   - **the geographic origins of the ethnic group;**
   - **the push/pull factors that influenced the person's decision to immigrate to Canada;**
   - **the number of immigrants from this country in the past ten years;**
   - **where these immigrants have settled in Canada;**
   - **the neighbourhood patterns and cultural imprints this ethnic group has created.**

   Present your information in a visual display to be shared with the class.

Include a map indicating the journey the person you interviewed made to Canada, including the distance travelled, the method(s) of transportation, and the time it took to complete the journey.

Historical imprints

Many of the cultural imprints of early settlers have remained with us over the centuries. These **historical imprints** are evident in Canadian society. The most enduring social imprint is the bilingual nature of our country. But early settlers left lasting physical imprints as well. Some of these historical imprints are evident in our rural land-use patterns.

Prior to European settlement in North America, there was no land ownership as we know it today. The aboriginal peoples lived off the land, taking from it only what they needed to survive. The concept of land ownership did not exist in these societies. However, the Europeans introduced their own traditions, among them the idea of ownership of the land. As they established their settlements, other traditions made a lasting impact on the landscape.

Land-use patterns in Quebec

Original contact between early French settlers and aboriginal peoples was for the purpose of developing the fur trade. As this trade flourished, commercial activities began to extend beyond hunting and trapping. By 1760, Montreal and Quebec were thriving communities. As the French colony expanded, 60 000 farmers began to cultivate the land. They created a unique historical imprint that is still evident today.

18 Figure 13.13 shows the banks of the St. Lawrence River near Trois Rivières, Quebec. Locate this area on an atlas map using the gazetteer.
   a) Describe how the farmland has been divided in relation to the river.
   b) The river was important to French settlers. What advantages would a river location have?

Prior to 1760, French settlers were the dominant European influence in what is today eastern Canada. They established a distinctive land-use pattern that remains a unique feature in much of southern Quebec and the St. Lawrence Valley.

In the late 1600s and early 1700s, the king of France granted tracts of land in what is now Quebec to landlords, or **seigneurs**. In return for the land, the seigneurs were responsible for settlement of the area. French peasant settlers, or **habitants**, were offered land grants, or **roture**, by the seigneurs.

The area was originally covered by dense forest. The roture were established along the rivers to provide the settlers with access to water for transportation. In return for the land, the habitants paid the seigneurs an annual tax; the amount depended on the width of their rotures. Because the river was so important, these **seigneuries**, as the land lots were called, stretched back from the river in long, narrow plots. This created the opportunity for more waterfront lots, which gave river access to a greater number of habitants.

According to French tradition, when a farmer died his land was divided equally among his sons. If he had two sons, for example, the land was split in half lengthwise so that both lots had access to the river. This tradition continued well into the twentieth century. It produced a unique pattern of fragmented, narrow agricultural strips.

Figure 13.13
Seigneurial farm system near Trois Rivières, Quebec

19 Refer to Figure 13.13, which shows the layout of farms around the St. Lawrence River near Trois Rivières, Quebec.
a) Use the scale to measure the approximate length of the lots.
b) Copy Figure 13.15 into your notebook. Each lot should be 20 cm long and 2 cm wide. (The scale of 1 cm:75 m is only approximate to the actual proportions.) Indicate the scale on your diagram. Number the lots from 1 to 5. This repre-

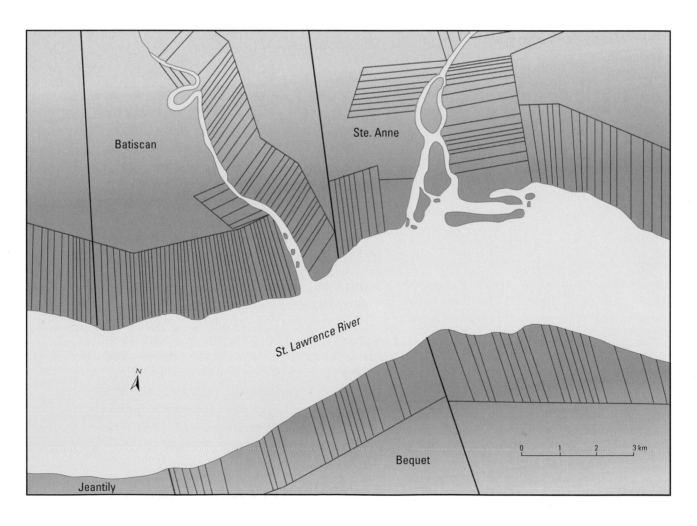

Figure 13.14
The long-lot field pattern in southern Quebec

sents the lots given to five families around the mid-1700s.

c) Based on the information provided below, divide your lots.
- The family on Lot 1 has two sons.
- The family on Lot 2 has four sons.
- The family on Lot 3 has one son.
- The family on Lot 4 has four sons.
- The family on Lot 5 has three sons.

d) For each of these new lots, place a farmhouse as close to the river as possible. What pattern emerges?

e) What are the disadvantages of these long, narrow strips of farmland?

Once all the land along the shore had been granted, another row of long lots was created behind the first row. (See Figure 13.16.) These lots had access to a road, which served the same function as the

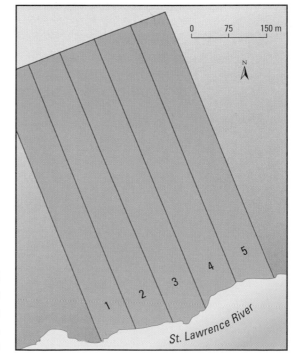

Figure 13.15
Detailed plan of a seigneurial farm layout

Figure 13.16 Development of the seigneurial system away from the river

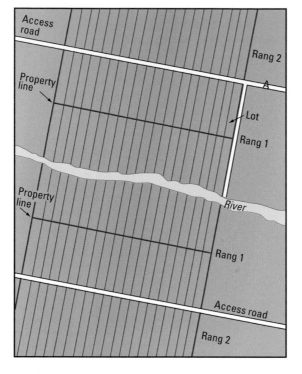

Figure 13.17 Air photo of Bourg Royale and Charlesbourg, near Quebec City *Evaluate the radial land pattern shown here. Do you think this pattern had more advantages or disadvantages over the seigneurial system?*

river. Each row of seigneuries was called a **rang**. Those along the river's shore were the first rang. The second row beyond the access road was the second rang, and so on. This created a unique settlement pattern of linear, or strip, villages in southern Quebec, with all of the homes located in parallel lines at the end of the rangs.

Originally there were 240 seigneuries on 3.2 million hectares of land in southern Quebec. In recent times, however, farmers have bought adjoining plots to create larger, and thereby more efficient, farms. But remnants of the seigneurial system can still be found in some parts of the region.

This system of land use was not unique to Quebec alone. In parts of New Brunswick, Nova Scotia, Ontario, and Manitoba the seigneurial system was adopted by early settlers. It was not the only settlement pattern in Quebec, either. Figure 13.17 shows a **radial land pattern** at Bourg Royale and Charlesbourg near Quebec City. In these settlements, land was surveyed outwards from a central community, with the lots becoming wider and wider.

Land-use patterns in southern Ontario

In 1760, the huge area north of the Great Lakes was colonized by Britain. Like their French counterparts, the British settlers brought with them their own traditions. These included British land-use patterns that were quite different from those in France. Figure 13.18 shows the imprints settlers left on the land in southern Ontario in the early eighteenth century.

Figure 13.18
Survey
patterns in
southern
Ontario

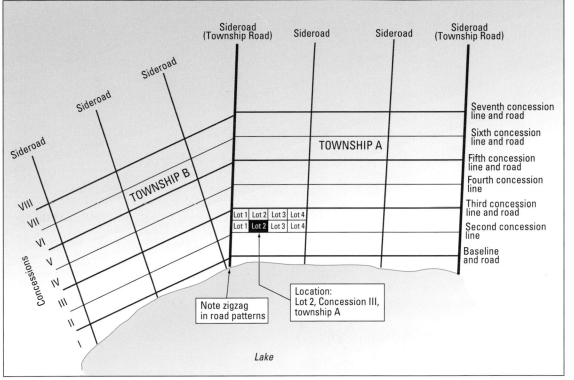

The British governors of Ontario wanted to create blocks of land called townships. The creation of these townships began by surveying lines away from important bodies of water, such as Lake Ontario and the St. Lawrence River. A survey line, called a base line, was drawn parallel to the shore. Roads were built parallel to the base line approximately 2 km apart. The roads dividing these parcels of land were called concession roads; the land in between was called a concession. Each concession contained two parallel rows of property called lots; each lot consisted of 100 acres (40.5 ha). Farmers were given a whole lot, or sometimes just part of a lot, which produced very small farms. Concession roads were usually numbered with Roman numerals, beginning at the base line. (Today, however, many of these roads have names.) In southern Ontario, most concession roads were established in an east-west direction. But in order to make the base line run parallel to the shore of the lake or river, many of the roads had slight zigzag patterns—a source of frustration for some of today's motorists!

For better access to all areas, but especially north and south, sideroads were built at right angles to the concession roads. The distance between these roads was the same as the concession roads about 2 km. Farm homes and barns were usually built near the roads, and neigh-

Figure 13.19
Settlement
patterns in
southern
Ontario

bours often built their farms side by side. Why do you think they would do this?

The historical imprint of this survey system has proven to be inconvenient and expensive to maintain. There is an excessive number of small roads in southern Ontario. Many of these are unpaved and are continually damaged in winter, requiring costly repairs each spring. In addition, most of the early 100 acre (40.5 ha) lots given to farmers proved to be too small for the processes of mechanization that eventually developed. As a result, many farms became less competitive. In time, some of these farms were abandoned.

Simulation: surveying land-use patterns in the Prairies

Settlers in the Prairies in the late 1800s found large areas of relatively flat, open space. What imprint did they leave on this vast land?

Imagine you are a land surveyor in 1875. Your objective is to encourage farming in the Prairies. Your task is to create a plan for dividing the vast farmland of this region. The population must be spread out and evenly distributed. This land-use pattern will stretch from the Ontario-Manitoba border across the Prairies to the Rocky Mountains.

Figure 13.20
Land division
in the Prairies

20 a) Draw a line 18 cm long near the bottom of a piece of paper. This is the base line. It represents the 49th parallel, which forms the border between Canada and the United States.

b) Draw three horizontal lines, each 6 cm apart, above the base line and running parallel to it. Label the area between each of these lines a township, beginning with township 1 at the border with the United States. The actual distance between each township line is 9.66 km. Each township contains an area of 93.3 km².

c) Along the base line, draw four vertical lines 18 cm long and 6 cm apart. From right to left, label the first space range 1, the second space range 2, and so on.

Shade the square that represents township 3, range 2, and label it.

d) Each township must now be divided into thirty-six equal squares called **sections**. Subdivide the area identified as township 2, range 1, into thirty-six sections. Each section should measure 1 cm x 1 cm. Number each section according to the method in Figure 13.21.

The sections in a township total 259 ha. But this is still too large for settlers to farm successfully. The sections must be divided again, this time into sixteen subdivisions. Each family is entitled to a quarter of one section, or four subdivisions. This is called a homestead. Each homestead should measure 64.8 ha. In return, the settlers must

Figure 13.21
Division of
townships

36	35	34	33	32	31
25	26	27	28	29	30
24	23	22	21	20	19
18	17	16	15	14	13
7	8	9	10	11	12
6	5	4	3	2	1

A

| NW | NE |
| SW | SE |

To complete the process of land division, additional base lines had to be drawn every 39 km north of the original base line. Because the meridians running from north to south narrow as they move northwards, the new north-south survey lines were placed a little further to the west. These new base lines were called correction lines.

pay $10 and agree to stay on the land for at least three years. The homesteads are labelled according to their location within the section—northwest (NW), northeast (NE), southeast (SE), southwest (SW). (See Figure 13.21). (It should be noted that sometimes subdivisions were allocated for purposes other than farming. Some were left vacant. As their value rose, they were sold to help pay for churches, schools, and the expansion of the railway. The government also awarded a substantial number of subdivisions as compensation to the Hudson Bay Company, which once claimed ownership of this land.)

21 On your plan, shade the following farm addresses: i) SW, section 6, township 1, range 3; ii) NW, section 2, township 2, range 2.

The survey system in the prairies worked very well. Settlement was helped by a network of roads and railways. Roads were built every one mile (1.6 km) from east to west and every two miles (3.2 km) from north to south. Up to 1 million immigrants settled in this area between 1885, when the Canadian Pacific Railway was built, and 1914, when the First World War began.

Today there has been much consolidation of farmland in the Prairies as individual farms have expanded. The early homestead of 64.8 ha has almost disappeared. Today, the average size of farms in Saskatchewan is between 300 and 350 ha. This has allowed farmers to grow more grain and raise more livestock while reducing many of their costs. There are fewer farmers in any one township and settlements are further apart than in the early days.

Settlement patterns in Atlantic Canada

Much of the early settlement of Canada took place in the Atlantic region. Because of the geography, the grand settlement patterns that were later established in Ontario, Quebec, and the Prairies were impossible. Much of the Atlantic region has poor soils, a hilly landscape, and a climate that is less favourable for agriculture. Settlements were confined to more fertile river valleys and the flatter coastal plains. Instead of agriculture, mining, logging, and fishing were the primary reasons for the establishment of many settlements. As a result, settlement patterns are dispersed, or scattered. Because of this, there are frequently long distances between communities. Transportation routes tend to be coastal. Only major highways link towns and cities located inland.

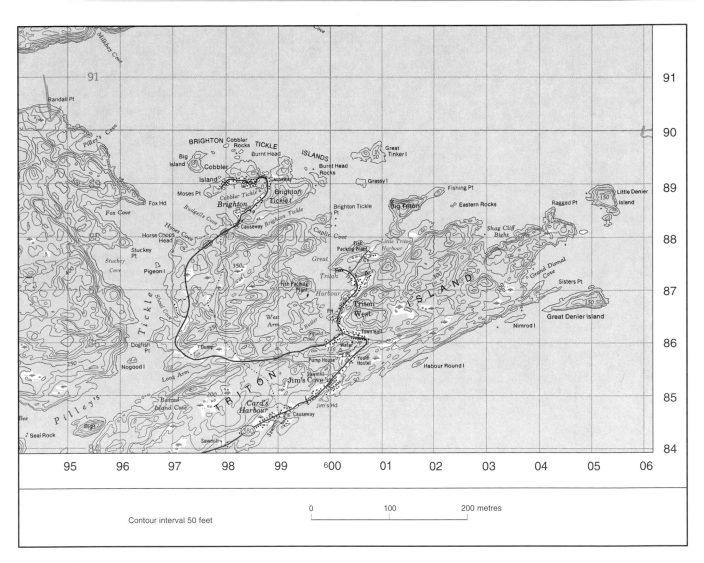

Figure 13.22
Topographic map of Triton Island, Newfoundland
A causeway is a road, often made with a base of rocks, that links islands together. Identify the causeways on this map.

One of the best examples of dispersed settlement is found along the coast. Here communities were established to harvest the once-rich Atlantic fishing resources. Many of the villages in Newfoundland are completely isolated and can be reached only by boat. Figure 13.22 is a topographic map of Triton Island in Newfoundland. It is typical of the settlement patterns found throughout the Atlantic region.

22 Refer to Figure 13.22.
 a) **On a piece of tracing paper, sketch an outline of the area shown on the topographic map. Include a red line to indicate the main highway and black dots to show settlements. Label Brighton, Triton West, Jim's Cove, and Card's Harbour.**
 b) **Which do you think came first on Triton Island, the highway pattern or the villages? Explain your answer.**

c) **In your notebook, describe the settlement pattern around Triton Island.**

23 a) Study the contour lines on the topographic map in Figure 13.22. What do they tell you about the physical landscape of this area? How might the landscape have contributed to the settlement pattern?
 b) **Identify the traditional economic activities on Triton Island. Use evidence and references from the map to support your answer.**

24 a) A *tickle* is a stretch of narrow water where ice moved by tidal currents tickles, or rubs, the sides of fishing boats. Give the references for tickles on the topographic map.
 b) **What other names are used to describe coastal features in the region?**

Culture changes with each generation. Often, these changes are gradual—so gradual, in fact, that we may not notice them until we look back at old photographs or videotapes. Society can usually adapt to gradual change. But what happens when cultural change is not gradual? How does a society cope with change that may be overwhelming?

In Canada, one of the most dramatic examples of cultural change has occurred in the lifestyle of aboriginal peoples. The term **aboriginal**, or **Native**, **peoples** describes the descendants of Canada's first inhabitants. The most generally held anthropological theory states that Canada's first people migrated here over 40 000 years ago over a land bridge that once extended across the Bering Sea from Asia. These nomadic peoples spread throughout North, Central, and South America. As they did so, they formed separate cultural groups. In Canada, six cultural regions were formed.

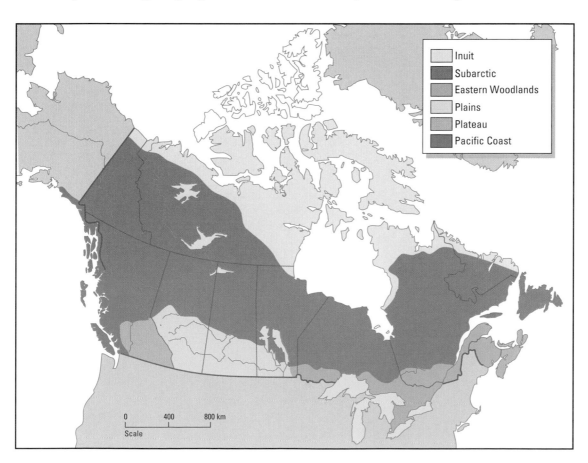

Figure 14.1
Native cultures in Canada
Cultural groupings were based on how each group adapted to the natural environment.

Legend:
- Inuit
- Subarctic
- Eastern Woodlands
- Plains
- Plateau
- Pacific Coast

0   400   800 km
Scale

(See Figure 14.1.) Within each cultural group, there was a variety of different dialects and languages. Thus Canada had great cultural diversity long before European settlement. Contact with Europeans, however, would change these aboriginal cultures forever.

A simulation: Inuvial

Inuvial is an imaginary northern land. The history of Inuvial reveals how the traditional culture of its people changed over time, and why.

Figure 14.2
Inuvial

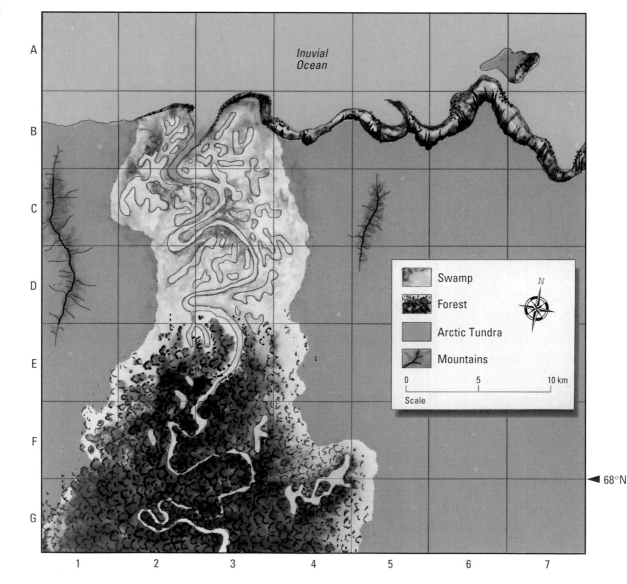

Period A (pre-1700)

Inuvial is one of the most northern regions in the world. Located at about 68°N, the climate is a cold one. Winters are long, with temperatures averaging -27°C! The short summer lasts only six to eight weeks, when the temperature rises to 10°C.

A large river flows northward into the Inuvial Ocean. Although there are mountains west of the river, the rest of the landscape is flat. For most of the year it is covered with snow and ice. During the brief summer, lichens, mosses, and colourful plants and flowers appear. The river valley in the south is dotted with small trees, while swampland surrounds the mouth of the river.

The Inuviat who live here are hardy people. Their ancestors were hunters who followed the herds to this land 40 000 years ago. The Inuviat still hunt today. Their survival is dependent on their knowledge and understanding of nature, and their lifestyle and culture are in harmony with it. These values are passed on to their children. Women are treated as equals in Inuviat society. They are respected as the first educators of their children. They are also defenders of their community.

Using bows and arrows and harpoons, the Inuviat hunt caribou, seal, fish, walrus, whale, musk-ox, and bear. Six caribou can sustain a family of five for a full year. Needles carved from bone are used to make clothing from animal hides. Everything the Inuviat need is created from the materials they have at hand. They take only what they need and waste nothing. This is called a **subsistence economy**.

The homes of the Inuviat reflect their **nomadic** way of life. When hunting, they live in snow huts or skin tents. Winter homes are usually built on the **permafrost**, the permanently frozen ground of the region. When the Inuviat stay in one place for a long period, they build domed houses of stone and turf. Beams of whalebone or wood support roofs of sod or animal hides.

During the winter, dog sleds, or komatiks, transport the Inuviat over the ice and snow. Kayaks or longer umiaks are used to travel the water in summer.

The Inuviat language is unique to the people of these northern lands. Like the rest of their culture, their language is at one with nature. The seven Inuviat words that describe the winds are as varied as the winds themselves.

1 a) **Copy the map in Figure 14.2 onto a blank piece of paper. Use the same number of squares and the same numbers and letters for the grid. Label the map and add the legend and scale.**

   b) **Each square represents 25 km². This area provides enough food for a family of five for a year. Using a pencil, draw dots on your map to represent the distribution of this nomadic population of 130 people. (Be sure to use a pencil; you will be asked to relocate some of these dots later.) Spread the dots over the whole map to show nomadic movement. Use one dot for every five people.**

2 a) **In a chart similar to Figure 14.3, describe the culture of the Inuviat. (NOTE: The column "Changes from previous period" does not apply to Period A.)**

Figure 14.3
Culture chart

TIME PERIOD FROM _____ TO _____		
	CULTURAL CHARACTERISTICS	CHANGES FROM PREVIOUS PERIOD
Housing Food Clothing Language Economy Transportation Hunting methods		

b) What cultural imprints have the Inuviat left on their environment?

Period B (1700-1920)

During this period, significant changes are affecting the Inuviat way of life. In the 1700s, British, French, Icelandic, and Scandinavian explorers begin navigating the Inuvial Ocean in search of trade routes. Those Inuviat who hunt near the northern coast are the first to make contact with the crews of these ships.

The explorers are impressed by the abundance of wildlife they find. As the news spreads, hunters and trappers arrive from the south. The impact of their presence is quickly felt. The Inuviat are introduced to guns and metal traps, which enable them to kill their prey more easily. But they still rely on the traditional sleds and canoes to get to the hunting grounds.

Once the Inuviat discover that fur and skins are valued by the newcomers, their attitude towards hunting begins to change. Some are persuaded to hunt for profit and not just for food and clothing. A trading company establishes a trading post. At the post the Inuviat exchange their furs and skins for material goods. Sometimes they are paid scrip, or tokens, for their goods, which they can exchange later for other southern items. The Inuviat are beginning to move towards a **trading economy**.

A few Inuviat families move into permanent timber homes near the trading post. Most, however, continue to be nomadic and come to the trading post only between hunting expeditions. But many Inuviat are now beginning to learn the language of the visitors.

Sailors continue to navigate Inuviat waters. Now they are not exploring, but hunting for whales; whale oil and bone is considered valuable in their societies. Soon the whale population is almost extinct. As the stocks are depleted, the whaling trips become less profitable. Eventually the ships stop coming. Unfortunately, the sailors have left behind a legacy of diseases that were previously unknown among the Inuviat. These diseases kill many Inuviat, whose immune systems cannot cope with the "new" germs.

3 On your map from activity 1, select a coastal site for the trading post. This will develop into a community of fifty people. It will include a family of five non-Inuviats who will run the trading post. Relocate some of your population dots to represent Inuviat workers in the village. Give your community a name.

4 **a)** On your chart from activity 2, describe the culture of the Inuviat during this period. Indicate any changes and new cultural imprints.
   b) What impact did the introduction of more efficient hunting methods have on the balance of nature?

Period C (1920-1960)

The Inuviat face more changes. In the late 1920s, valuable minerals are discovered in the mountains in the west. (See square 1D in Figure 14.2.) Bush planes transporting mining and trading officials begin regular flights to the area. The federal government wants to establish its authority, so government officials, including police, also arrive. Towards the end of this period, the military builds a radar installation base here. (See square 6C.)

More Inuviat have now settled in the trading and mining communities. They are becoming dependent on a **wage economy**. Those people who work for the mining companies earn good salaries. There is little exchange of goods as in the past; now there is only the buying and selling of goods for money.

The government has provided permanent timber homes, heated with oil-burning stoves, for all the families. Although some Inuviat still hunt for their food and clothing, the majority buy food brought in from the south. Many Inuviat wear southern clothes, including boots, baseball hats, and T-shirts. A few Inuviat now drive trucks and snowmobiles, which are beginning to appear in the region for the first time. Over the next decade they will replace traditional methods of transportation.

The Inuviat also have radios now and listen to broadcasts from the south. The federal government has taken even greater control. A boarding school for Inuviat children whose parents do not live in the community has been established. The teachers, books, and other learning materials are from the south. The children are learning English as their primary language, and they are losing their ability to speak Inuviat. The role of women in Inuviat society is changing as a result of outside influences. Instead of the traditional society in which both men and women are valued equally, women now have inferior status.

5 **a)** With the increased number of southerners who have moved to the area, more accommodation is needed. On your map, establish a second community for the mining operation and the military installation.
   b) Assume another fifty Inuviat have been given jobs with the new resource companies. Relocate some of your population dots from their traditional nomadic locations to the new community.

c) **Assume that small airports are being built close to your original community, the mining operation, and the military base. Add these airports to your map and draw in the roads that will link them to the communities.**

6 **Complete the culture chart for this time period, indicating any changes or new cultural imprints.**

Period D (1960-present)

Many significant changes are now taking place in the region. Several oil companies have been searching for oil and gas, and a major oil discovery has been made. (See square 4C.) The impact of this discovery is substantial. Much more heavy equipment is being brought in from the south to recover the oil. The trading post community is now the headquarters for the new oil operations. Money is flowing into the area. Wages are high. It is a boom time for the Inuviat!

The Inuviat are experiencing a culture clash, however. Some of the older generation, who still dress in traditional skins, fondly remember the hunting, fishing, and nomadic lifestyle of their youth. The younger generation, however, dress in blue jeans and sweaters. They have no interest in learning the skills needed to make clothes from animal hides, and they prefer to eat foods from the south. In addition, it is now necessary to have a federal licence to hunt and trap, and the licence is expensive.

The Inuviat of the younger generation like working for the oil companies. The wage economy is so strong that many people work long hours to earn bonuses so they can buy luxury items like all-terrain vehicles. Most Inuviat now live in prefabricated houses brought in from the south in sections and assembled on site. English is the first language of their children. Members of the older generation can only shake their heads in despair.

Environmental issues are becoming a concern in Inuvial. One of the main issues involves the transporting of oil to southern markets. The oil companies favour building a pipeline, which would extend across the landscape for hundreds of kilometres. Many Inuviat, as well as some people in the south, are concerned about the potential dangers the pipeline poses to the fragile northern environment.

The question of land ownership is also becoming an issue. Some Inuviat are claiming legal possession of the land and its resources. They argue that, since their ancestors were the original inhabitants, they have aboriginal land claims to the area. They feel that any resource wealth should be under their control rather than that of the federal government or private enterprise.

7 a) **On your map, indicate the changes that have resulted from resource exploration and recovery, especially in terms of transportation and population.**
 b) **Add to your map any other changes that may result from the new activities. (Consider settlement patterns.)**
 c) **Relocate some of your population dots to show how resource-related job opportunities might affect population distribution.**
 d) **On your map, indicate a possible route the proposed pipeline might take through Inuviat.**

8 Complete the culture chart for this time period, indicating any changes or new cultural imprints.

9 a) Using the words independence and dependence, explain the difference between the traditional Inuviat lifestyle of a subsistence economy and the wage economy created by the resource companies.

b) What social problems might the Inuviat experience as a result of this change in their lifestyle?

10 In chart form, highlight arguments for and against the land claims of the Inuviat.

Period E (the future)

Bad news! Too much oil is being produced in the world. Prices are falling and are expected to stay low for some time. Oil companies are closing fields that are too expensive to operate. This includes those in remote northern areas like Inuvial.

11 How will falling oil prices affect the Inuviat people i) economically and ii) socially?

12 a) Which cultural changes make it impossible for the Inuviat to return to their traditional lifestyle?

b) Do you think it is possible for the Inuviat to balance tradition with modernity? Explain your answer.

The Inuit in Canada

Assimilation occurs when people from one culture become more like people from another culture. The story of the Inuviat is an example of how a people can be assimilated. While this story is only a simulation, it is based on the real-life threat to the unique culture of the Inuit in Canada.

The majority of Inuit people live in the northern regions of Canada. The largest Inuit population is in the Northwest Territories. This is a landscape much like fictional Inuvial. The region is huge—3 426 320 km². That's more than three times larger than Quebec and four times larger than Ontario or British Columbia! Yet the population of the Northwest Territories is only 57 430. Of these, 21 355 are Inuit. They live mostly in the extreme northern and eastern parts of the territory, usually around the frozen coastline. Like the fictional Inuviat, the Inuit are being assimilated into the non-aboriginal culture. But the process has resulted in a culture clash between the traditional ways of older Inuit and the contemporary lifestyle of Inuit youth. Many young people find themselves caught between their traditional culture and the lifestyle brought to the region by white people. The older Inuit refer to these teenagers as *aqunnaaki*, meaning "between two skins."

Over 65 per cent of Inuit living in the Arctic are under the age of twenty-five. A declining infant mortality rate has created a baby boom. The Inuit population is growing four times faster than the national average. Yet there are not enough jobs for the growing number of people. Unemployment is close to 80 per cent. The prospects for the future are not promising because the population is growing much faster than the economy. Many Inuit believe the solution may lie in a return to traditional activities.

13 At what stage in the Inuvial simulation are the young Inuit? Give reasons to support your answer.

14 You have been asked by the government of the Northwest Territories to recommend steps that could be taken to help Inuit teenagers. What five recommendations would you make?

Native subgroups in Canada

The Constitution Act of 1982 recognized the Inuit, **North American Indians**, and **Métis** as Canada's three aboriginal peoples. **Status Indians** are registered under the Indian Act; **Non-status Indians** are not. The Indian Act establishes the administrative and legal framework for the rights of Status Indians; Non-status Indians do not share these rights. The Department of Indian and Northern Affairs has responsibility for the affairs of Status Indians.

Many Status Indians live on **reserves**. They are exempt from paying income tax on money earned on the reserve and from paying property tax. Within the regulations established by the federal government and the Indian Act, the band councils on the reserves have limited jurisdiction over community matters.

Métis are people of mixed Indian and European ancestry. They are often described as the forgotten people and as the most dispossessed aboriginal people in Canada. In spite of the significant role Métis have played in Canadian history, they have no official status. Today they seek equal treatment with other aboriginal peoples, includ-

ing settlement of land claims and equal funding. They also want the same rights to hunt, fish, and trap as other aboriginal peoples.

15 Research the Indian Act. What rights are guaranteed to Status Indians?

16 Métis representatives have been negotiating with the federal government in constitutional talks. Find out what progress has been made in realizing the goals of Métis.

Social and economic conditions on Indian reserves

Many Status Indians living on reserves try to preserve the traditional ways. Yet they are faced with many social and economic challenges.

Demographics

The **infant mortality rate**—that is, the rate of death of children under one year— has declined from 18.2/1000 in 1985 to 12/1000 in 1993. While this is an improvement, it is still almost twice the rate in the rest of Canada—6.8/1000.

Life expectancy has also improved. Although it is still less than the Canadian average, the gap has narrowed since 1975. (See Figure 14.6 on page 296.) However, deaths from unnatural causes, such as accidents, suicides, and homicides, are much higher than the national average.

Between 6 and 7 per cent of the Indian population is over the age of fifty-five; in the total Canadian population, the figure is 21 per cent. Over 38 per cent of the Indian population is under the age of

TYPE	DEFINITION	POPULATION	LOCATION (% of population)	LANGUAGE (% of population)
STATUS INDIAN	Registered Indians under the Indian Act. Special rights guaranteed by the federal government. Most receive government aid.	573 657 (303 898 on reserves)	2 250 reserves for 607 bands on 26 525 km² Prairies 38.6 Ontario 24.0 BC 18.5	Native 46.6 English 46.4 French 1.8
NON-STATUS INDIAN	Those not registered under the Indian Act. Do not have rights or obligations under the act. Groups may not have signed treaties.	167 113	Ontario 34.7 BC 25.4 Prairies 24.7	Native 9.5 English 79.5 French 6.6
MÉTIS	Those of mixed aboriginal/non-aboriginal blood. Have no rights or obligations under the Indian Act.	212 650	Prairies 66.2 6 out of 10 live in urban areas	Native 13.9 English 75.0 French 8.9
INUIT	Native peoples of Canadian Arctic	49 255	NT 63.0 Northern Quebec 19.2 (Mostly on bays, river mouths, inlets, and fiords)	Native 74.1 (Inuktituk) English 24.2 French 0.9

Source: Adapted from Statistics Canada and the Department of Indian and Northern Affairs Canada, 1995.

Figure 14.4 Categories of Native people in Canada
a) What is the total number of Native peoples in Canada?
b) The population of Canada in 1994 was 29 248 000. What percentage of the population is Native?
c) Calculate the percentage of the total number of Native peoples in each category.

Figure 14.5
Status Indian population by region, 1994
a) Which province has the largest Indian population?
b) Which region has the largest Indian population?

REGION	BANDS	ON RESERVE	ON CROWN LAND	OFF RESERVE POPULATION	TOTAL
Atlantic Canada	31	14 910	7	7 463	22 380
Quebec	39	38 269	1 129	16 450	55 848
Ontario	126	63 950	2 271	63 928	130 149
Manitoba	61	56 744	1 622	29 795	88 161
Saskatchewan	70	45 060	1 538	42 259	88 857
Alberta	43	44 528	2 209	24 560	71 297
British Columbia	196	50 480	345	45 983	96 808
Yukon	16	666	3 010	3 272	6 948
NT	25	236	9 669	3 304	13 209
Canada	**607**	**314 843**	**21 800**	**237 014**	**573 657**

Source: *Indian Register by Population.* Indian and Northern Affairs Canada, 1995.

fifteen, compared with 21 per cent of the total Canadian population.

Housing

Housing on many reserves is often substandard. Many of these homes are prefabricated units of less than 90 m². Often there is only one bedroom for a family of five or more people. Families living in overcrowded conditions are placed on a waiting list for more suitable housing. But some of these waiting lists are reported to be as long as ten years. The federal government has allocated more and more funds to building and improving housing on reserves. But it has not been enough to keep up with demand. The rising birth rate and the return to reserves means the populations on reserves are increasing faster than housing problems can be resolved.

Education

There have been dramatic improvements in education. Native councils are assuming more control of schools on reserves. The number of band-operated schools has risen from 262 in 1988 to 372 in 1994. There are more aboriginal teachers teaching Native languages, culture, and values. The result has been a steady increase in the number of students on reserves that stay in school.

The number of Indians enrolled in colleges and universities has increased from

Figure 14.6
Life expectancy (years)

	STATUS INDIANS		TOTAL CANADIAN	
	MALE	FEMALE	MALE	FEMALE
1975	59.2	65.9	70.2	77.3
1980	60.9	68.0	71.7	78.9
1985	63.9	71.0	72.8	79.6
1990	66.9	74.0	73.2	80.3
1995	69.1	76.2	74.0	81.0

Sources: Indian and Northern Affairs Canada and Statistics Canada, 1995.

	TOTAL HOUSING ON RESERVES	ADEQUATE HOUSING	ADEQUATE WATER SUPPLY	ADEQUATE SEWAGE DISPOSAL
1988	58 756	24 702	49 951	43 793
1994	73 683	33 665	67 826	63 069

Adequate housing: housing that does not require renovation
Adequate water supply: water delivered to a housing unit through pipes, wells, trucks, etc.
Adequate sewage disposal: piped connections to septic systems, main drains, treatment plants, etc.

Figure 14.7
Housing on reserves

14 242 in 1988 to 23 388 in 1994. Many universities now offer Native studies programs. The federal Postsecondary Student Support Program provides tuition as well as travel and living expenses for aboriginal students for the first four years of postsecondary education. The funding program has allowed more Native peoples to seek careers in professional occupations. Yet there is still a need for greater access to postsecondary education for all aboriginal peoples. In addition, the number of Native teachers and language and cultural programs must be increased to reflect enrolment of aboriginal students.

Employment

Many Indians living on reserves have tried to maintain their traditional ways. But this has often been difficult. Much of the reserve lands are unsuitable for hunting, fishing, and trapping. The growth of anti-trapping and animal rights movements has also hurt the economy. The drastic drop in demand for animal furs means that aboriginal peoples are no longer able to earn a living in the fur trade. In many remote communities, there are few other opportunities for work. Some people earn a living fishing or making crafts; others work as firefighters in the battle against the forest fires that rage each summer. But much of this work is seasonal. The result is underemployment or unemployment. The lack of an economic base on

Figure 14.8
A student in a surveying class in Yellowknife

	STATUS INDIANS		TOTAL CANADIAN	
	MALE	FEMALE	MALE	FEMALE
	(%)		(%)	
1971	48.7	22.5	77.3	39.4
1981	50.6	27.8	75.4	48.9
1991	54.9	38.5	74.8	58.2

Figure 14.9
Employment over the age of 15

Figure 14.10
A young boy performs traditional Inuit drumming

which to support themselves means that many Native people are forced to rely on government assistance.

Economic conditions are better on reserves that have developed nontraditional industries, such as resource development, manufacturing, and tourism. In northwest Alberta, for example, the Dene Tha band formed a construction company to meet the needs of the Norman Wells oil field and pipeline project. In Saskatchewan, Indian bands own and operate over 700 businesses: Kitsaki Industries in Prince Albert manufactures saw and pulp logs; J-Sid Manufacturing makes canvas products; and Northland Processors produces smoked meat. Over 800 businesses are owned and operated by Native groups in Ontario. The Mohawks of the Bay of Quinte band manufacture jogging shoes for the Bata Shoe Company. The Batchewana band runs a 156 ha industrial park near Sault Ste. Marie. The Mount McKay ski area near Thunder Bay is owned and operated by the Fort William band. Walpole Industries, a tool and die company that supplies zinc and aluminum products for the auto industry, is operated by the Walpole Indian band in southwestern Ontario. More economic opportunities are developing as a result of the Canadian Aboriginal Economic Development Strategy. This is a partnership between the federal government and aboriginal communities to improve the economic well being of aboriginal peoples.

17 a) Which three issues affecting the social and economic conditions on reserves do you think the government should give top priority?
b) Which social condition do you think is the most difficult to improve? Explain your answer.

18 Create the front page of a brochure for the Department of Indian and Northern Affairs. The purpose of the brochure is to heighten public awareness of industries owned by aboriginal peoples.

Case study: Inkameep Vineyards

In the early 1960s, life for the Osoyoos Indian Band was an uncertain one. They lived near the town of Oliver in the southern Okanagan Valley in British Columbia. There was little local employment. The adults worked across the US border at Oroville and Omak in Washington state, a southern extension of the Okanagan Valley. They worked in the orchards, pruning and picking fruit until the fall. After the harvest, they returned to their reserve, where they spent the winter hunting and fishing. The elders of the band stayed on the reserve year-round, spending most of their time hunting, fishing, and growing vegetables.

The incomes of the Osoyoos were very low and seasonal. Most lived at the subsistence level—that is, all of the money they earned was spent on necessities. Luxuries were scarce. A few families had a television, but there were no cars. The people lived in large, extended family units, with lots of relatives under one roof. Housing conditions were generally poor.

In the late 1960s, two projects helped the Osoyoos. BC Hydro hired band members to work on the construction of power lines through the reserve. The South Okanagan Land District built a canal in the area and hired local labour. The income from these projects helped to ease the financial problems for the short term, but had little long-term benefit.

The real turning point came when Andres Wines contracted to build a vineyard near the reserve. Many band members offered to work two days a week at the vineyard for free in order to learn the craft of growing grapes. The rest of the week they worked preparing their own land to become a vineyard. This included supplying water by hand until an irrigation system was built.

In order to keep the workforce on the reserve, the Department of Indian and Northern Affairs set up a payroll system. This provided band members with a steady income year-round. Gradually the band members' hard work paid off and Inkameep Vineyards was born.

Today Inkameep Vineyards Ltd. is run by the board of directors and the general manager, Sam Baptiste. The band's population has grown since the vineyard was established. Today it is just under 200. The population is stable year-round as the reserve has become an attractive place to live. The majority of people live in modern subdivision-type homes and 90 per cent of families have a car. The average family size is also smaller than in the past.

The vineyard's success can be traced back to 1976. In the early 1970s, most of the grapes grown in the struggling vineyard were French hybrids. They grew easily in the sandy soil and could survive the harsh winters. But competition from other Canadian and Californian wine producers inspired Inkameep to develop a premium-quality Canadian wine. Since the climate is similar to wine-growing regions in Germany, Inkameep decided to import 85 000 pure vinifera grape plants to produce an international-quality wine. These vines produce quality grapes for a considerable period of time. But specialized skills were needed to grow this particular variety. In addition, the project required government loans and grants of $2 million. The Osoyoos also received government funds to train band members in agricultural science and management.

Today the vineyard farms 95 ha of vines. Alfalfa and fruit trees are grown on another 20 ha of land that are considered unsuitable for vineyards. In 1995, there was an abundant crop yield of over 12 500 kg of grapes per hectare. Once harvested, most of the grapes are crushed on site. Twenty-five per cent of the juice is shipped by tanker truck to Andres Wines at Port Moody, some eight hours away; the rest is shipped to markets across North America.

Today the vineyard is prosperous. Inkameep employs about 20 people for pruning and 100 people for harvesting. Most of the part-time harvesters live in British Columbia. The company maintains a hiring policy that gives preference to band members and other Native peoples living on the reserve. Even though there are now job opportunities off the reserve, most Osoyoos prefer to stay and work for Inkameep.

Today Inkameep produces premium wines that can compete with the highest quality wines anywhere. Many observers believe that Inkameep will play an important role in the future of the Canadian wine industry.

19 Using the gazetteer in an atlas, locate Oliver, British Columbia.
   a) Describe the relative location of Oliver—that is, its location relative to other places, such as physical landforms and towns.
   b) Using the climate map in an atlas, describe the temperature and precipita-

tion patterns for Oliver. What climate factors influence these patterns?

20 a) Compare the social conditions of Indians described in the text with the conditions experienced by the Osoyoos before the development of the vineyard.
   b) Describe two significant events that improved the economic and social conditions for the Osoyoos.

21 Imagine that you were a visitor to the Osoyoos reserve in 1960. You are making a return visit to the reserve today. Describe the major changes you would observe.

The Royal Commission on Aboriginal Peoples

In 1992, the Royal Commission on Aboriginal Peoples held its first round of hearings. Between April and June, the commission conducted meetings across the country. Aboriginal and non-aboriginal peoples were invited to voice their concerns and to offer solutions to the problems experienced in Native communities. The hearings laid the foundation for future changes in the relationship between aboriginal and non-aboriginal peoples in Canada.

The concerns and solutions of aboriginal groups varied, depending on factors such as history, language, status, and location. However, there was a common foundation: that aboriginal history and traditions lie in their relationship with the environment, and that this relationship must be central to a new relationship with non-aboriginal society. The commission recommended that concern for the survival of aboriginal culture, language, and spirituality should be reflected in all future developments in health, education, and other services, and that these services should be provided by aboriginal peoples.

22 A meeting has been arranged between two representatives of Canada's aboriginal peoples and two federal officials responsible for aboriginal affairs. They are to discuss the current social and economic status of aboriginal peoples in Canada. Their objective is to reach an agreement on how social, economic, and health conditions can be improved within the framework recommended by the Royal Commission on Aboriginal Peoples.
  a) Form groups of four students. Decide which two students will represent the aboriginal peoples and which two will represent the government. Before conducting the mock meeting, each pair should discuss their opinions and the positions they will take.

b) Once both sides are prepared, begin your meeting. Assume a further allocation of $500 million will be made from the federal government to aboriginal development over the next five years. Make a group decision as to how this money will be allocated. Share your results with other groups.

Aboriginal land claims

Traditionally, aboriginal groups have not had a united voice. This was largely due to the diversity of Native cultural groups. In recent years, however, Native groups have joined together to create a more powerful force for aboriginal rights, land claims, and self-government.

Native land claims are based on aboriginal title to land a group may have traditionally occupied. The Canadian government will consider a land claim providing the aboriginal group can prove:

Figure 14.11 Land claims under negotiation, 1996

AREA	GROUP	POPULATION
208 857 km² in NT (North Slave region)	Dogrib (Métis and Dene)	4300
Offshore islands, Labrador, and Quebec	Inuit of northern Quebec	7500
Coastline, interior, and offshore of northern Labrador	Labrador Inuit Association	4000
Central Labrador and northern Quebec	Innu	1500

- that it was and still is an organized society;
- that it alone has occupied the territory since before European settlement;
- that to some degree the land is used for traditional purposes;
- that it has never entered into a treaty affecting rights to the land and its resources;
- that it has never given up its legal aboriginal title to the land.

The first major land claim settlement was in 1975. It gave Cree Indians and Inuit in northern Quebec exclusive use of 13 696 km^2 of land, together with $267.5 million in cash and a further $226.3 million in additional programs. Another four land settlements were reached in 1989. These gave full or partial control over 600 000 km^2 to Native peoples and traditional land-use rights on another 1 200 000 km^2. This was accompanied by a cash payment of $1.5 billion. In 1990, the Dene and Métis of the western Arctic were awarded 18 per cent of the land in the region in addition to subsurface mineral rights and compensation of $500 million. In February 1996, the Nisga'a in northern British Columbia reached a tentative land settlement in which they would receive 2000 km^2 and $200 million. The deal also includes fishing rights and limited self-government. Other land claims being negotiated are outlined in Figure 14.11.

A new territory

On 1 April 1999, a new territory will be created in Canada—**Nunavut** (Inuktitut for "our land"). Nunavut includes the central and eastern parts of the Northwest Territories—a total of 1 916 602 km^2. This represents the largest land claim settlement in Canadian history. The 17 500 Inuit who live in the region make up 80 per cent of the population. In their agreement with the federal government, they will have direct ownership of 350 000 km^2 of the new territory—about 18 per cent of the total. (See Figure 14.12.) The rest of Nunavut will remain under the control of the federal government.

Within their specific land area, the Inuit will have guaranteed rights over wildlife and the harvesting of resources as well as policies for the protection of the environment. Resource development in Nunavut must now take Native interests into account. In addition, the Inuit will receive a financial settlement of $1.14 billion, to be paid over fourteen years. The Inuit will have greater authority in education, health, and social services. In return, they have agreed to give up any further land claims within Nunavut. The creation of Nunavut marks the first time that the work, culture, and government of any Canadian province or territory will represent the interests of an aboriginal group.

23 a) **What are some of the advantages for the Inuit in having greater authority in the administration of Nunavut?**
   b) **What are some of the challenges facing the new territorial government?**
   c) **Should the creation of Nunavut be the first step towards the territory becoming a province? Give reasons for your answer.**

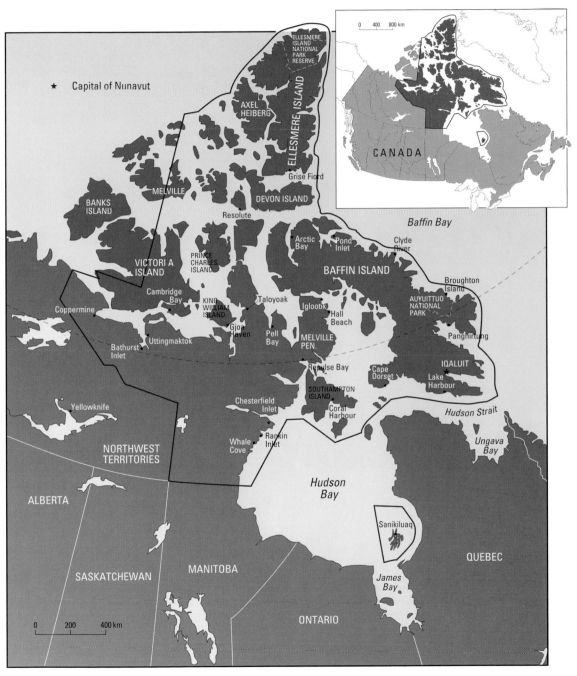

★ Capital of Nunavut

ELLESMERE ISLAND NATIONAL PARK RESERVE

AXEL HEIBERG

ELLESMERE ISLAND

Grise Fiord

MELVILLE

DEVON ISLAND

BANKS ISLAND

Resolute

Baffin Bay

VICTORIA ISLAND

PRINCE CHARLES ISLAND

Arctic Bay

Pond Inlet

Clyde River

BAFFIN ISLAND

Broughton Island

Cambridge Bay

KING WILLIAM ISLAND

Taloyoak

Iglootik

Hall Beach

AUYUITTUO NATIONAL PARK

Coppermine

Gjoa Haven

Pell Bay

MELVILLE PEN.

Panghirtung

Uttingmaktok

Bathurst Inlet

Repulse Bay

Cape Dorset

IQALUIT

Lake Harbour

Yellowknife

SOUTHAMPTON ISLAND

Chesterfield Inlet

Coral Harbour

Hudson Strait

Ungava Bay

NORTHWEST TERRITORIES

Whale Cove

Rankin Inlet

ALBERTA

Hudson Bay

Sanikiluaq

SASKATCHEWAN

MANITOBA

QUEBEC

James Bay

ONTARIO

0   200   400 km

CANADA

0 400 800 km

Figure 14.12
The territory of Nunavut

Unit 5

URBAN CANADA

The real Canadian scene is a cityscape: smooth pavements and squared-off walls, crowds of people at lunch-time, flowing night-time expressways....Canadians and their activities are becoming more and more concentrated in a hundred or so urban areas which occupy less than one per cent of the land area.

James and Robert Simmons, *urban canada*, 2nd edition

Big Town by Janet Mitchell/Courtesy Masters Gallery, Calgary

The term **urban** refers to cities and towns. An urban environment contains all the things we associate with city life—office buildings, high-rise apartments, single-family homes, shopping malls, theatres, restaurants, and a network of busy roads. At one time, all urban areas were **rural**. First they were in their natural state, covered by forests and grasslands. Later, these areas may have been developed for agriculture. Eventually, the cities took over these sites. As today's urban centres expand, they continue to encroach on the rural landscape that surrounds them.

     Urbanization describes the process in which an area is transformed from rural to urban. As towns and cities expand, the amount of quality farmland that surrounds them shrinks. As urbanization takes place, it is sometimes difficult to determine whether the edges of the towns and cities are rural or urban. This area is called the **urban fringe**.

Figures 15.1
A variety of urban and rural settings

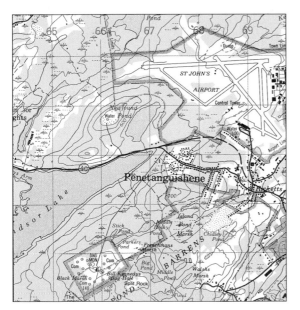

Defining urban

How do we define what is urban? Each
country has its own definition. In some
countries, the term urban may apply only to
large centres; in others, it may include small
communities. In the United States, for
example, a community must have a population of at least 2500 to be classified as urban.
In Nigeria, the figure is 5000. In Japan, it
takes 30 000 people to create an urban community. But in Denmark, it takes only 200!

Statistics Canada classifies urban as
any community of 1000 people or more, or
any place in which the population density
is at least 1000 people per 1.6 km^2. Under
these guidelines, even large villages or
small towns are considered urban. So is a
rural area if 1000 people live within an area

Figure 15.2
Rural-urban population growth in Canada, 1891-1994

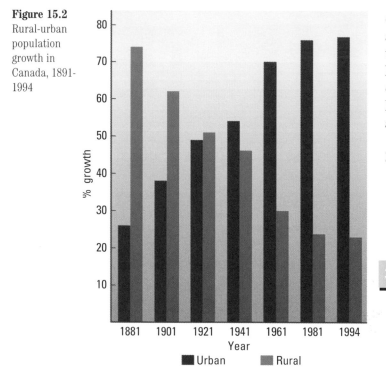

of 1.6 km^2. Sometimes, of course, urban areas are huge and sprawling. The largest type of urban centre in Canada is a **Census Metropolitan Area**, or **CMA**. This is a city and its surrounding area with a population of 100 000 or more. In Canada, there are twenty-five CMAs.

2   a) Why do you think there are different definitions of urban in different countries?
    b) What do you think is a reasonable definition of urban? Give reasons for your answer.

3   a) Using the information in Figures 15.2, 15.3, and 15.4, write a statement summarizing urban growth in Canada.
    b) What do you think the trend in urban growth will be twenty years from now? Give reasons to support your answer.

Figure 15.3

Percentage of population in urban areas by province, 1911–1991

a) Which three provinces had the highest percentage of urban population in 1991? Which three provinces had the lowest percentage?
b) Which provinces became more urbanized between 1971 and 1991? Which provinces became less urbanized?

PROVINCE	1911	1931	1951	1971	1991
British Columbia	50.9	62.3	68.6	75.7	80.5
Alberta	29.4	31.8	47.6	73.5	79.8
Saskatchewan	16.1	20.3	30.4	53.0	63.0
Manitoba	39.3	45.2	56.0	69.5	72.1
Ontario	49.2	63.1	72.5	82.4	81.8
Quebec	44.5	59.2	66.8	80.6	77.6
New Brunswick	26.7	35.4	42.8	56.9	47.7
Nova Scotia	36.7	46.3	54.5	56.7	53.5
Prince Edward Island	16.0	19.5	25.1	38.3	39.9
Newfoundland	-	-	43.3	57.2	53.6

Source: Statistics Canada, Cat. No. 93-301, 1995.

4 a) On an outline map of Canada, indicate the location of each city in Figure 15.4 using a bar 5 mm in width. The base of the bar should be at the actual location of the CMA. Use a vertical scale of 3 mm for every 100 000 population.
   b) Estimate the population of the current five largest metropolitan areas in the year 2011. To do this, calculate the actual growth in population for the twenty-year period between 1971 and 1991. For example, Edmonton grew by 362 000.

Divide this number by the population in 1971 (495 000), then multiply the answer by 100. This will produce a percentage growth figure for the twenty-year period. (For Edmonton it is 73 per cent.) Let's assume that Edmonton will grow by another 73 per cent between 1991 and 2011. Calculate 73 per cent of the 1991 population (625 000); add this to the 1991 population. This gives an estimated population for Edmonton in 2011 of 1 482 000.

CITY	1961	1971	1981	1991	1994
			(000s)		
Toronto	1 919	2 628	2 998	4 040	4 282
Montreal	2 215	2 743	2 828	3 215	3 322
Vancouver	826	1 082	1 268	1 649	1 775
Ottawa-Hull	457	602	718	953	1 010
Edmonton	359	495	656	857	889
Calgary	279	403	592	754	815
Quebec	379	480	576	646	684
Winnipeg	476	540	584	652	681
Hamilton	401	498	542	600	640
London	226	286	283	382	410
Kitchener-Waterloo	154	226	287	356	385
St. Catharines-Niagara Falls	257	303	304	365	384
Halifax	193	222	277	321	339
Victoria	155	195	233	288	313
Windsor	217	258	246	262	279
Oshawa	na	120	154	240	266
Saskatoon	95	126	154	210	219
Regina	113	140	164	192	199
St. John's	106	131	154	172	178
Sudbury	127	155	149	158	166

Figure 15.4
Population of the top 20 Census Metropolitan Areas, 1961–1994

Source: Statistics Canada, Cat. No. 91-213, 1995.

From rural to urban

Often people in other countries think of Canada as a land of lush forests, sparkling lakes, towering mountains, and vast prairies. They may not always think of the hustle and bustle of thriving cities like Toronto, Vancouver, and Montreal. But the reality is that Canada is an urban nation. Most Canadians today live and work in cities. But this was not always the case. For decades, Canadians lived off the land farming and harvesting the country's abundant natural resources. How did Canada change from a rural country to an urban one? What factors led to the creation of urban communities?

Early settlement in Canada

Most early pioneers in North America emigrated from Europe. Some were farmers who were lured overseas by the promise of greater opportunities in a vast land of rich, fertile soil. They arrived with the hope that their knowledge and experience would help them start a prosperous new life. Others abandoned the growing industrial towns of western Europe where they worked long hours for little pay. These newcomers looked to Canada for an opportunity to escape the harsh poverty of Europe's growing urban centres.

When these early settlers arrived in Canada, their first task was to establish roots in a place that would enable them to fulfil their dreams. What factors influenced these settlers in establishing their communities? Let's see what choices we might have made if we had been settlers in the early 1800s.

Simulation: a site game

It is the early 1800s. A group of settlers are trekking across the land that will one day be known as Canada. They have left their homelands for many reasons, including poverty, overcrowding, and war. They have been lured to this distant land by the promise of new opportunities for a better life.

The settlers

The settlers consist of thirty-five people from six families. The group includes:

- *A farming family:* The husband and wife have five children. They have left a small farm in Europe where they grew wheat and kept a small dairy herd. They dream of owning a large wheat farm and raising some livestock.
- *A fishing family:* This couple has three children. The husband fished with his father in their homeland. His dream is to own his own fishing boat.
- *A trader:* This man worked in a small European town, trading in the new machinery that was being mass produced in the Industrial Revolution. Although business was good, he dreamed of better possibilities. His sister, a seamstress, decided to join him.
- *A miner:* This mining prospector believed his knowledge would lead him to rich mineral deposits. He decided to move with his wife and six children in search of this wealth.
- *A woodcutter/carpenter:* This husband and wife have four children. They believe they can find security in a land covered with vast forests. His skills will be useful to the settlers building their homes.

- *A weaver:* This couple is looking for an opportunity to start a small business. With a growing population, there will be the need for a clothing industry. They have five children.

With such a long journey ahead, the settlers were forced to leave home with few belongings. Their most valued possessions are the tools of their trades, which they will need once they are settled. On the east coast, they purchase wagons for their journey overland. The trip takes its toll, however. The woodcutter's wagon is lost when the axle is damaged; the family must split up and ride with other families in their wagons. Later a lame horse has to be destroyed. As the weather begins to turn colder, the settlers' situation is becoming desperate. They must find a suitable place to establish their roots!

The settlers are looking for a place that will help each family realize its dreams and ambitions. Their first priority is to ensure that they can fulfil the basic needs of food, water, and shelter. Safety is another factor. They cannot afford to lose any members of the group in this unfamiliar and untamed land. They also need a source of power to fuel their businesses as well as to heat their homes. They need a location that offers transportation routes, which will allow them to trade with other communities. They agree that the minimum amount of land they need to establish their settlement is 1 km².

5 Form groups of six students. Have each member of the group represent one of the families. Make a list of the settlers' common needs. Then add the personal needs of your family to the list. For example, the weaver needs a place with fast-running water to power a mill that can make cloth. Areas for the grazing of sheep would help in the supply of wool.

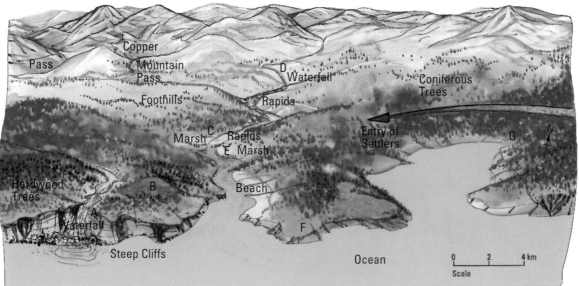

Figure 15.5
The settlers' situation

Figure 15.6
Site selection
organizer

	ALTERNATIVES		
	?	?	?
Safety			
Food			
Shelter			
Freshwater			
Power			
Trade			
Personal needs			

6 a) Figure 15.5 shows the general area, or **situation**, the settlers have reached. Describe the main features of this situation.
   b) Possible locations, or **sites**, for the settlers' community are indicated by the letters A to G. Review each site from your family's point of view. Select three possible sites that suit your family's needs. Enter the appropriate letters under Alternatives in a decision-making chart like the one in Figure 15.6.
   c) Now you must choose the best site for your family. For each criteria listed in the left column of the organizer, score each alternative site as most suitable (3), suitable (2), or least suitable (1). Add the total score for each site. Which one emerged as the most suitable site for your family?

Wait! Before you commit yourself, review the alternatives again. Are there any other important criteria *not* consid-ered here that might have affected the out-come? If so, now is the time to reconsider your decision!

7 Once you are satisfied with your site selection, discuss your choice with your group members. If all members of the group have selected the same site, chances are you have chosen the best location. If there is disagreement, howev-er, you must repeat the decision-making process. Sometimes individual needs are not in the best interests of the community as a whole. This time consider the needs of the group instead of those of your indi-vidual family. Try to reach a **consensus** and select a site on which everyone agrees.

8 This site game gave you the opportunity to follow a decision-making process. This process helps us to make informed deci-sions rather than educated guesses. List the steps in the decision-making process in the site game.

9 Congratulations! Your settlement has grown into a city of 20 000 people today.
   a) Draw an outline of the map in Figure 15.5. Include physical features such as rivers, mountains, etc.
   b) Draw where you believe the city of the 1990s would be situated. You will need 1 km^2 for every 2000 people.
   c) Remember that a city of 20 000 people will contain roads, rail lines, and bridges and industrial, commercial, and residential areas. Keeping in mind the needs of a modern community of 20 000 people, what problems might there be

with your site? (For example, a city located on a waterfront limits the direction in which development may take place. The city is forced to stretch out, which means a greater commuting distance between the outskirts of the city and the city centre.)

d) Do you think the present-day population would be content with the site you chose? Give reasons for your answer.

Site selection

It is hard to imagine that today's modern Canadian cities are the result of the kinds of decisions you made in the site game. But it's true! The needs of the settlers were matched to the advantages of a particular site. If their most important need was water for transportation, they looked for a site next to a river or lake. Figure 15.8 lists the factors that may influence site selection.

Figure 15.7
Identifying the advantages of a site
Identify and describe the site advantages in each of these communities.

1 Defence: An elevated location or an island is easily defended.

2 A junction: An area where a number of routes meet at a mountain pass or a river crossing serves as an important junction.

3 A resource base: An area that has a valuable resource such as minerals or forests will attract related industries.

4 Trade: A point where rivers meet is a good place to trade with travellers.

5 Transportation: The mouth of a river, a lakehead, or the coastline are locations where goods can be transported to other destinations.

6 Scenic location: A location of particular scenic beauty will attract people.

7 Port facilities: A deep harbour in a sheltered bay makes an excellent port.

8 Service centre: A central position in a large agricultural region is a good location for an agricultural service centre.

10 Copy Figure 15.9 into your notebook. Working with an atlas, match one site-selection factor in Figure 15.8 to each city. The same reason can be used for more than one city.

11 Conduct your own research into the community in which you live. Determine the main advantages that this site provided.

Case study: St. John's

The premier city of Newfoundland is St. John's. The site of Canada's most easterly provincial capital has served the city well. St. John's is located on the eastern edge of Newfoundland's main island, adjacent to what are potentially some of the most productive fishing grounds in the world. It has a

CITY	REASON #
Niagara Falls, ON	(#6) A location of particular scenic beauty
Halifax, NS	
Calgary, AB	
Thunder Bay, ON	
Regina, SK	
Winnipeg, MB	
Sudbury, ON	
Vancouver, BC	
Thompson, MB	
Montreal, PQ	
Kingston, ON	
St. John's, NF	

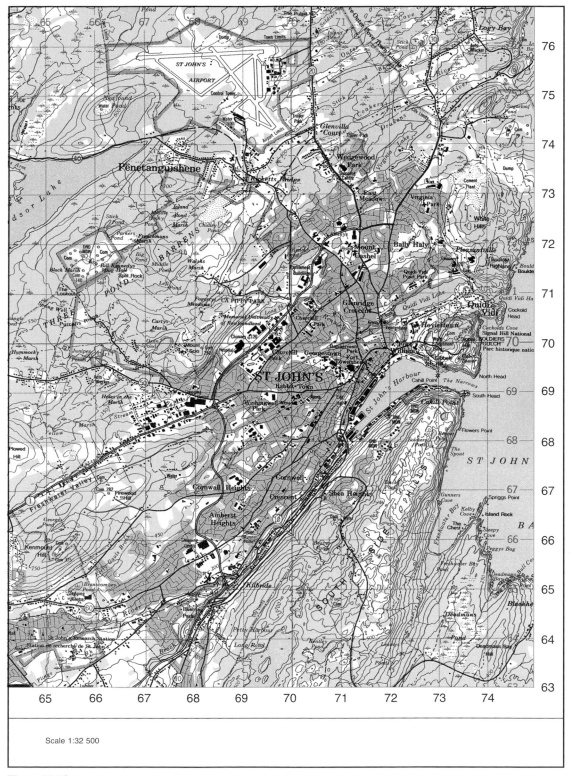

Figure 15.10
Topographic map of St. John's

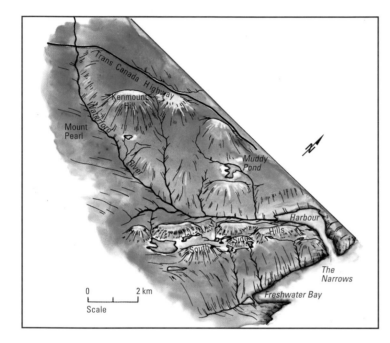

0   2 km
Scale

Figure 15.11
Sketch of site
of St. John's

South Side Hills. These are steeper than the land to the north, so development has been limited.

While the fishing industry has played a significant role in the development of St. John's, the city has other resources that help to diversify its economy. In recent years, St. John's has become a service centre for the exploration and development of offshore oil and gas deposits. Yet the city retains its distinctive Atlantic maritime character, with its steep, winding streets, colourful buildings, and busy harbour. The unique characteristics of St. John's make it an intriguing tourist destination.

12 a) Using Figure 15.10, identify the following features of St. John's: Signal Hill; South Side Hills; the container port; the Central Business District; the government facilities on the southeast side of the harbour.
   b) How have the hills surrounding St. John's influenced i) transportation (rail, road, air) and ii) urban growth?
   c) Why do most transportation facilities converge on the western edge of the harbour?

13 On a tracing-paper overlay on the topographic map of St. John's, sketch i) the coast, lakes, rivers, and harbour; ii) the extent of the built-up area; iii) the main transportation routes; iv) important features. Shade each section appropriately.

14 Assume you are a developer. Which sites would you suggest for future development in St. John's? Give reasons for your recommendations.

well-protected natural harbour, carved out of the surrounding hills of sandstone, shale, and slate. Usually ice-free year-round, the harbour makes St. John's an important trading port and a centre for both the local and transatlantic fishing industries.

The land to the north of the main harbour slopes upward towards a ridge. There it gently dips down to form a valley. Here is where most of the urban development has taken place as the city has spread back from the harbour. Development also extends to the southwest along the Waterford River, which flows from the west into the main harbour. It is believed that the river is responsible for cutting the channel through the sedimentary rocks into the Atlantic Ocean millions of years ago; the valley was later deepened by glaciers during the Ice Age. To the south of the harbour lie the

The growth of settlements

In the eighteenth and nineteenth centuries, Canada was primarily an agricultural country. Settlers cleared the forests for farmland. As more farms developed, scattered settlements began to emerge. Some of these eventually grew into villages where farmers could find a general store and the services of a blacksmith and a few other tradespeople. These **service centres** provided the farmers with their basic everyday needs. Travel to the village was either on foot or by horse, so trips were limited. Farmers usually attended to all of their business in the village in a single trip.

As the number and size of the villages grew, a few developed into larger towns. These served a greater area in the region and provided specialty items like stoves and ploughs that the local villages could not supply. Farmers had to travel greater distances to these towns, and the trips occurred less frequently than those to the local village.

As rural Canada gradually became more prosperous, incomes from farm sales increased. So, too, did the population. People began to demand expensive luxury items like radios! But people buy expensive goods much less frequently than other products. Few villages or towns could afford to stock these luxury items. They were found only in the cities where the larger populations meant there was more demand. So farmers had to travel long distances to buy luxury goods.

Modern settlement patterns

The same pattern exists in communities across Canada today. We buy everyday items such as newspapers and bread from a local convenience store. These are called **low-order products**. To be profitable, stores specializing in low-order products must sell a variety of items. Because there is little profit to be made on inexpensive goods, a store must have a steady flow of regular customers. The number of regular shoppers needed to make a store profitable is called the store's **threshold population**. A small store selling low-order products needs about 200 families shopping at the store regularly to make a reasonable profit.

There are many products that we don't purchase on a daily or regular basis but that we still need from time to time. These might be such things as lightbulbs, batteries, or a new pair of socks! We are usually willing to travel a little further to buy these **middle-order products**. Because we buy them less often, a store selling middle-order products needs a larger threshold population than a store selling low-order products. Not every village has enough shoppers for a hardware store to operate profitably, for example. Therefore a larger community is needed to support businesses providing middle-order products.

But what about those expensive items that we buy infrequently, like cars or computers? Businesses specializing in these **high-order products** need a lot of customers to be profitable. When we buy one of these products, it may be years before we buy another one. Therefore high-order businesses need a large threshold population.

Figure 15.12
Products and services

15 a) Make a list of the things your family buys on a daily or weekly basis.
   b) How far do you travel to buy these things?
   c) In what kind of store do you purchase these items?
   d) Are these expensive or inexpensive items?

16 Refer to the products and services in Figure 15.12.
   a) Describe each product.
   b) How often would people buy each of these products?
   c) Indicate each item as a low-, middle-, or high-order product.

17 How would the threshold population for a store selling multi-media computer systems compare with that of a hardware store?

18 Copy Figure 15.13 into your notebook.
   a) Calculate the threshold population for a video store. To do this, add the total population of the six communities, then divide the sum by the total number of video stores. This figure is the average number of customers needed to run a profitable video store.
   b) For each community, calculate the population per store. (Divide the population by the number of stores.) Based on the threshold population, which community would be the best place to open a video store? Which would be the worst?
   c) What other factors might influence a decision about the location of a new store in an established community?

Figure 15.13
Threshold population for a video store

COMMUNITY	POPULATION	NUMBER OF STORES	POPULATION PER STORE
A	120 000	6	
B	80 000	5	
C	100 000	4	
D	60 000	4	
E	100 000	5	
F	160 000	5	

19 a) Using the Yellow Pages of your telephone directory, find one example each of a typical low-, middle-, or high-order product or service.
b) Count the number of places in your community that provide this product or service. If you live in a large urban centre, use your municipal boundaries or election ward as your community.
c) Divide the population of your community by the number of stores offering this product or service. This will establish the threshold population.
d) Use the addresses of these stores to plot their distribution on a map of your community. Use different colours to plot the low-, middle-, and high-order products and services.
e) Write a conclusion about the distances between places offering the same level of product or service.

20 Assume the role of an entrepreneur who wants to establish a fast-food franchise in your local community. Develop a list of considerations that need to be addressed before a final decision is made.

21 a) Develop an inventory of leisure and recreational activities which could be developed in your community. Base your decision on population as well as physical and cultural attractions.
b) Determine which activity has the greatest potential for success in your community.
c) Develop a tourist brochure to promote the activity you selected.

Community distribution

Most regions in Canada contain many small communities or villages, a fewer number of towns, and very few large urban centres. As we have seen, the villages provide low-order products and services, the towns offer a wider range of middle-order products and services, and major urban centres provide a variety of goods and services, including specialized products. This pattern of community distribution is called a **service hierarchy**. A hierarchy ranks things in order from largest to smallest. Figure 15.14 shows a community hierarchy, with one large metropolitan centre, four smaller cities, ten towns, and twenty-four villages. Figure 15.15 ranks communities by population.

Each service community has a **zone of influence**. This is the area from which

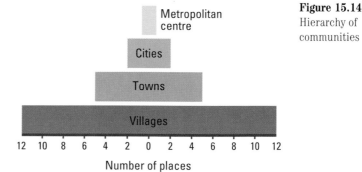

Figure 15.14
Hierarchy of communities

Metropolitan centre: over 100 000 people
City: between 10 000 and 100 000 people
Town: between 1000 and 10 000 people
Village: between 100 and 1000 people
Hamlet: less than 100 people

Figure 15.15
Community populations in Canada

Figure 15.16
Distribution of small communities in an agricultural region

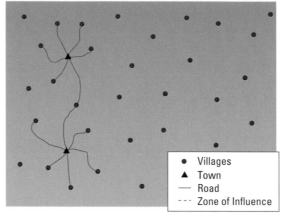

Legend:
- ● Villages
- ▲ Town
- — Road
- --- Zone of Influence

Figure 15.17
Distribution of settlements

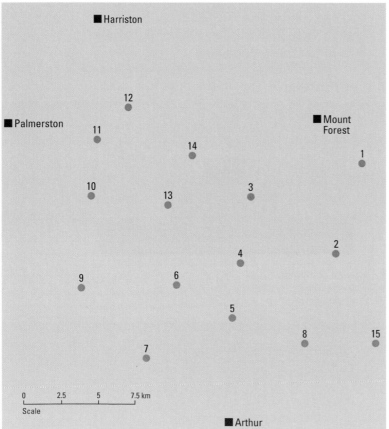

■ Harriston

■ Palmerston

12

■ Mount Forest

11

14

1

10

13

3

2

4

9

6

5

8   15

7

0   2.5   5   7.5 km
Scale

■ Arthur

the village, town, or city draws its customers. It is also the extent of the area that is influenced by newspapers, radio, and television that originate in a particular service centre. The extent of the zone of influence is proportional to the size of the community. The zone of influence for a village, for example, may be only 10 km, while the zone of influence for a major city may be more than 200 km.

22 Create a service hierarchy of communities within a 100 km radius of your own community. You will need a provincial road map and a compass. Use the scale on the map to draw the 100 km radius around your community. Use the legend to determine the size of the communities within this radius. Don't forget to include your own community in the hierarchy.

23 a) Figure 15.16 shows the distribution of small communities across a large agricultural region. Copy this figure onto a piece of paper. Notice that two of the villages have developed into towns. Decide which other villages will become towns. (Remember: Towns usually offer the same kinds of goods and services as one another, therefore you should keep them the same distance apart.) Mark the towns with a box and add the roads linking the towns and villages.
    b) Draw a broken line around the zone of influence for each town.

24 You are the manager of a rock band that is touring Canada. You would like to give as many Canadians as possi-

ble the opportunity to see your band. However, you can only include eight destinations in your concert schedule.

a) On an outline map of Canada, choose and label the locations where your band will perform. Shade the zone of influence around each centre; this is the area from which you will draw your audience. Give your map an appropriate title that includes the name of your band.

b) Explain your schedule using the terms *service centre* and *zone of influence*.

We have established that, in theory, we would expect to see many small towns providing low-order products and services and a few larger communities providing middle-order products and services. Now let's examine an area in southern Ontario to see if the distribution pattern of towns is really true in practice.

25 a) Copy Figure 15.18 into your notebook. Refer to Figure 15.17 to find the information for Column B. This map shows the distribution of settlements in an area of southern Ontario. Using the map scale, measure the distance between each village and its nearest neighbour. An example has been done for you.

b) Total the distances between all fifteen villages. Divide this figure by the total number of villages. Your answer will be the average distance between communities offering low-order products.

c) Now measure the distance between each of the four towns and complete Column B. Follow the process outlined in part b). Your answer will be the average distance between towns offering middle-order products and services.

	A VILLAGES	B DISTANCE TO NEAREST NEIGHBOUR (km)
1	Clare	6
2	Derrynane	
3	Riverstown	
4	Kenilworth	
5	Petherton	
6	Olivet	
7	Riverbank	
8	Gordonville	
9	Rothsay	
10	Teviotdale	
11	Cotswold	
12	Glenlee	
13	Wagram	
14	Farewell	
15	Stoneywood	
TOWNS		DISTANCE TO NEAREST TOWN (km)
Mount Forest		
Harriston		
Arthur		
Palmerston		

Figure 15.18 Distribution of settlements in southern Ontario

d) What evidence is there that some communities expand to offer more goods and services to a wider area?

Town-forming and town-serving activities

The sale of products and services contributes to the growth of a community. The income generated by businesses makes the community more prosperous. More jobs are created to provide the products and services a prosperous community demands. These employment opportunities encourage more people to move to the community, which contributes to a growing population. Any businesses that bring money into a community are called **town forming**. Consider a factory that manufactures farm equipment. The owner of the factory decides to locate in a rural community close to customers. Sales are brisk. Some of the money is paid out as wages to the factory employees. In turn, the employees spend their money on goods and services in the community. Many of Canada's large towns and cities have been created in part because they have successful town-forming businesses.

Jobs that do not attract new income to the community are called **town serving**. Instead of attracting new money, these businesses circulate the money that is already in the community. Fast-food restaurants are typical town-serving activities.

26 Make a list of jobs in your community that could be described as town forming.

27 You have just spent $10 at a fast-food restaurant. Describe how your money might be passed on to five other people in your community.

28 Classify each of the following jobs as either town forming or town serving: i) police officer; ii) school custodian; iii) oil refinery engineer; iv) long-distance truck driver; v) city hall clerk; vi) computer chip manufacturer.

29 Assume you are the business development officer for your community. Prepare a presentation, either oral or written, to attract town-forming businesses to your community. Include all the advantages in your community in your report. (You may have to do some research!)

Simulation: locating a shopping mall

We have seen that some villages grow to become towns. Some towns in turn expand to become cities. A similar pattern of distribution is evident *within* large urban centres themselves. Metropolitan areas have become so large that mini towns—in the form of shopping malls—have developed within them. Malls offer a variety of goods and services under one roof; in this way, they function much like a town. Urban centres also have villages and hamlets. The villages are represented by local shopping plazas, while convenience stores serve the same purpose as hamlets.

How are these urban towns, villages, and hamlets distributed? In most urban areas, there are too many convenience stores and shopping plazas to map and study their distribution patterns. So let's focus on the distribution of the largest centres—shopping malls—to see if they share a similar distribution pattern to towns and cities in a region.

Figure 15.19 shows the distribution of the twenty-five largest shopping malls in the **Greater Toronto Area (GTA)**. This region encompasses Metropolitan Toronto (the cities of Toronto, North York, Scarborough, Etobicoke, and York and the borough of East York) and the four regional municipalities of Durham, York, Peel, and Halton. Figure 15.20 shows the population density of this

Name	Address		Location	No. of Stores	No. of Parking Spaces	Floor Space (000s) (m²)
1. Eaton Centre	220	Yonge Street	Toronto	326	1050	160.3
2. Yorkdale Shopping Centre	3401	Dufferin Street	North York	247	6566	148.6
3. Square One	100	City Centre Drive	Mississauga	280	6300	128.0
4. Scarborough Town Centre	300	Borough Drive	Scarborough	221	5200	101.0
5. Oshawa Centre	419	King Street West	Oshawa	160	5966	101.0
6. Bramalea City Centre	25	Peel Centre Drive	Brampton	225	5025	97.9
7. Sherway Gardens	25	The West Mall	Etobicoke	242	5700	96.3
8. Upper Canada Mall	17600	Yonge Street	Newmarket	216	N/A	94.5
9. The Promenade		Bathurst Street & Highway 7	Vaughan	219	3595	83.9
10. Fairview Mall	1800	Sheppard Avenue East	North York	292	4250	83.2
11. Pickering Town Centre	1355	Kingston Road	Pickering	205	4166	74.5
12. Burlington Mall	777	Guelph Line	Burlington	106	3634	69.7
13. Erin Mills Town Centre	2700	Eglinton Avenue West	Mississauga	230	N/A	69.2
14. Centre Point Mall	6212	Yonge Street	North York	119	2204	61.8
15. Dixie Value Mall	1250	South Service Road	Mississauga	120	2100	61.6
16. Woodbine Shopping Centre	500	Rexdale Boulevard	Etobicoke	193	3424	60.1
17. Shoppers World	499	Main Street South	Brampton	211	4500	59.3
18. Oakville Place	240	Leighland Avenue	Oakville	108	2294	52.6
19. Dufferin Mall	900	Dufferin Street	Toronto	135	1800	52.2
20. Hillcrest Mall	9350	Yonge Street	Richmond Hill	110	3136	51.0
21. Don Mills Centre	939	Lawrence Avenue East	North York	130	2400	46.5
22. Eaton Sheridan Place	2225	Erin Mills Parkway	Mississauga	200	2000	46.5
23. Mapleview Mall	900	Maple Avenue	Burlington	N/A	N/A	46.0
24. Markville Mall	5000	Hwy 7	Markham	135	3009	45.5
25. Bayview Village	2901	Bayview Avenue	North York	114	2000	43.1

Figure 15.19
The 25 largest shopping malls in the Greater Toronto Area

Source: Metro Toronto Planning Department, *The Municipality of Metropolitan Toronto, Key Facts–1995.*

Halton Region
Peel Region
York Region
Durham Region
Metropolitan Toronto

Figure 15.20
Population
density in the
Greater
Toronto Area

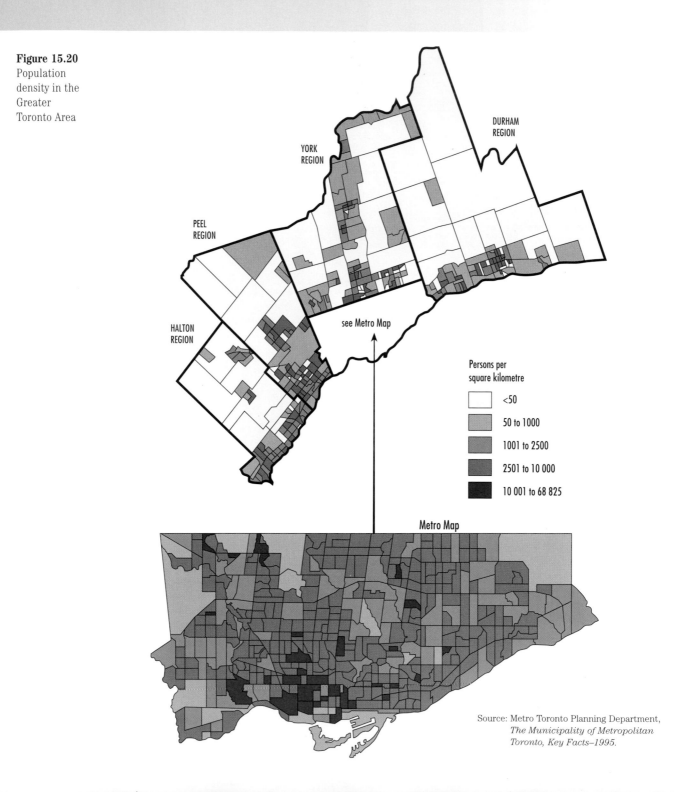

DURHAM
REGION

YORK
REGION

PEEL
REGION

HALTON
REGION

see Metro Map

Persons per
square kilometre

<50

50 to 1000

1001 to 2500

2501 to 10 000

10 001 to 68 825

Metro Map

Source: Metro Toronto Planning Department,
*The Municipality of Metropolitan
Toronto, Key Facts–1995.*

area and Figure 15.21 shows population in the GTA.

A major developer has asked your consulting firm to recommend the location of another shopping mall in the Greater Toronto Area.

30 a) Add together the total population of the municipalities. Divide this total by 25. The result represents the average number of people served by a single shopping mall—that is, its threshold population.
   b) Divide the population of each municipality by the number of shopping malls in that municipality. For example, in York Region there are four shopping malls (numbers 8, 9, 20, 24) and a population of 504 961. The average number of people per shopping mall is therefore 504 961 ÷ 4 = 126 240.
   c) Which municipalities have a higher than average population per shopping centre? Which have a lower than average population per shopping centre?
   d) Based on the information you have gathered, where would you recommend building a new shopping centre in the Greater Toronto Area? Give reasons for your choice.

31 A more accurate assessment of shopping malls would take into account the size of the shopping centres.
   a) Total the amount of floor space in all of the malls in the Greater Toronto Area.
   b) Divide the total population of the GTA by the total floor space. The result is the average shopping floor space per person. Repeat this exercise for each

MUNICIPALITY/REGION	POPULATION	% OF GTA
Toronto	635 395	15.0
York	140 525	3.3
East york	102 696	2.4
Scarborough	524 598	12.4
North York	562 564	13.3
Etobicoke	309 993	7.3
Total Metro	**2 275 771**	**53.7**
Durham	409 070	9.7
York	504 961	11.9
Peel	732 798	17.3
Halton	313 136	7.4
Total GTA	**4 235 736**	**100.0**

Figure 15.21 Population in the Greater Toronto Area

municipality. Which municipalities have higher than average shopping floor space per person? Which have lower than average shopping floor space per person?
   c) On an outline map, use a symbol to represent the location of shopping malls in each of the following categories: small—less than 70 000 m²; medium—70 000 – 100 000 m²; large—greater than 100 000 m². How might this information help to determine where a new shopping mall should be located?
   d) Based on this information, where would you locate the new shopping centre? Explain your answer.

32 An alternative to building a new shopping centre is to expand an existing one. Based on the information you have gathered, where would you recommend that expansion of an existing shopping mall take place?

The core and periphery

We have seen that the distribution pattern of large urban centres across Canada is an uneven one. Like many countries, Canada has a particular region with a large concentration of population clustered together in large towns and cities. This highly urbanized area is called the **core**. The regions beyond the core are called the **periphery**. The periphery is less densely populated than the core. While it may contain large cities, they are not usually clustered together as they are in the core.

FEATURES	CORE	PERIPHERY
1 Transportation (Network density? Accessibility?)		
2 Industry (Primary? Secondary? Tertiary? Quaternary?)		
3 Income levels		
4 Employment levels		
5 Population (Density? Average age?)		
6 Number of services (Hospitals? Schools? Entertainment?)		
7 Advantages for industry (Market? Labour supply? Services? Accessibility?)		

Most manufacturing takes place in the cities of the core. The periphery often supplies these industries with the raw materials they need. New businesses are usually attracted to the core because of its large market and the availability of supplies and services. The core also attracts many young people from the periphery because of the job opportunities it provides. As a result, the average age of people living in the core is usually lower than that of people living in the periphery.

On average, people living in the core tend to be wealthier. This is because there is less unemployment and higher incomes. Facilities in the core are more extensive than elsewhere. There are more universities and hospitals, for example, and extensive mass transit systems. Many of the national road, rail, and air traffic routes also focus on the core. They radiate from it like the spokes from the centre of a wheel.

The core is the financial centre of the country. As such, it contains the majority of corporate head offices. Because it has such a large population, the core also has many political representatives in the federal parliament. These factors give the core a lot of economic and political influence.

33 Copy Figure 15.22 into your notebook. For each feature, list the characteristics of the core and periphery.

34 What do you think might be the attitude of some people living in the periphery towards the core? Why?

Figure 15.22
Features of the core and periphery

The core and periphery in Canada

Is it possible to see the development of a core and surrounding periphery in Canada?

35 a) On an outline map of Canada, draw individual columns to represent each Census Metropolitan Area in Figure 15.23. The columns should be drawn at their geographic location on the map.

The height of the column should represent 3 mm for every 100 000 people. The width of the column should be 5 mm.

b) The dominant function of each CMA is the most important activity in that city. Choose a different colour to represent each of these functions. Shade each column according to the city's dominant function.

c) Can you identify an area with a concentration of CMAs in which manufacturing

CITY	1994 (000s)	MAIN FUNCTION
Toronto	4 282	Manufacturing
Montreal	3 322	Manufacturing
Vancouver	1 775	Transportation
Ottawa-Hull	1 010	Public administration
Edmonton	889	Public administration
Calgary	815	Extraction
Quebec	684	Public administration
Winnipeg	681	Manufacturing
Hamilton	640	Manufacturing
London	410	Manufacturing
Kitchener-Waterloo	385	Manufacturing
St Catharines-Niagara Falls	384	Manufacturing
Halifax	339	Public administration
Victoria	313	Public administration
Windsor	279	Manufacturing
Oshawa	266	Manufacturing
Saskatoon	219	Community services
Regina	199	Public administration
St. John's	178	Community services
Sudbury	166	Extraction

Source: Statistics Canada, Cat. No. 91-213, 1995.

Figure 15.23 Population and main function of the top 20 Census Metropolitan Areas

is the dominant function? Draw a line around this area.

When you completed activity 35, you probably drew a line around an area stretching 1150 km from Windsor, Ontario, to Quebec City, Quebec. This is called the **Windsor-Quebec City Axis**. It contains 60 per cent of Canada's population and 75 per cent of its manufacturing industry. Can the Windsor-Quebec City Axis be considered Canada's core?

36 a) What similarities are there between the Windsor-Quebec City Axis and what is usually described as the core? What differences are there?

b) Consider the dominant functions of the CMAs outside the Windsor-Quebec City Axis. To what extent do these cities reflect the characteristics of the periphery?

c) Based on this information, would you consider the Windsor-Quebec City Axis to be Canada's core? Give reasons to support your answer.

Urban Patterns

The towns and cities across Canada vary in size, shape, and character. The physical landscape, such as rivers, valleys, hills, and plains, has had a significant influence on these urban patterns. But these patterns are also the result of human factors, including history and economics. These patterns have not been created by chance. They are the result of thoughtful decisions about how land should be used.

1 Figure 16.1 shows six different growth patterns. Each has been influenced by the physical structure of the original site of the settlement. Describe the urban pattern of each community. What features of the surrounding landscape may have influenced each of these patterns?

A good way to analyse urban patterns is to view them from above. With today's technology, satellites enable us to get incredible pictures of the earth's surface from high in space. Electronic images are taken by a satellite that orbits the earth every 100 min at a distance of 900 km. The satellite transmits electronic signals to computers at the Canada Centre for Remote Sensing at Prince Albert, Saskatchewan. There the signals are transformed into photographic images.

Satellites can transmit information about entire cities or about areas as small as a backyard playground. These electronic devices can even collect ground information through cloud cover. Figure 16.2 on page 331 is a satellite image of Ottawa-Hull and its surrounding area. It clearly reveals the shape of our nation's capital and illustrates the physical features that have influenced the growth and development of Ottawa-Hull.

Satellite images enable geographers to observe the expansion of urban centres and the impact this growth has on the landscape and the environment. These images also help geographers map remote regions with greater accuracy than has ever been possible before. The information obtained by satellites can be digitally processed by computer **geographic information systems** (GIS). Different categories of information can be isolated, counted, and processed by computers as maps or graphs. This enables us to obtain valuable information about the earth's surface almost at our fingertips!

2 Study the satellite image of Ottawa-Hull in Figure 16.2.
   a) Describe this urban pattern. What physical and human features have influenced this pattern? Explain.
   b) What physical imprint reflects the influence of early French settlers?
   c) What time of the year was this image taken? How can you tell?

3 a) The satellite image of Ottawa-Hull shows a contact zone where two distinct landform regions meet. Find the contact zone on the satellite image, then locate this area in an atlas. What are these two landform regions?
   b) Name the waterways shown in the satellite image. In which direction is the water flowing? How do you know?

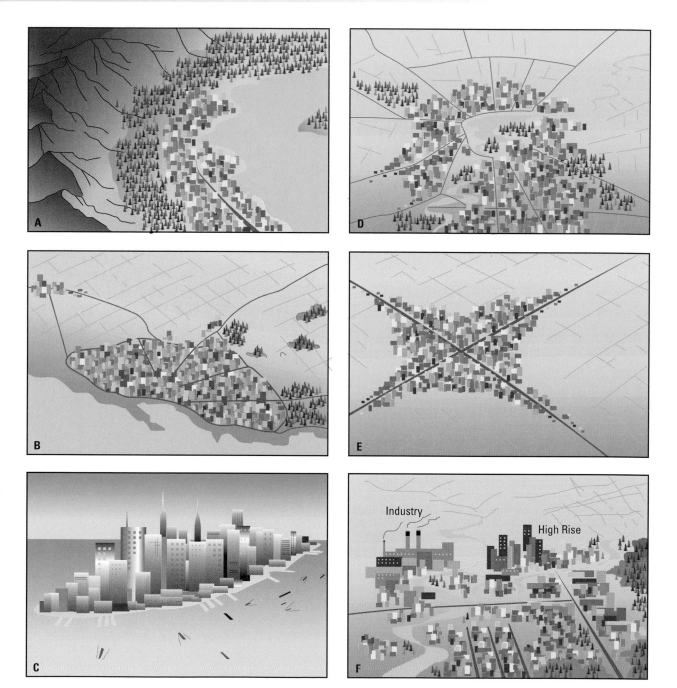

Figure 16.1
Urban growth patterns

Figure 16.2
A satellite image of Ottawa-Hull
This satellite image uses natural colour wave bands,
which depict the earth much as we see it.

4 Using a detailed map of Ottawa-Hull,
   locate the following features on the satel-
   lite image: the Rideau River and Canal;
   Gatineau Park; Parliament Hill; the Central
   Experimental Farm; the Green Belt; Ottawa
   International Airport.

   Infra-red satellite images are used to
observe and evaluate ground vegetation.
Healthy vegetation appears as dark red;
unhealthy vegetation appears much lighter.
Soils appear as turquoise. This kind of information is useful to geographers and scientists. It enables them to monitor the health
of forests, calculate the amount of wetlands
that provide habitats for unique wildlife,
and offer advice to farmers about crops.

5 Look at the infra-red satellite image of
   Ottawa-Hull in Figure 16.3.
   a) Why does the tree vegetation on the
      Shield north of Ottawa appear to be
      healthier than it does in the natural
      colour satellite image in Figure 16.2?
   b) Explain why there is a patchwork of
      colours in the fields to the south of the
      Ottawa River.
   c) Coniferous trees appear as pale red
      because they reflect less radiation than
      broadleaf deciduous trees. Locate these
      trees on the Shield.
   d) What other uses could infra-red images
      have in providing information about the
      Canadian landscape?

Figure 16.3
Infra-red satellite image of Ottawa-Hull

Land-use patterns

Land use is one of the most important aspects of any community. Urban land has many purposes. Each purpose serves the needs of individuals, businesses, and the community at large. But while there are many land uses, there is a great deal of similarity in the ways in which cities design their living and working space. Urban land-use categories are indicated in Figure 16.4.

6 Construct a divided circle graph to illustrate the land-use percentages in Figure 16.4. Multiply each percentage figure by 3.6 to obtain the number of degrees in the circle. Shade the different land-use categories in your graph according to the colour code.

Figure 16.4
Urban land-use categories
The colour code shown here is the one most commonly used on urban land-use maps in Canada.

7 The aerial photograph in Figure 16.5 shows a variety of urban land uses.
   a) Identify each land use.
   b) Place a piece of tracing paper on top of the photograph. Outline the residential land-use areas and shade these yellow.
   c) Repeat the process for all of the land uses in the photograph. Colour each land use according to the categories in Figure 16.4. Add a legend and label your sketch appropriately.

8 Obtain a land-use map of your community from your municipal government. What does it reveal about land use in your community?

	PERCENTAGE	COLOUR CODE
Residential	40	yellow
Commercial	4	red
Industrial	6	blue
Institutional and public buildings	10	grey
Transportation	33	turquoise
Open space and recreational	7	green

Residential land use

Residential land is where people live. Residential housing takes many forms. Single-family homes are separate houses with their own yards. Semidetached homes are two houses joined together by a common wall. Duplexes are buildings that house more than two dwellings, either side-by-side or one above the other. Townhouses are rows of small houses attached together. Apartments are multiple-dwelling buildings that can be either low-rise or high-rise. All of these types of housing can be found in Canada's cities. Figure 16.6 is an aerial photograph of a residential area in one Canadian community.

The size of residential properties varies. Lot sizes in suburban subdivisions tend to be larger than those in older neighbourhoods in the inner city. Usually the largest properties are found in the outer fringe where land prices are lower.

Housing density is the number of housing units and people living in them in a given area. Housing densities vary by location. Often the highest housing densities are found in the downtown area where limited space means there are more multiple-dwelling buildings. The lowest densities are usually in the outskirts of the city where land

Figure 16.5
Mixed land use

is more abundant. The average housing densities in Canada are described in Figure 16.7.

9 Figure 16.6 shows an area of mixed-density housing. Place a piece of tracing paper over the photograph. Outline the areas of low-density housing and shade them light yellow. Next outline the areas of medium-density housing and shade them dark yellow. Finally, outline the areas of high-density housing and shade them orange.

A housing survey

Now let's find out about housing in your own neighbourhood. Working in groups of three or four students, select a small residential area within walking distance of your school; no two groups should choose

the same area. Plan a walk through your neighbourhood with your group. Before

Figure 16.6
Mixed density housing
Identify the types of housing shown in this photograph.

Figure 16.7
Average housing densities in Canada

DENSITY	NUMBER OF UNITS (per hectare)	NUMBER OF PEOPLE	TYPE OF DWELLING
Low	Less than 30	75	Single-family, semidetached, small duplexes
Medium	30–70	150	Townhouses, large duplexes, low-rise apartments
High	More than 70	300	High-rise apartments

Figure 16.8
Housing survey— a sample study block

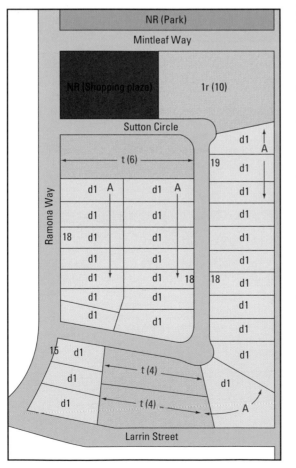

you begin, draw an outline of the study block, complete with street names. During the walk, record your observations on the outline map using the following codes:

Type of housing

Note each type of housing in your neighbourhood. For multiple-dwelling buildings, note the number of units after the letter code. For example, a townhouse complex with fifteen units would be marked *t15*.

Detached: **d1**
Semidetached: **d2**
Townhouse or duplex: **t**
Low-rise apartments: **lr**
High-rise apartments: **hr**
Other (e.g., apartment above a store): **o**
Non-residential: **nr**

Age of housing

Estimate the period in which the housing was built. Record this information as follows:

Pre-1945: **A**
1946-1959: **B**
1960-1979: **C**
1979-1989: **D**
Since 1990: **E**

Lot size

If there are detached homes in your study, measure the approximate width of the lot frontage using long steps about 1 m in length. Do this only for every fifth house. Record this information on your outline map.

10 a) Transfer the information from your working outline map to a second map of your study area.

b) Shade the residential areas on the second map as follows: low density (detached and semidetached homes)—light yellow; medium density (townhouses and duplexes)—dark yellow; high density (apartments)—orange.

c) Count the total number of housing units in each of the three categories. Write the totals on your map. Multiply each total by 3.6, which is the average number of people in a Canadian housing unit. The answers are estimates of the total population in each housing-density category in your neighbourhood. Indicate these totals on your map.

d) Add the three totals together. This gives you the estimated total population of your study block. Indicate this total on your map.

11 Create an overall picture of the residential neighbourhoods in your community by displaying all of the maps together.

a) What is the estimated total population in each housing-density category?

b) What is the estimated total population of the entire area studied by the class?

c) Do the maps reveal any relationship between high-density areas and major roadways? Explain.

12 Total the lot frontages you measured in your study. Divide this figure by the number of homes measured to find the average lot frontage of detached homes in your neighbourhood.

13 Is there a relationship between lot size and i) the age of the housing and ii) the distance away from the residential centre? Explain.

14 Using the data on the age of housing in your study area, it is possible to create a residential growth map.

a) Place a piece of tracing paper over your neighbourhood map. Using a different colour to represent each time period, shade in the housing developments according to your age estimates.

b) Describe the pattern on your map. What does it reveal about the direction of residential growth in your area?

Commercial land use

Commercial land is reserved for the buying and selling of goods and services in the retail business. Commercial properties occupy 4 to 5 per cent of urban land. While this may be a small percentage, retail businesses are extremely important to a community's well being. They provide goods and services for the people of the community. They also serve important economic functions. They create outlets through which money enters the community and provide jobs.

There are three different types of commercial land—the Central Business District, shopping centres and malls, and local service centres and ribbons.

The Central Business District

A good starting point for any study of commercial land use is the Central Business District, or CBD—sometimes known simply as "downtown." Although it is called the "Central" Business District, the CBD is not always located at the geographic centre of an urban area.

15 Figure 16.9 shows the CBD of Toronto. What feature in this photograph suggests that the CBD is not located at the geographic centre of the city?

If we cannot always find the Central Business District at the geographic centre, how do we locate it? The easiest way is to look for the area with the tallest buildings. The CBD is considered the prime business area and many companies want to locate there. This may be because they need to be near other businesses or because they need to be near a lot of people. As a result, there is a great demand for the limited amount of space available in the CBD. High demand makes the cost of land very expensive. To be cost effective, office space spreads upward instead of out! High-rise office buildings are filled with hundreds of businesses and thousands of employees. So if we want to locate the Central Business District, we simply look for the tallest buildings!

Within the Central Business District, there are usually specialized districts. These are areas where many similar businesses and activities concentrate together. Businesses that offer the same product or service, such as clothing stores, often locate close to one another to attract a larger number of customers. Some businesses, like law firms and banks, conduct a lot of their business activities with other law firms and banks. It makes sense for these businesses to be located close together. In Toronto, the head offices of several banks are clustered together in towering skyscrapers along Bay Street, creating Canada's most important financial district.

16 Figure 16.10 shows the location of the banking industry in downtown Toronto. Using the street names, describe the location of the specialized area known as the *banking district*.

Figure 16.9 Toronto and the CBD *Large urban centres like Toronto have huge office buildings known as skyscrapers in the CBD. The tallest skyscraper in Canada is Toronto's seventy-two-storey Bank of Montreal, shown here.*

Source: City of Toronto Planning and Development Department, Research and Information Systems Section 1996

Figure 16.10
Location of banking office blocks in downtown Toronto

Blocks in which banking office uses occur

17 a) List five types of businesses that need to be located where there is a large number of people. Explain why.
b) List five types of businesses that need to be located near one another. Explain why.

18 Studies indicate that retail stores attract more customers when they are located next to a competitor. Why do you think this is so?

19 Land values are usually higher at a place where two main streets meet. The intersection where the two most important streets meet in a downtown area is called the **peak value intersection**. In Figure 16.10, this area is at the corner of Bay Street and King Street in the financial district. Where is the peak value intersection in your community? What evidence is there of this?

Shopping malls

Shopping malls are most often located in urban areas. As service centres, they offer a range of goods and services similar to those provided by large towns.

Malls usually have one or more anchor stores. These are large chain or department stores that sell a wide range of products, from children's clothing to household appliances. The number of anchor stores usually reflects the size of the mall. A shopping mall with two, or perhaps even three, anchor stores usually has a large number of other retail outlets as well. The advertising power of these retail giants makes them the most important drawing card in a mall.

In addition to anchor stores, shopping malls house a number of businesses offering low-, middle-, and high-order goods and services. (For a review of low-, middle-, and high-order products see page 317.) This variety enables customers to shop for a wide range of products at one location. It also provides the opportunity for comparison shopping: shoppers can compare selection, quality, and price in several shops in a single trip. Malls also have the advantages of a climate-controlled environment and lots of parking space. These features combine to make these shopping centres popular with today's consumers.

Not everyone loves shopping malls, however. Businesses in older parts of the community, such as the main street, may suffer because their customers now do most of their shopping at the mall. Many of these businesses can survive only if they offer specialized products or services that are not found in the mall. There are some shoppers, too, who do not like malls. They may find them too impersonal and lacking in character. Or they may find them just too busy!

20 In a comparison organizer, list the advantages and disadvantages of shopping malls.

21 Most customers at a shopping mall arrive by car or bus. Therefore, easy road access is essential for a mall. If there is a mall in your community, how well is it served by important roads or highways?

22 Obtain a plan of the stores in your local shopping centre.
a) Create a colour-coded legend to indicate stores selling low-, middle-, and high-order goods and services. Colour these on the plan.
b) List the categories of stores and services on the plan, such as clothing, hardware, restaurants, etc. Count the number of stores in each category and use these totals to create a bar graph. The vertical axis should indicate the number of stores. Plot the number of stores in each category as a bar graph along the horizontal axis.

c) Mark the areas in the shopping centre where you believe there will be the highest pedestrian traffic. These will be places near major entrances, at meeting places, or near food and beverage facilities. Which stores are located near these places? Why?

Simulation: designing a shopping mall

You have been asked to design a shopping mall. The shops and services must meet the needs of your particular community, including all age groups. In designing your mall, you will have to make strategic decisions about the locations of the anchor stores and other shops and services. You will also have to consider the easy flow of shoppers through the mall and other key shopping attractions.

The shopping centre must not exceed 32 000 m^2 and must include a 5000 m^2 mall spine or walkway. Figure 16.11 lists the stores and services your mall must contain.

23 a) Use squares to represent floor space, with each square representing 25 m^2 of space. Therefore a store with 150 m^2 will consist of six squares. NOTE: Sketch out a rough plan of your mall on small pieces of graph paper first. Once you have done some preliminary sketches, begin outlining your mall on large pieces of graph paper.

Figure 16.11
Stores and services to be included in a shopping mall

TYPE AND NUMBER OF BUSINESSES	AREA PER BUSINESS(m^2)
Anchor stores (2)	7 500
Food stores (supermarket) (1)	1 500
Food stores (specialty) (4)	150
Drug (2)	500
Shoes (5)	100
Men's clothing (3)	200
Women's clothing (8)	200
Children's clothing (4)	200
Appliances (1)	300
Furniture (1)	300
Books, stationery (2)	150
Florist (1)	100
Hardware, paint (1)	200
Music (2)	50
Jewellery (2)	150
Camera (1)	100
Toys/hobby (2)	200
Art (1)	200
Luggage/leathers (1)	200
Banks (2)	200
Medical (2)	100
Restaurants (4)	100
Video arcades (2)	100
Hairdressers (2)	100
Computers (2)	150
Travel agencies (2)	100
Pet stores (1)	150
Vacant (2)	200
Vacant (1)	150
Vacant (1)	100

Total amount of floor space for stores: 27 000 m^2 (1080 squares)
Spine (walkway) area: 5 000 m^2 (200 squares)
Total mall area: 32 000 m^2 (1280 squares)
Each square represents 25 m^2 of space.

Local service centres and ribbons

Most commercial businesses in local communities are small. Some are located on their own, sometimes at street corners, and are appropriately called corner stores. They serve the daily needs of the people in the immediate neighbourhood. Some retail businesses cluster together in plazas. Plazas usually offer a limited range of services for the local community, such as drug stores, dry cleaners, and banks. Ribbons are commercial outlets that are lined up in a strip or row along a single street. Their customers are local people and perhaps casual passers-by. Some ribbons specialize in particular products or services, such as furniture and appliances or auto dealerships. These are called specialty ribbons. They attract customers from a wider area who are comparison shopping for specific items.

24 In a comparison chart, list the four types of local shopping facilities. For each one, identify the source of most of its customers.

Industrial land use

Industrial land is important to any community. It provides for the processing, manufacturing, storing, and shipping of products. It also includes businesses that serve the needs of these industries, such as banks and trucking companies. Most products produced by these businesses are sold outside the community. These sales generate money for these industries, some of which finds its way back into the community. These businesses also pay taxes, which help local governments provide vital community services. But while industrial land is important, on average it occupies only 6 per cent of land use in a community.

There are four types of industrial land—the Central Business District, ribbon industries, industrial parks, and business parks. Figure 16.12 shows these four industrial land uses.

There is a trend in many communities today for older industries in or near the Central Business District to relocate to more modern and spacious facilities in industrial parks in the outer fringes. This is because there is more land available here at lower cost. This means businesses can custom design their new plants to meet their current needs. At the same time they can take into account their expansion needs in the future. Businesses are also attracted by lower property taxes in the urban fringe. The exodus from the Central

Business Parks
• modern and spacious
• variety of businesses and services (manufacturing, banks, restaurants)
• may contain small office units

Industrial Parks
• businesses collected together in planned area
• low-rise buildings with roads and truck docks
• designed for trucking service
• small-scale manufacturing (auto parts, computers)

Ribbon Industries
• along highways and rail lines
• built as city expanded
• businesses sometimes spread apart
• bulk products (lumber, animal processing)

Central Business District
• near transport (docks, rail lines)
• bulk industries (flour, sugar)
• many warehouses for storage
• may make products for downtown businesses (printing)
• often rundown as businesses leave for more spacious suburbs

Figure 16.12
Types of industrial land use

Business District, however, may leave many old buildings in the downtown core empty. Sometimes these are leased and occupied by other businesses. Often they are sold for redevelopment as condominiums, retail outlets, or parking garages. Some waterfront cities have taken advantage of the move to the fringes to redevelop parts of the Central Business District into revitalized "people places."

25 Refer to Figure 16.12.
  a) Describe the four types of industrial land uses.
  b) What are the advantages of having industries gathered together in industrial parks?

Sometimes existing industries are incompatible with land uses that develop in the surrounding area. With the increasing cost of land, some developers may build residential communities next to older industrial areas. A housing complex, for example, may develop next to the site of a glue factory. Even with modern emission controls, unpleasant odours from the glue plant may spread throughout the neighbourhood. Trucks travelling to and from the glue factory may also cause noise and safety problems on residential streets.

26 a) Find two examples of incompatible land uses in your community.
   b) Why do modern business parks sometimes locate next to residential subdivisions?

Some businesses have a complementary relationship—that is, they do business with one another. A printing company, for example, may print all the stationary and business literature for an insurance company. In turn, the insurance company may provide the insurance coverage for the printing company and its employees. These complementary relationships attract businesses into business parks because of the potential to earn money from other businesses. A restaurant owner, for example, may find a large business park an ideal location because of the high volume of lunch-time trade.

27 Research a local industrial or business park. List the businesses as either manufacturing or service. Which businesses do you think would offer complementary goods or services to one another?

28 Some business parks specialize in research and technology. These complexes are called research and science parks. What types of businesses would you expect to find in these parks?

Open space and recreational land

An average of 7 per cent of land in urban areas is classified as open space and recreational. This includes undeveloped areas that have been left in their natural state as well as landscaped parks and gardens. Most urban centres have a variety of parklands. Small parcels of green space found in suburban subdivisions are called parkettes. Larger neighbourhood parks may contain a baseball diamond or soccer field. Community parks are larger still and may include walking trails in addition to multiple sports facilities. Recreational land also includes sports arenas, community facilities, and fairgrounds.

29 a) Survey the recreational land uses in your community. On a map of your community, shade all of the parklands green. Label each of the parks as either a parkette, a neighbourhood park, or a community park. Note the facilities each park contains and label these on your map.
   b) Create a colourful brochure promoting the recreational facilities in your community.

30 Review your map. Are there any facilities your community doesn't have that you feel are needed? Where do you think these facilities should be located? Write a letter to your municipal council recommending

the building of these facilities. Give reasons to support your position.

Studying urban land use

To study urban land use, geographers often use a **transect**. This is a linear slice or cross-cut through an area. A survey of the transect reveals the land-use patterns.

Figure 16.13 shows a transect of Metropolitan Toronto from the Central Business District to the eastern fringe. Five planning areas, called basic planning units, show typical land uses. Basic planning units are small areas in which urban planners plan development in detail. Like census tracts, basic planning units allow planners to count such things as people and housing and to plan development with these factors in mind.

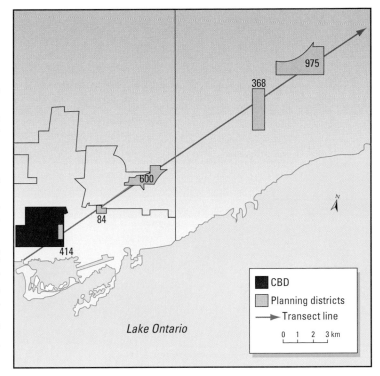

Figure 16.13
A transect through Metropolitan Toronto

BASIC PLANNING UNIT	414	84	600	368	975
Total population	4 114	6 682	2 359	4 147	25 363
% under 35	65.7	52.1	40.1	43.9	66.1
NUMBER OF DWELLINGS BY TYPE					
Single detached	3	372	733	980	2 256
Single attached	5	504	0	1 052	1 846
Row condominiums	111	0	0	12	665
Apartment condominiums	860	4	0	13	2 141
Duplexes	1 265	354	52	30	489
Apartments	28	98	303	85	525
Collectives (rooming houses)	962	2	0	371	0

Source: Metropolitan Toronto Planning Department, 1995.

Figure 16.14
Basic planning units in Metropolitan Toronto

31 Refer to Figure 16.14.
  a) Which basic planning unit has the largest population?
  b) Which two basic planning units have the highest percentage of young people? What might explain this?
  c) Which basic planning unit contains the greatest variety of housing type?

d) Add the total number of housing units for each basic planning unit. Divide this total by the population of each planning unit. The result is the number of persons per unit. Which basic planning unit has the most persons per unit? Which has the least? Can you explain why?

Figure 16.15
Area 1—Planning District 414
Residential area just east of the CBD

Distance from CBD: 1 km

32 Refer to Figure 16.15.
  a) What evidence is there that i) this is at the edge of the CBD and ii) the population density is high?
  b) What conclusions can you make about the age of the population in basic planning unit 414 compared with the other planning units? What might this indicate?

Figure 16.16
Area 2—Planning District 84
Older residential area to the east of the City of Toronto

Figure 16.17
Area 3—Planning District 600
Older residential and industrial area in the Borough of East York

Distance from the CBD: 5 km

Distance from the CBD: 8 km

33 What evidence is there that people are moving closer to the CBD and renovating older homes? Refer to Figure 16.15 to help you.

34 a) This area contains early suburban subdivisions. Describe the single-family homes in terms of i) the size of the house and the lot; ii) design; iii) materials used for construction; iv) services such as telephone wires and lighting.

b) Some of the first industrial parks were built in this area. Describe the design of these buildings in terms of their size, height, and landscaping.

Figure 16.19
Area 5—Planning District 975
New residential and industrial area on the fringe of the City of Scarborough

Figure 16.18
Area 4—Planning District 368
Suburban industrial area in the City of Scarborough

Distance from the CBD: 16 km

35 a) Describe the street patterns in this newer suburban area.

b) Shopping malls are a feature of outlying suburbs. Describe the Scarborough Town Centre in terms of i) land use and ii) its location relative to major transportation routes.

Distance from the CBD: 20 km

36 a) Compare these single-family homes with those in unit 600.

b) What evidence is there that the suburbs are mixing low and high density?

c) Compare the industrial park with the one in unit 600. Include the size and design of the buildings as well as landscaping and parking facilities.

Simulation: creating a town

You have an exciting opportunity. You are part of a team that is to plan a new community at the site shown in Figure 16.20. Your planning team consists of yourself and two or three other students. Discuss ideas for your development with your team and prepare some rough sketches before you begin. It's a good idea to read through all of this activity before you get started.

37 a) Write out your objectives for this community in the form of an official plan. Your plan should state what type of community you intend to create. Be sure to consider the following aspects of the development:
• population (target for 24 000)
• housing types and distribution
• job opportunities
• physical appearance
• features of the natural environment
• shopping facilities
• schools and other public buildings.

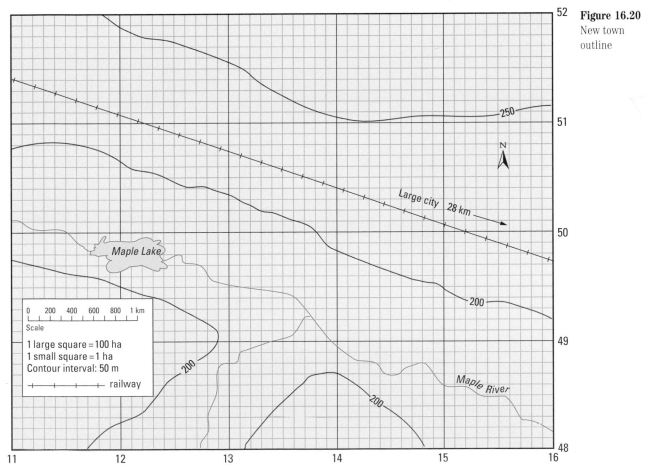

Figure 16.20
New town outline

b) Draw a plan of the area. Make the plan as large as possible but retain the scale. Each large square represents 100 ha, or 1 km^2; each small square represents 1 ha (100 m x 100 m). Note the contour lines and the drainage pattern.

c) Your plan must include the land-use zones indicated below. When you have decided where to locate each zone, outline the area on your plan. Do this lightly at first in case you need to make changes.

i) *Residential:* Use a total of ten large squares to indicate the following categories:
  - Low density (single-family homes; twenty-five people per hectare). This will cover 60 per cent of all residential land (six large squares).
  - Medium density (semidetached homes, townhouses; fifty people per hectare). This will cover 30 per cent of all residential land (three large squares).
  - High density (apartments, condominiums; seventy-five people per hectare). This will cover 10 per cent of all residential land (one large square).

ii) *Commercial (retail and business):* The community should have a Central Business District or main street that takes into consideration the following factors:
  - For every 20 000 people there should be one large shopping centre covering 10 ha.
  - For every 5000 people there should be a community plaza.

  - For every 2500 people there should be a local plaza.

iii) *Industrial:* The total industrial area should be 100 ha. Decide on the industrial uses and choose suitable sites for each one.

iv) *Institutional or government:* Choose suitable locations for:
  - a city hall (2 ha)
  - a hospital (10 ha)
  - three elementary schools (5 ha each)
  - one secondary school (10 ha)

v) *Open space and recreational:* Your community should have:
  - one town park (50 ha)
  - three community parks (10 ha each)

vi) *Transportation:* Plan only main arterial roads and collector streets. A rail line already exists, but you may want to plan a rail station for commuter service to the city.

c) Once you have outlined all of the land-use zones, colour them according to the appropriate land-use colours. Make sure your plan is fully labelled and contains all the necessary information. Display your plan in the classroom.

38 a) Describe the site pattern, or shape, of your community. What physical features influenced this pattern?

b) Which land use occupies the greatest amount of land?

c) Are there areas where conflicting land uses are close together?

d) If this community were to expand, where would this expansion take place? Why?

39 a) Where would you choose to live in this community? Why?
    b) What should the city council do to keep this community one of which its residents are proud?

40 How well did you meet the objectives of your official plan? Explain your answer.

41 Choose another group's plan and compare and contrast it with your own.

42 A landfill site for the town's garbage is needed in your community. The site will cover 25 ha (25 small squares). Many people are unhappy about having a landfill site in the community. It is the responsibility of your planning group to recommend a suitable location that will satisfy the greatest number of people.
    a) List five criteria, such as accessibility, zoning, and weather patterns, that should be considered in selecting a landfill site.
    b) With these criteria in mind, select a site and indicate its location on your town plan. Label it as the landfill site.
    c) Be prepared to respond to public criticism by writing a statement explaining your reasons for selecting this site.

Canada is an urban society. Eight out of ten Canadians live in an urban environment. This means that, for most of us, our lives involve crowds of people, heavy traffic, shopping malls, fast-food outlets, and other things we commonly associate with city life.

There are many things we enjoy about our urban lifestyle—the convenience, the variety, the entertainment. But there are also many things that we find less desirable—the crowds, the noise, the crime. Even so, towns and cities act as magnets, drawing thousands of people who want to live in them. One of the strongest attractions of urban life is the variety and availability of jobs.

1 Look through the employment section of a city newspaper. How many jobs can you count in i) manufacturing and ii) service industries? Prepare a written summary of your findings.

2 a) What kinds of jobs are available for young people in your community? For example, are most jobs part-time or in certain industries? List the five most common types of jobs.
   b) Contact the Canada Employment office closest to your community. Find out what kinds of jobs are available in your community for people between the ages of sixteen and twenty-five. Classify these jobs as either part-time or full-time and as service or manufacturing.
   c) Ask your teacher to arrange to have an employment counsellor or your school's guidance counsellor speak to the class about job opportunities for young people.

In order to produce a skilled and educated workforce, many towns and cities have postsecondary institutions. Often local colleges and universities offer special courses to match the needs of local employers. For example, the colleges near the Canadian Shield offer geology and mining courses.

3 a) Ask your school guidance counsellor for a list of postsecondary institutions in your province, with their enrolment figures. Produce a map showing the location of each institution and the number of students.
   b) Look through the course calendars for the community colleges and universities closest to your community. Are any of the programs these institutions offer designed to supply trained workers for local industries? Explain.

For many people, the variety and convenience of services and activities are some of the advantages of urban living. Cities offer a variety of cultural and recreational activities. There are shops, restaurants, and theatres; museums, art galleries, and cultural centres; amusement parks, sports events, and specialty shows. These attractions are not just for the benefit of people who live in cities. They also attract visitors who are eager to sample urban life.

4 Obtain a map of your community. Using symbols, mark the locations of the follow-

ing businesses and services on your map:
movie theatres; hospitals; Italian restaurants; new car dealerships; sports arenas.
The Yellow Pages may help you obtain
this information. Be sure to include a legend to explain your symbols.

5 Design a poster advertising the attractions
of your community. It should convey all of
the ways in which your community is a
great place to live and to visit!

Figure 17.1
Urban life

The pros and cons of urban living

Urban life means different things to different people. Some people see more advantages to life in the city than disadvantages. Others have the opposite point of view. The following accounts of city life by two Canadian teenagers present very different opinions.

So much to do!

City life has its good points—and so many of them! There are all kinds of conveniences close at hand, like stores, restaurants, sports facilities, and rec centres. I can shop for bargains because I can compare prices at different stores—there's so much variety, and there's always a sale somewhere! There are so many things to do—go to a movie or a museum or a sports event. And the concerts! It's great to be able to see my favourite bands. Life in the city is very exciting!

A lot of people live in the city. This means that we have more services, like buses, hospitals, and police and fire departments. We also have more job opportunities and more choices about the kinds of jobs we want. More people also means more power, so we have a greater voice in government. To me, the city has everything to offer.

Too many people!

The city is a concrete jungle! People don't care about other people. They are too self-centred. The poor and the homeless are cast aside and ignored by the more fortunate people who have jobs and homes. City people close their eyes to violence and crime—as long as it doesn't affect them personally. Most of these problems are the result of too many people in too small a space. People only look out for themselves.

The pace of city life is too fast—and it's getting faster all the time. Everywhere you look, people are rushing. No one has a minute to spare. I think this prevents people from communicating with one another.

I don't like the sights, sounds, and smells of the city, either. There's too much traffic. Too much noise. Too much pollution. Too much crime. Too many people! The city might be an interesting place to visit, but I wouldn't want to live there.

6 Construct a PMI (Plus, Minus, Interesting) evaluation chart. Under the Plus column, list those things you consider to be positive about city life. Under the Minus column, list those things you consider to be negative about city life. Under the Interesting column, list those things you consider to be neither positive nor negative—just interesting! Summarize your chart in a paragraph describing what life in the city means to you.

7 If you were a teenager from a rural area visiting a large city for the first time, describe the most significant differences you would notice.

Challenges for Canadian cities

Physical challenges: urban blight

Our cities are growing older. The aging process is evident everywhere. Many grand old buildings now display the effects of time. Older neighbourhoods are slipping into decay as people leave the city centre in favour of the suburbs. Rundown buildings are being abandoned and boarded up. Pollution has cast a dirty blanket across once-gleaming monuments and buildings.

The deterioration of the urban landscape is called **physical blight**. It is usually the result of two factors: the decaying of original building materials and a lack of money for maintenance. Eliminating physical blight involves restoration and renewal. This is an ongoing challenge for cities, and a costly one.

Functional blight occurs when an area is no longer used for its original purpose. A once-quiet residential street, for example, may have become a busy thoroughfare, and the traffic may pose a danger for young children living there. Sometimes, however, functional blight can become positive. Old buildings or industrial waterfronts can be converted into people places with restaurants, art studios, and shops.

Frictional blight occurs when conflicting land uses are found side by side. An outdoor stadium next to a residential area is an example of frictional blight. The noise levels from sporting events and concerts may be disturbing to residents, particularly at night.

8 Give examples of i) physical blight, ii) functional blight, and iii) frictional blight in your community. What do you think should be done to eliminate these instances of urban blight?

Not all blight is part of the visual landscape. Excessive noise is another form of

Figure 17.2
Urban blight
*What examples
of blight are
illustrated
in these
photographs?*

urban blight. Noise levels in our cities are rising at a rate of 5 per cent a year. Excessive noise can damage our ear drums and may lead to some degree of hearing impairment. Figure 17.3 on page 354 shows normal noise levels in an urban environment. Note that our downtown streets regularly emit a noise level of seventy decibels. This is only ten decibels below the maximum comfort level for human hearing! What is even more disturbing is that as higher noise levels become a part of our lives, we take noise pollution for granted. This makes us even less aware of the damage noise may be inflicting on our hearing.

9 a) Using the noise levels from Figure 17.3, create a "noise map" of your community. Plot the maximum decibel figure you would expect to hear at various locations. For example, you may plot 75 dB along the side of a busy expressway and 45 dB within a normal subdivision.

Plot as many readings as you can.

b) Draw "contour lines" around the noise levels. For example, draw a line that connects all places with 50 dB of noise in a circle, then draw a second line for 60 dB, and so on. (You may want to

Figure 17.3
Noise decibel
levels in urban
communities

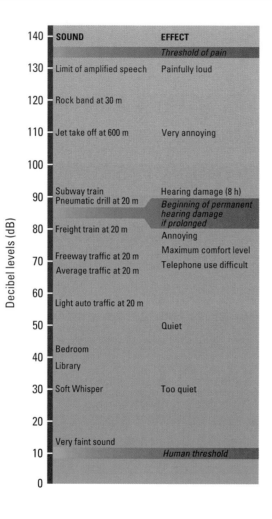

review contour lines on page 39 before
you begin.)
c) Use the graded shading technique to
colour the different noise levels. The
darkest shade should represent the
loudest noise levels.
d) Where is the noisiest place in your
community?
e) What could your community do to
reduce noise pollution?

Social challenges: alienation, poverty, and crime

Alienation

It is often said that cities are less friendly places than rural areas. Sociologists believe that areas of dense population influence human behaviour. While living in a city demands a lot of human interaction, it also leads people to become more reserved with one another. Psychologists have suggested that this is because we are faced with so many situations each day that we screen out those things that are least important to us. Therefore we tend to talk with people only when it is in our interests to do so. So even though we may be surrounded by people, we are often isolated.

Unfortunately, isolation can lead to loneliness. This loneliness is called **alienation**. It is a feeling of being apart or separate from everyone else. Many people living in cities experience problems that stem from alienation. These include addiction, unemployment, homelessness, poverty, criminal behaviour, and feelings of suicide. Most cities have a variety of social agencies that offer help to people who feel alienated in society.

Poverty

Although we live in a wealthy society, poverty is a serious problem in Canadian cities. The high cost of urban life makes it difficult for many people to support themselves. Generally, it is more expensive to live in urban centres than in rural areas, and the cost of living increases with the size of the community. Therefore it takes more money to live in a community of 500 000 than to live in a community of 30 000.

Poverty is also determined by family size. The larger the family, the more money is needed to support its members. In Canada in 1993, over 4.9 million people lived below the poverty line; this included 1.5 million children. The majority of these are lone-parent mothers and their families.

When we think of urban poverty, we may first think of homeless people who are forced to live on the streets. But there are also many people who have jobs and earn regular paycheques yet are still poor. This is because their wages are not enough to support their families. They must rely on food banks and other social service agencies to meet their basic needs.

10 Make a list of the social service agencies in your community. Select one of these agencies and find out more about the work it does in your area. Find out what you can do to help and present this information to your class.

Crime

Many people associate crime with urban life. Indeed, crime is a problem in most urban areas. The public perception is that the **crime rate**—that is, the overall number of crimes that are committed—is increasing steadily. In reality, however, the crime rate fluctuates. In Metropolitan Toronto, for example, the number of criminal offences from 1992 to 1993 dropped by 5.2 per cent; this included a decrease of 10.8 per cent in the number of homicides. But the number of sexual assaults, robberies, and breaking and entering offences increased.

Theft is the most common type of crime in Canada. In Montreal, for example, over 100 000 serious crimes are committed each year; more than half of these involve theft. But is crime more common in large cities like Montreal, Toronto, and Vancouver? Are we more likely to be a victim of crime in the hustle and bustle of the city or in the relatively calmer environment of the suburbs? Most people assume that the greatest opportunities for crime are in the city centre because of the large number of businesses and people. But is this really true? Let's examine the crime statistics in Metropolitan Toronto to discover if there are any geographic patterns to crime.

11 There are seventeen police divisions serving Metropolitan Toronto.
  a) For each category of crime in Figure 17.5, rank the divisions from most crimes to least crimes. For example, Division 52 ranks first in the "Robberies" category. (There may be some ties in your rankings.)
  b) Count the number of times each police division ranks in the top three (the most crimes) or the bottom three (the fewest crimes). Award each division +1 for every top three ranking and –1 for every bottom three ranking. Total the points to reach a final plus or minus score.
  c) On a copy of the police division map in Figure 17.4, draw two columns to represent the plus and minus totals in each division. Colour the plus column red and the minus column green. The scale should be 1 cm for every plus or minus.
  d) Which police divisions have the lowest crime rates? Which have the highest?

12 Compare the map in Figure 17.4 with the statistics in Figure 17.5. Which police divisions cover Toronto's Central Business District? Which crimes would you conclude to be typically "downtown" crimes? Which crimes would you conclude to be typically "suburban" crimes? Can you explain why?

13 a) Create a column graph showing the crime totals in the police divisions that run along the lakeshore: 21, 11, 14, 52, 51, 55, 41, and 42.

b) Describe the crime pattern from the west of the city through the Central Business District to the east of the city.

Does this pattern bear any similarity to a downtown skyline?

14 a) Which police division has the most crimes relative to its population? To calculate a crime rate for each police division, divide the total number of crimes by the population and multiply by 1000. The answer will be the total number of crimes per 1000 population in that police division. For example,

Division 11 $\dfrac{11\,961 \text{ crimes}}{91\,465 \text{ people}}$ × 1000 = 130.8.

b) What conclusions can you reach about the crime pattern in Metropolitan Toronto?

Figure 17.4
Metropolitan Toronto police district and divisional boundaries

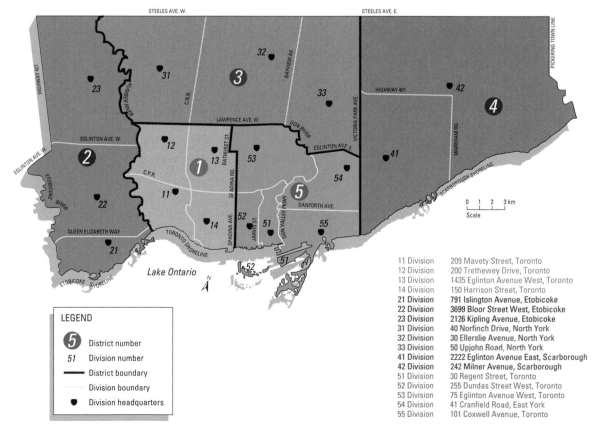

11 Division   209 Mavety Street, Toronto
12 Division   200 Trethewey Drive, Toronto
13 Division   1435 Eglinton Avenue West, Toronto
14 Division   150 Harrison Street, Toronto
21 Division   791 Islington Avenue, Etobicoke
22 Division   3699 Bloor Street West, Etobicoke
23 Division   2126 Kipling Avenue, Etobicoke
31 Division   40 Norfinch Drive, North York
32 Division   30 Ellerslie Avenue, North York
33 Division   50 Upjohn Road, North York
41 Division   2222 Eglinton Avenue East, Scarborough
42 Division   242 Milner Avenue, Scarborough
51 Division   30 Regent Street, Toronto
52 Division   255 Dundas Street West, Toronto
53 Division   75 Eglinton Avenue West, Toronto
54 Division   41 Cranfield Road, East York
55 Division   101 Coxwell Avenue, Toronto

LEGEND

5 District number
51 Division number
— District boundary
— Division boundary
● Division headquarters

| POLICE | | | | | | | VEHICLE | | | | |
DIV.	POPUL'N	DEATH	ASSAULT	ROBBERY	B/E	THEFT	FRAUD	THEFT	WEAPONS	OTHER	TOTAL
11	91 465	3	1 285	190	1015	486	560	3 820	166	3 232	11 961
12	86 025	9	1 469	232	1021	580	237	2 959	189	3 016	10 663
13	30 942	4	1 391	218	1 190	577	1003	3 685	210	3 049	12 468
14	145 484	16	2 907	501	2 749	748	764	8 687	471	7 932	27 448
21	53 270	2	755	71	519	291	178	1 364	108	2 129	6 062
22	124 241	3	774	158	1 061	734	588	4 246	120	3 677	12 603
23	140 822	9	1 854	304	1 264	1 361	675	5 107	194	3 922	16 094
31	177 947	28	2 328	460	1 345	1 412	713	5 826	352	4 893	19 566
32	183 556	11	1 240	241	1 448	960	997	6 368	230	4 337	18 204
33	172 525	4	1 227	165	1 288	975	697	5 179	109	3 312	14 489
41	210 199	9	2 916	479	2 376	1 866	1 312	7 728	422	7 250	27 337
42	326 046	17	2 950	564	2 664	2 026	1 113	8 831	519	7 212	28 813
51	59 883	16	1 734	448	1 041	479	244	3 575	460	5 426	14 310
52	63 065	8	2 202	585	1 669	596	1 913	12 887	393	10 564	32 613
53	126 680	2	848	119	1 145	424	550	4 410	65	2 313	10 908
54	23 561	9	1 407	198	1 425	753	301	3 585	187	3 112	12 055
55	110 589	19	1 955	332	2 140	902	441	6 260	306	5 013	18 745

NOTE: "Death" includes first- and second-degree murder, manslaughter, and attempted murder.
"Assault" includes common assault and sexual assault.
"B/E" means Breaking and Entering.

Source: Metropolitan Toronto Police Department, *Annual Report*, 1993.

Figure 17.5
Reported Criminal Code offences in Toronto, 1993

The expansion of cities

Urban sprawl

The population of Canada is growing at a rate of 1.1 per cent a year. That's about 350 000 people annually. Most of these people are being added to our towns and cities. This has an important impact on urban land use.

An influx of people affects a city in two ways. The population density may increase as more people are added within existing boundaries. Or the city may physically expand as land on the outskirts is developed to accommodate the growing population. In Canada, outward expansion is the usual result of population growth.

Urban areas have been experiencing this outward "push" for many years. The desire for single-family homes in quiet neighbourhoods began in the 1920s when cars were first introduced. Before cars, most people had little choice but to live close to the city centre. The only means of transportation were horse-drawn vehicles and later electric trams and streetcars. The introduction of Henry Ford's Model T automobile allowed people to move to quieter neighbourhoods away from the busy downtown core. More roads were added to accommodate the cars. Eventually this enabled people to live almost anywhere. The result was low-density housing subdivisions called the **suburbs**. The continued expansion of the suburbs into the surrounding countryside is known as **urban sprawl**.

There are four types of urban sprawl. **Normal sprawl** is the logical extension of development at the outer edges of an urban centre. **Linear sprawl** is urban

Figure 17.6
A typical urban fringe area

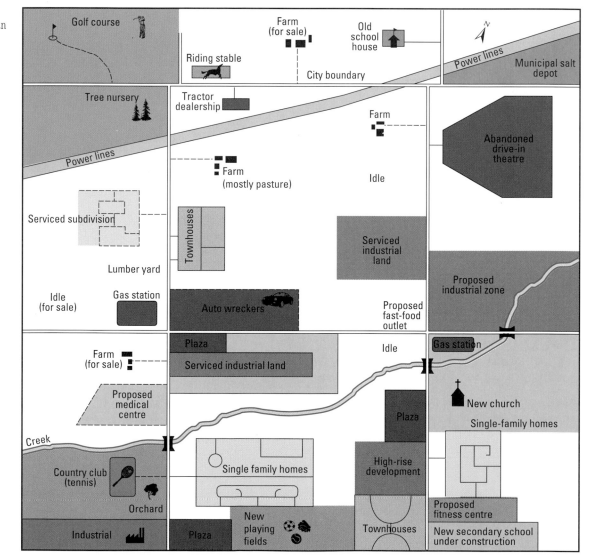

growth that follows important transportation routes into and out of a city. **Leapfrogging** is the development of lower-priced land well removed from present urban development. **In-filling** is the development of the less desirable areas of land that remain after leap-frogging.

The border area between our urban landscapes and the undeveloped land beyond the cities is called the **urban fringe**. The fringe is easily recognized because of its mixed land use. Here we find new subdivisions, plazas, schools, and industry mixed together with farmland, tractor dealerships, and roadhouses. Some land uses in the fringe are classified as non-farm. This means that although they are located in a rural area, they do not earn an income from farming.

15 Look at Figure 17.6.
   a) What land uses indicate that this is an urban fringe area?
   b) What do you predict this area will be like five years from now? Illustrate your prediction on a land use map.

16 Figure 17.7 shows an area where building permits have been granted to a number of developers. Describe which of the four kinds of urban sprawl will result from the development. Refer to the letters identifying each site in your answer. For example, "A" will contribute to a linear sprawl pattern.

Problems in the suburbs

Once, the most attractive part of living in the suburbs was the quiet, almost country-like, atmosphere on spacious lots not far

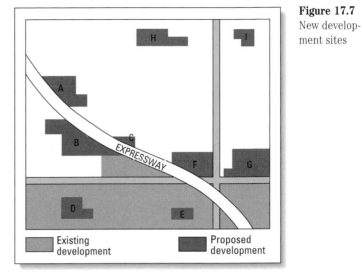

Figure 17.7
New development sites

from downtown. Today, however, continuous outward growth has pushed the suburbs further and further away from the city centre. In some cities, new suburban neighbourhoods may be an hour's drive from the downtown core.

In outlying areas, residential densities are much lower than downtown. But the fewer number of people means that these municipalities receive less revenue from property taxes. This makes community services in the suburbs more costly. As a result, services are often limited. In response, municipalities try to entice other tax-paying land users, such as businesses and industries, to the area in order to increase their tax base.

Urban sprawl carries with it considerable public expense. Extensive road networks and freeways have to be built to connect people in the outlying areas to the city. Commuter trains and mass transit systems must be developed to shuttle people between their homes and their jobs. Shopping centres must be built to satisfy the needs of these suburban consumers. Still, many people in the suburbs complain about the lack of entertainment and other social and cultural activities.

Yet thousands of people move to suburbia every year. The advantages of suburban life are that land costs are lower, therefore overall housing costs are less than in the city. There is also a wide selection of new homes that are more spacious and modern than many homes in the city. Couples with young families may also be attracted by the new schools and recreational facilities.

17 Design a brochure advertising a new subdivision on the outskirts of the city. The development is 30 km from downtown but only 4 km from a city-bound expressway. The homes are reasonably priced to attract first-time buyers. Give your subdivision an appealing name.

18 The aerial photograph in Figure 17.8 shows a fringe area in Markham, Ontario.
a) What evidence is there of mixed land use?
b) Can you identify any areas of incompatible land use? (Notice the rail line across the upper part of the photograph.)

Figure 17.8
Urban fringe in Markham, Ontario

c) Why do you think there are more incompatible land uses in the suburbs today than twenty years ago?

d) Is there any evidence that the municipality is trying to increase the population density?

e) Estimate the percentage area taken up by each land use in this fringe. You can do this by using a grid of squares copied onto a transparency. Count the number of squares that cover each type of land use. Then calculate each land use as a percentage of the total.

19 Your municipal council is considering an application to build a large sports arena in a residential neighbourhood in the suburbs.

a) As a reporter for the community newspaper, write an article outlining the advantages and disadvantages of the proposal.

b) Assume the role of editor-in-chief of the community newspaper. Write an editorial either in favour of or against the proposal.

Case study: the Greater Toronto Area

The Greater Toronto Area, or GTA, stretches for 7000 km² around Lake Ontario. It consists of the six municipalities of Metropolitan Toronto (the cities of Toronto, North York, Scarborough, Etobicoke, and York and the borough of East York) and the four surrounding regional municipalities of Halton, Peel, York, and Durham.

The impact of growth in Toronto

Population

Since 1971, the population in the GTA has grown by 1.5 million. In 1994, a total of 4.4 million people lived in the region. Within the next ten years, it is expected that Canada's population will grow by 2.7 million. About half of this growth, 1.3 million, will be in Ontario; two-thirds of this, 682 000, will be in the GTA. Figure 17.10 shows the area's past and projected population growth.

From 1961 to 1981 nearly all the added population spilled over onto land in the outskirts of Metropolitan Toronto. This was partly due to a large amount of leap-frogging sprawl. Figure 17.11 shows the amount of migration away from Metropolitan Toronto into the fringe.

20 What three factors might account for the population growth in the Toronto region?

Figure 17.9
Population of the GTA and Metropolitan Toronto

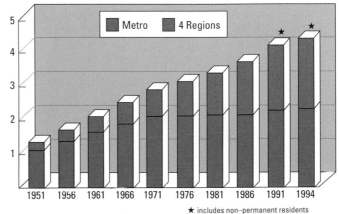

★ includes non–permanent residents

	1961	1971	1981 (000s)	2001	2011
City of Toronto	703	713	599	603	567
Metro	1 620	2 089	2 137	2 502	2 689
Fringe	484	830	1 280	2 520	2 952
Total GTA	**2 104**	**2 919**	**3 417**	**5 022**	**5 641**

Source: Adapted from Metropolitan Toronto Planning Department, 1995.

Figure 17.10
Past and projected population growth in the Toronto region

21 Refer to Figure 17.10. Describe what has happened to the populations of i) the City of Toronto; ii) Metropolitan Toronto; iii) the four municipalities of the fringe; iv) the Greater Toronto Area (GTA).

22 Refer to the projected population statistics in Figure 17.10. Describe what you think will be the impact of projected growth on:
a) school construction in Metro Toronto and the fringe;

Figure 17.11
Movement of people in the GTA

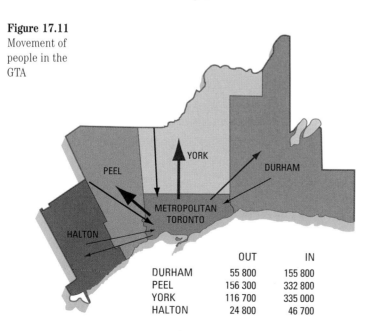

	OUT	IN
DURHAM	55 800	155 800
PEEL	156 300	332 800
YORK	116 700	335 000
HALTON	24 800	46 700

b) transportation networks;
c) the importance of Toronto's CBD;
d) the surrounding farmland.

Housing

In 1981, the baby boomers (those born between 1945 and 1964) made up 36 per cent of the population in the Toronto region. As these people became adults and established their own households, housing requirements in the Toronto area increased. At first demand was for apartments in Metro. Then it was for single-family homes in the fringe areas. Today young adults between eighteen and twenty-four are the largest age group moving into Metropolitan Toronto. In contrast, there has been significant movement of adults between twenty-five and forty-four to the urban fringe. Most are young couples buying their first home and starting to raise a family. This influx of people places enormous pressure on the fringe regions to provide housing, schools, and community facilities. Many of these new suburbanites return to Metro each day to work. In a region where people are four times more likely to travel by car than by public transit, this places enormous pressure on the roads.

Figure 17.12
Housing construction completions in the Toronto region, 1993

	TOTAL
Metro Toronto	7 168
Fringe	14 401
Total GTA	**21 569**

Source: Metropolitan Toronto Planning Department, 1995.

23 Figure 17.12 shows the number of housing construction completions in the Greater Toronto Area in 1993.
  a) Calculate the percentage of new homes built i) within Metropolitan Toronto and ii) in the fringe. Illustrate this information in a divided circle graph.
  b) What is the difference between housing construction in Metro Toronto and the fringe? How will this affect the population densities of each region?

REGION	1986	1991	2001	2011
		(000)		
Metropolitan Toronto	1 360	1 459	1 664	1 818
Fringe	730	920	1 189	1 392
Total GTA	**2 090**	**2 379**	**2 853**	**3 210**

Source: Adapted from Metropolitan Toronto Planning Department, 1995.

the percentage of jobs located in Metro and in the fringe.
  b) What conclusions can you make about the pattern of the labour force? What might be the consequences of this pattern?

Figure 17.13 Past and projected labour force in the Toronto region

Employment

While the GTA has experienced substantial population growth, it has experienced an equal amount of new employment opportunities. This has centred largely in the surrounding regions of Halton, Peel, York, and Durham. These are the areas in which the majority of new industrial parks have been created. Businesses have been lured to the fringe regions by lower land costs and municipal incentives such as tax breaks and new roads and facilities to service their needs. As a result, employment in the four regions grew by over 30 per cent between 1986 and 1991. The largest increase, at 32 per cent, was in York Region. This has become the headquarters for Canada's computer industry, with companies like IBM, Apple, and Compaq establishing their Canadian head offices here. Figure 17.13 shows the projected growth in the labour force in the Toronto region.

24 a) Construct divided bar graphs for each year in Figure 17.13. Each bar should represent the total labour force in the region and should be divided to show

The loss of agricultural land

Canada has a land area of 9 970 600 km^2 and a population of 29 million. The Netherlands in Europe, on the other hand, has a land area of 37 300 km^2 and a population of 15.4 million. If we compare the population densities of these two countries, it would seem that we have lots of land to support our population. Right? Wrong! Fifty per cent of Canada is permanently frozen. Only 13 per cent of our land is suitable for agriculture, and only about half of this is suitable for growing crops. Land is classified into seven categories according to its suitability for agriculture. Class 1 is the best soil; class 7 is swampland, incapable of supporting any crops.

The earliest settlements were located in areas that provided a good local food supply. As a result, most of our present towns and cities are located on top quality soils—classes 1 or 2. It is estimated that 50 per cent of Canada's population lives on the best 5 per cent of our farmland. As these urban areas begin to expand, they consume even more valuable agricultural soil. It is estimated that Canadian cities will have consumed another 400 000 ha of quality farmland by the year 2000.

25 It takes 40 ha of land to feed 100 people. If Canada loses 400 000 ha of farmland to urban expansion, how many fewer people will our farmland be able to support?

Simulation: evaluating proposals for urban development

Lofthouse is a suburban borough north of Metropolitan Wakefield. Wakefield is an expanding urban centre with a population of over 800 000. The borough of Lofthouse has 54 000 people but it is growing quickly. At present, recreational facilities include two community centres. Crosstown Community Centre has an indoor pool, a gymnasium, and a hockey arena. Lofthouse Recreational Centre has a large outdoor pool, a baseball diamond, a sports field with spectator stands, and tennis courts. The Valley View Golf Course is 30 km east of Lofthouse.

While Lofthouse has grown steadily over the past five years, it is now facing an expansion crunch. Up until now, development has taken place on land between existing developments—a classic example of urban in-filling. Now, however, the only remaining area for expansion is high-quality classes 1 and 2 agricultural land. There is also an environmentally sensitive area of woodland surrounding Ardsley Creek; this flows into Lofthouse from the north through the agricultural land. The creek flows through a broad valley with wide sweeping turns until it reaches the residential development. Here it has been straightened and its banks reinforced with concrete to protect against floods and stormwater runoff.

Figure 17.14 shows the extent of present development in Lofthouse and highlights four proposals for development over the next five years. Working with a group, you must present these proposals and determine which one is best for Lofthouse.

26 a) Form groups of five. Assign one person to represent each of the interest groups described in the briefing notes on page 366–367. Students playing the same roles should gather together to discuss their positions. (For example, all those playing the role of a representative from Megacorp Housing Developments should discuss their position.) Each group should decide on five important points to raise in a discussion with the mayor. The mayors should discuss what their response will be to each interest group.

b) Following your discussions, return to your original group and conduct your meeting. Each person should present his or her proposal without interruption; the others should note the main points of the proposal. Questions may be asked once all proposals have been made. Following the discussions, the mayor must decide which proposal(s) will be presented to the Lofthouse Council. These should be highlighted in a point-form presentation.

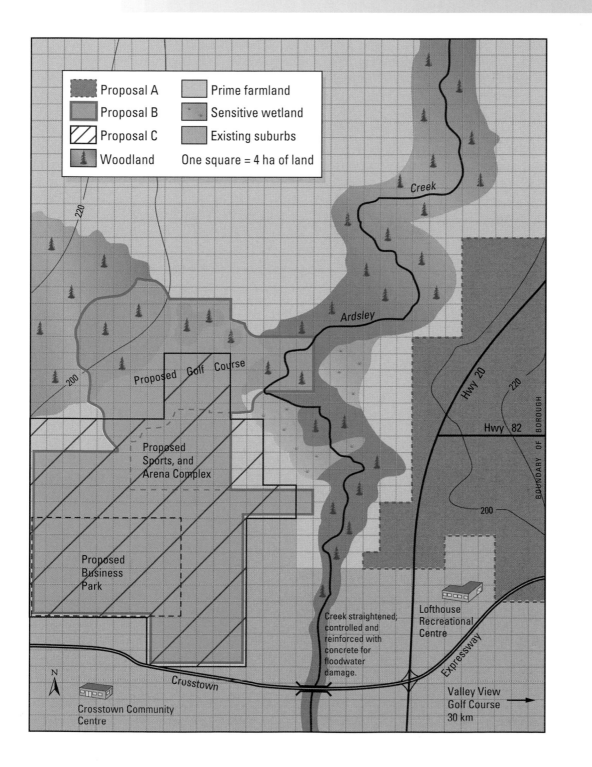

Figure 17.14
Proposals for Lofthouse

Proposal A

Proposal B

Proposal C

Woodland

Prime farmland

Sensitive wetland

Existing suburbs

One square = 4 ha of land

220

200

Creek

Ardsley

Proposed Golf Course

Proposed Sports, and Arena Complex

Proposed Business Park

Crosstown

Crosstown Community Centre

N

Hwy 20

220

Hwy 82

200

BOUNDARY OF BOROUGH

Lofthouse Recreational Centre

Creek straightened; controlled and reinforced with concrete for floodwater damage.

Expressway

Valley View Golf Course 30 km

Proposals for development

Proposal A: This project calls for a new high-density housing development extending into the farmland east of Ardsley Creek. The development will consist of both detached homes and townhouses and will accommodate approximately 12 000 people. Although it will increase the tax base, it will also mean that additional services such as schools and a fire station must be provided. A new commuter road linking Lofthouse to Wakefield will not be necessary because Highway 20, which connects to the Crosstown Expressway, can be widened to meet the traffic demand. The total cost of new services will be $140 million, but the tax base will increase by $24 million annually. The project will result in the loss of 604 ha of prime farmland.

Proposal B: This complex consists of detached homes, townhouses, and high-rise apartments, along with a recreation centre complete with golf course, sports arena, and playing fields. The development will be constructed around the west side of Ardsley Creek and some of the woodland areas will be incorporated into the golf course. In total, the project will consume 980 ha of farmland—552 ha for housing, 84 ha for the sports complex, and 344 ha for the golf course. This high-density project will house 8000 people and will provide an additional $16 million in taxes annually. The initial public spending will be $38 million.

Proposal C: This proposal calls for a mix of low-density housing and a well-designed business park on a large, flat area of land west of Ardsley Creek. This will accommo-

date 10 000 people, which will increase the tax revenue substantially. The new businesses will create jobs. They will also increase truck traffic, so new roads for the business park will be needed. These new services, including road construction, will cost $280 million; new tax revenue will be approximately $42 million annually. The project will result in the loss of 800 ha of prime agricultural land.

Proposal D: This recommends a freeze on further development in Lofthouse for ten years in order to conserve the environment. This will protect the environmentally sensitive ecosystems around Ardsley Creek, which is a unique waterfowl habitat. A walkway through the southern area of the creek will be designated a protected conservation area. Unfortunately, the current residents of Lofthouse will face an increase in taxes as there will be no new sources of revenue. The cost of creating the conservation area will be $8 million; half of this has been promised by the provincial government. No farmland will be lost.

Briefing notes

Megacorp Housing Developments: Your company stands to gain the most from Proposal A. Megacorp is willing to donate land for two new schools if this proposal is passed. This will reduce the cost to the borough by $8 million.

Wakefield Indurealty Inc.: Your company specializes in business parks and owns the largest business leasing and property management company in Wakefield. The company is willing to contribute to the construction of a major road linking the business park to the Crosstown Expressway. This will reduce the cost to the borough by $12 million.

Future Development Ltd.: This American company owns Sportsfutures Ltd., a firm specializing in the construction of residential golf communities. Along with the recreational facilities, your company is willing to contribute to the costs of a major access road to the sports complex and the golf course. This will reduce the cost to the borough by $16 million.

Wakefield Wetlands Society: Your conservation group wants development in Lofthouse kept at a minimum or stopped altogether. You want to preserve the wetlands around Wakefield and consider Proposal D the only alternative. The society is also concerned that local streams will be harmed by stormwater runoff in the northern fringes around existing development and from the increased amount of paved surfaces that would result from any new development. The Wetlands Society has support from the provincial government for the creation of a conservation area.

The mayor of Lofthouse: As mayor, you support further development in the borough. The cost of public services such as police and fire protection is high and more people and businesses are needed to increase the tax base.

27 Assume the role of editor of the *Lofthouse Gazette*. You have just attended a meeting of the Lofthouse Council in which the mayor has presented her/his recommendations. Write an editorial stating your opinion of this proposal.

Figure 18.1
Four types of industry
Identify each photo as primary, secondary, tertiary, or quaternary industry.

Canadians are busy at work. Over 13.7 million people are employed in thousands of different jobs. Each of these jobs contributes to a diverse Canadian economy.

This is a country with abundant natural resources. These resources must be gathered and harvested before they can be shipped to destinations around the world. Canada is also a country with a broad manufacturing base. Canadian industries range from giant iron and steel makers to state-of-the-art technology companies.

There are four basic types of industry. **Primary industries**, such as farming, forestry, fishing, and mining, provide raw materials for use by other industries. (See Unit 3.) **Secondary industries** involve manufacturing. **Primary manufacturing** produces usable products from raw materials; wood, for example, is processed into pulp and paper. **Secondary manufacturing** uses the products of primary manufacturing to make other products; paper, for example, is used to produce newspapers and books. **Tertiary** and **quaternary industries** do not manufacture products. Both of these are service industries. Tertiary industries provide services such as transportation and retail outlets. Quaternary industries provide information services like research and computer technology.

Employment in Canadian industries

Canadians are employed in all types of industries. Often these industries are interconnected. We seldom use a product in our daily lives that has not been changed considerably from the raw materials that were gathered to make it. Transforming raw materials into the products we use involves many different jobs. Figure 18.2 shows all the jobs that are involved in the calculator business.

1 Refer to Figure 18.2.
   a) Describe the jobs that are involved in the manufacturing, distribution, and sale of calculators.
   b) Select another product and create a similar diagram illustrating the jobs that would be involved in this process.

2 Figure 18.3 shows how work is connected in the shoe industry. Complete a similar chart for the following industries: road transport; plastics; forestry; coal mining.

3 Survey your class to determine the number of parents working in each of the four main industries. Create a bar graph to show the results.
   a) List the number of working parents along the vertical axis in intervals of five. Along the horizontal axis indicate the types of industries.
   b) Plot the results of your survey using different colours to illustrate each bar.

4 Figure 18.4 lists employment by industry for all people employed in Canada in 1995.
   a) Calculate the percentage of the total number of Canadians working in each of the main types of industry. For example, the total number of people employed in primary industry is determined by adding Agriculture (394) and Others (263). (Remember: These figures are in thousands of people.) The total of 657 is

Figure 18.2
The manufacturing, distribution, and sale of calculators *This flow diagram shows the variety of jobs in the calculator business, from the mining of raw materials to the sale of the final product to consumers.*

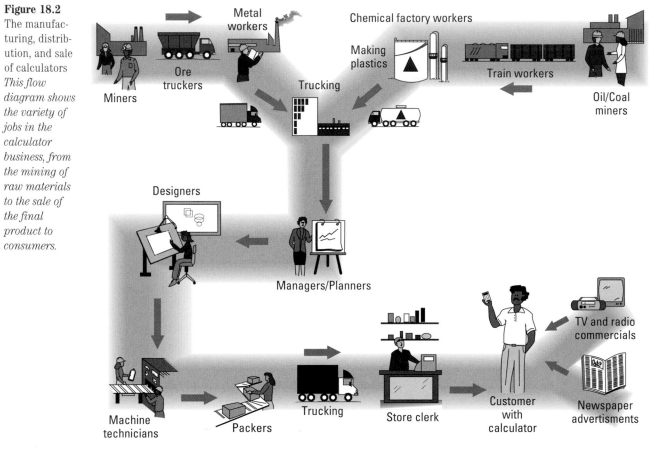

Figure 18.3
How work is connected

INDUSTRY	RAW MATERIALS USED	CATEGORY	PRODUCT	OTHER INDUSTRIES (IF ANY)	SERVICE INDUSTRIES SUPPLIED
Shoes	Leather Steel Oil Jute	Manufacturing	Shoes	Shoe stores	Warehousing Hydro Road and rail Transport Insurance Sales Advertising

EMPLOYMENT BY PROVINCE, 1995
(000)

CATEGORY	NF	PE	NS	NB	PQ	ON	MB	SK	AB	BC	TOTAL
PRIMARY											
Agriculture	–	–	6	5	60	116	36	68	86	17	394
Other (Mining, etc.)	14	–	17	13	40	35	6	11	75	52	263
SECONDARY											
Manufacturing	10	–	38	31	562	897	59	26	109	177	1 909
Construction	9	–	19	16	119	260	21	18	86	117	665
TERTIARY AND QUATERNARY											
Transportation, communication, and utilities	15	4	24	25	220	343	45	34	102	128	940
Trade and commerce	33	10	69	55	519	840	84	76	226	292	2 204
Finance, insurance, and real estate	7	–	20	13	157	333	26	23	67	98	744
Services	76	20	136	111 1	126	1 805	183	156	485	641	4 739
Public administration	17	6	35	24	198	298	34	27	68	96	803
Provincial total	**181**	**53**	**363**	**293**	**3 002**	**4 927**	**492**	**439**	**1 303**	**1 618**	**12 671**

Source: Statistics Canada. Cat. No. 11-001E, 1995.

divided by Canada's total employment of 12 671. The answer (0.0518) is then multiplied by 100. The percentage employed in primary industry is therefore 5.18 per cent.

b) Once you have calculated the percentages for all categories, construct a bar graph to show the results.

c) How does this bar graph compare with the previous one for working parents?

5 Refer to Figure 18.5.

a) Construct a continuous line graph to show changes in employment by industry between 1960 and 1995. Indicate the percentage employed on the vertical axis and the years on the horizontal axis.

b) Plot the percentage employed by each type of industry between 1960 and 1995 and connect these points with a continuous line. Use a different colour for each industry and identify these in a legend.

6 How do the national employment figures compare with those in your province? Calculate the percentages for each of the main industries in your province. Compare these figures with those for Canada. What are the similarities? What are the differences? Can you explain these?

Figure 18.4
Employment by province, 1995

Figure 18.5
Employment by
industry, 1960-
1995

INDUSTRY	1960	1970	1980	1985	1995
			(% of workers)		
Agriculture	11.5	6.3	4.5	4.3	3.3
Other primary	3.5	2.8	2.8	2.6	2.2
Manufacturing	24.7	22.7	19.7	17.5	15.2
Construction	7.0	6.0	5.8	5.2	6.2
Transportation, utilities, communication	8.6	8.8	8.5	7.8	7.3
Trade	16.5	16.1	17.2	17.7	17.9
Finances, real estate, insurance	3.8	4.8	5.7	5.6	6.0
Services	24.5	25.7	28.9	32.3	34.8
Government	na	6.2	6.9	7.1	6.6

na = not available
Source: Statistics Canada.

7 a) Refer to the latest *Canada Year Book* in your resource centre. Under the Employment section find out which ten jobs have shown the greatest increase in numbers over the past ten years.

b) Arrange to have a guidance counsellor visit the class to provide job descriptions and to discuss the changing job market.

c) Arrange a personal interview with the guidance counsellor to find out the best ways for you to prepare for the changing job market. This should include a personal education plan.

Primary industries:
steel manufacturing

Primary manufacturing industries transform raw materials into products that can be used to make other goods. Steel is one of Canada's most important primary manufacturing industries. It is made by combining huge amounts of iron ore, limestone, coal, and scrap iron. First these raw materials are smelted into a hot molten liquid. They are then refined to remove impurities. The result is pure steel. This complex process is illustrated in Figure 18.6.

8 Research the steps involved in making steel. Outline the process, then design a flow chart to illustrate each step. Figure 18.6 will get you started.

In 1994, Canada produced 14.4 million tonnes of steel and ranked thirteenth in the world in steel production. There are five huge steel corporations and fifteen smaller steel companies in Canada. Most steel is produced by the three biggest companies, Stelco, Dofasco, and Algoma. Stelco is located in Hamilton and Nanticoke in Ontario.

Step 1
Once the raw materials—iron ore, coal, and limestone—are mined, they are crushed into fine particles. The coal is heated to remove impurities, creating coke.

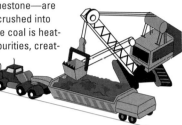

Step 2
The raw materials are transported to steel plants. The limestone and iron ore can be stored in the stockyards, but coke cannot withstand rehandling and must be used immediately.

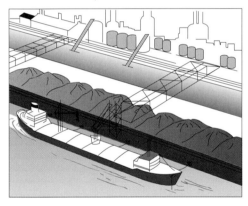

Step 3
The raw materials are loaded into a blast furnace. As the coke burns, the temperatures rise to over 1600°C. This melts the iron ore. The molten metal then flows downward, where it collects on the bottom as a white liquid called pig iron. The limestone acts as a cleansing agent; it mixes with impurities to form slag, which is then drawn off the surface.

Stock house

Raw materials hoisted into blast furnace

Blast furnace

Hot air

Ladle of molten iron

The molten iron is poured from the blast furnace every three to five hours. Some is cast into solid pig-iron blocks and sold.

Step 4
Most of the pig iron is fed into a basic-oxygen furnace and heated. Pure oxygen is mixed with the molten metal to burn off impurities such as silicon and carbon.

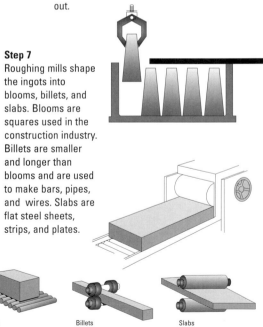

Basic oxygen furnace

Tap hole

Ladle of molten steel

Alloy addition

Step 5
After the steel has been refined, it is poured into a ladle through a tap hole. Alloys or other metals may be added at this stage to create different qualities of steel. The molten steel is then poured into moulds, where it hardens into ingots.

Step 6
The ingots are transported to soaking pits. These are furnaces that reheat the steel to a uniform temperature throughout.

Step 7
Roughing mills shape the ingots into blooms, billets, and slabs. Blooms are squares used in the construction industry. Billets are smaller and longer than blooms and are used to make bars, pipes, and wires. Slabs are flat steel sheets, strips, and plates.

Blooms

Billets

Slabs

Figure 18.6
The steel-making process

Dofasco's steel works are in Hamilton, while the Algoma plant is located in Sault Ste. Marie. Algoma is owned by Dofasco, which makes this Canada's largest steel operation.

Like many industries, steel manufacturing is undergoing change. New technology means that more steel can be produced by fewer people. In recent years, the number of employees in Canada's steel industry has dropped by 25 per cent. But production has continued to increase. New qualities of steel are also being developed. These high-strength, low-alloy metals are 50 per cent stronger than steel produced only a few years ago, but they are 30 per cent lighter.

Steel companies are also taking measures to reduce the negative impact their massive operations have on the environment. Large amounts of gases such as nitrogen oxide and sulphur dioxide are emitted into the atmosphere. These gases mix with water vapour, which eventually results in **acid precipitation**. This precipitation increases the acid levels in lakes, endangering fish and other aquatic life. Environmental experts believe that 15 000 Canadian lakes are "dead" and another 45 000 are "at risk" as a result of acid precipitation. It also contributes to the erosion of many buildings in our towns and cities.

Steel companies and other industries are investing large sums of money in new technology to protect the environment. For example, Stelco has spent $360 million on advanced scrubbers, filtering systems, and other devices. The company has also switched to energy sources with lower carbon levels to reduce pollution. Still, many people feel these measures are not enough to prevent further damage to the environment. Some environmental problems and their solutions are illustrated in Figure 18.7.

9 a) Assume you are a member of an environmental protection organization called Canadians for a Clean Environment. You are concerned about the negative impact of the steel industry in general and the proposals to build a new steel plant at a nearby community in particular. Write a letter to the Canadian Steel Producers Association expressing your concerns.

b) Assume you are the chairperson of the Canadian Steel Producers Association. Write a reply to the letter from the member of Canadians for a Clean Environment.

Case study: the new Stelco plant

In the 1980s, Stelco had to choose a site for a huge new foundry. A steel plant needs access to an extensive water transportation route; this is the least expensive method of transporting materials to and from the site. Both the east and west coasts of Canada offered such water transportation. So, too, did the Great Lakes. But Stelco also wanted ready access to the large markets in southern Ontario and the northeastern United States. This requirement eliminated the east and west coasts as potential sites. This left the Great Lakes Basin, in particular the industrial heartland of southern Ontario. Now the question was, *where* in southern Ontario?

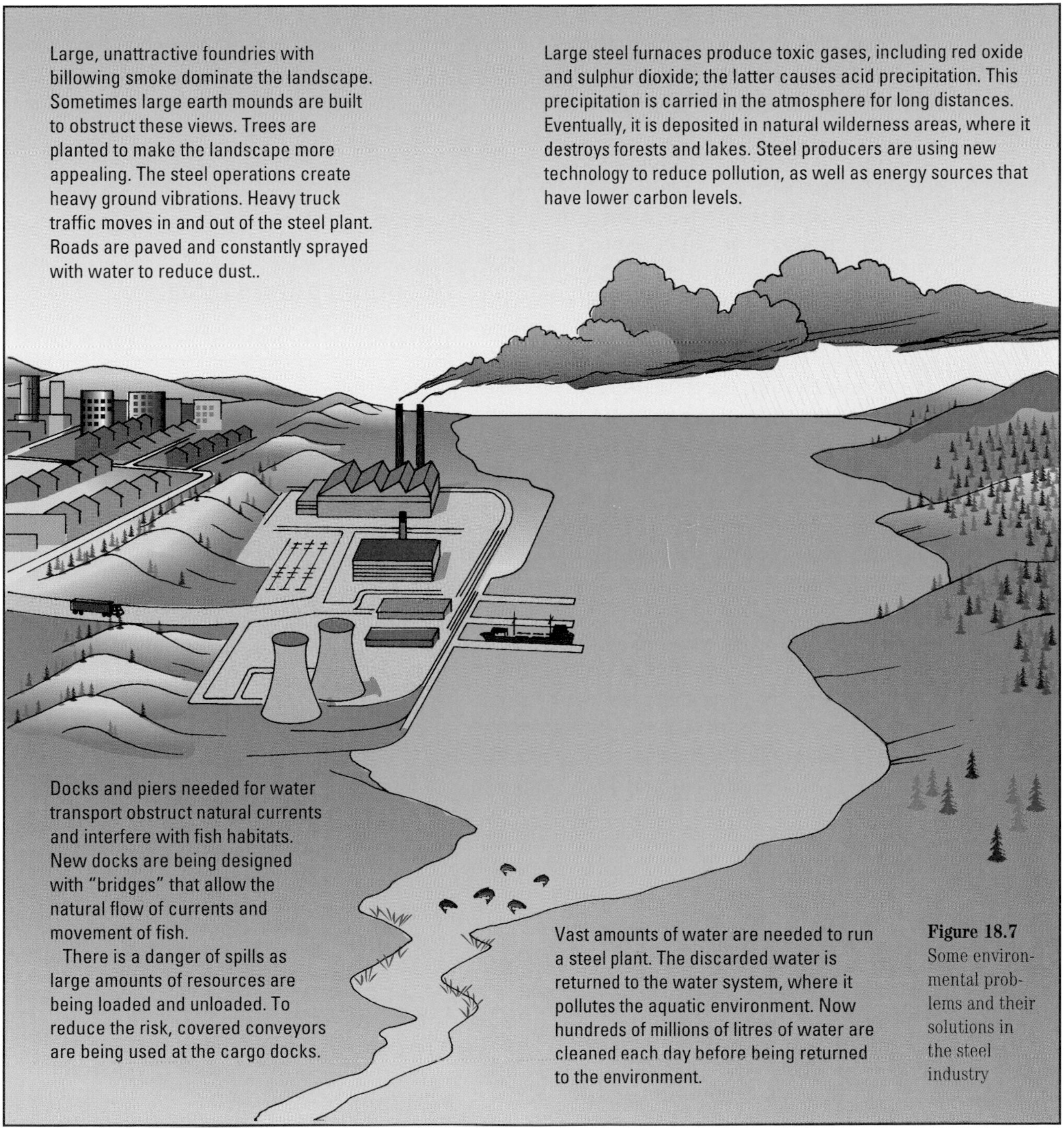

Large, unattractive foundries with billowing smoke dominate the landscape. Sometimes large earth mounds are built to obstruct these views. Trees are planted to make the landscape more appealing. The steel operations create heavy ground vibrations. Heavy truck traffic moves in and out of the steel plant. Roads are paved and constantly sprayed with water to reduce dust..

Large steel furnaces produce toxic gases, including red oxide and sulphur dioxide; the latter causes acid precipitation. This precipitation is carried in the atmosphere for long distances. Eventually, it is deposited in natural wilderness areas, where it destroys forests and lakes. Steel producers are using new technology to reduce pollution, as well as energy sources that have lower carbon levels.

Docks and piers needed for water transport obstruct natural currents and interfere with fish habitats. New docks are being designed with "bridges" that allow the natural flow of currents and movement of fish.

There is a danger of spills as large amounts of resources are being loaded and unloaded. To reduce the risk, covered conveyors are being used at the cargo docks.

Vast amounts of water are needed to run a steel plant. The discarded water is returned to the water system, where it pollutes the aquatic environment. Now hundreds of millions of litres of water are cleaned each day before being returned to the environment.

Figure 18.7 Some environmental problems and their solutions in the steel industry

Six locations were considered. One of the most important factors now was space. A steel plant needs a large area of flat land for the huge foundries and stockpiles of raw materials. Two sites, one on Lake Huron and the other on Georgian Bay, were too far from the main plant in Hamilton. A third potential site was east of Toronto on the north shore of Lake Ontario. But the land prices were extremely high. In addition, the raw materials would have to pass through the Welland Canal, where shipping tolls would be costly. Three other sites were located on the north shore of Lake Erie. Two of these were west of Long Point. But the sandy loam shoreline, combined with the prevailing winds, was vulnerable to erosion. The third Lake Erie site was Nanticoke, just east of Port Dover. Nestled behind Long Point, the area had a stable shoreline sheltered from the prevailing winds. The hard bedrock would support the heavy, vibrating equipment. There was ample space to build the 2640 ha facility and the price of land was reasonable. Bulk materials, such as coal from Pennsylvania, West Virginia, and Kentucky and ore from Michigan, Minnesota, and northern Ontario, could be shipped via the Great Lakes. The site was close to a limestone quarry at Beachville as well as the main plant in Hamilton and the largest markets. To top it off, a coal-fired generating station was located 1.6 km east of the site. Nanticoke had everything that Stelco required for its new plant.

10 a) What were the important factors Stelco had to consider in selecting the location for its new foundry?

b) Select a site for another large steel plant, keeping in mind the factors that influenced Stelco's decision. Use a variety of atlas maps, such as manufacturing, minerals, and population distribution, to help you make your decision. Prepare a rationale explaining why you made your choice.

Secondary industries: automobile manufacturing

Steel is one of Canada's most important primary manufacturing industries. But what happens to all of the steel that is produced in this country? One of the most important uses for steel is in automobile manufacturing. Cars are a way of life in our industrialized society. Four out of every five families in Canada owns a car. There are over 16.5 million vehicles on Canadian roads. In 1994, there were 1.25 million new cars sold in Canada.

The automotive industry is also one of Canada's biggest employers. An estimated one in six Canadian manufacturing jobs is in the auto industry. In total, 130 000 Canadians are directly employed by automobile manufacturers; the "big three"—General Motors, Ford, and Chrysler—account for 80 000 of this total. Another 300 000 people depend indirectly on the auto industry for their employment.

Case study: the General Motors Autoplex system

The automobile came to Canada in 1907. The McLaughlin Carriage Company began in Oshawa building motor vehicles using Buick engines. In 1908, the company became McLaughlin Motor Car Company. In its first year its labour force of 300 produced 154 cars. In 1918, a merger with an American company gave birth to General Motors of Canada.

A lot has happened to the automobile industry since those early days. Today, General Motors employs over 40 000 people and can build more than 700 000 cars and 300 000 trucks and vans a year! **Mass production** was responsible for this remarkable change in the number of vehicles a workforce could produce. The idea was introduced in 1913 by Henry Ford. He established an assembly line at his automobile plant in Detroit. A conveyor slowly moved the car along the assembly line. As it did so, workers performed their specialized tasks until the final product rolled off the assembly line. Mass production resulted in higher productivity—that is, more vehicles were being produced at a faster rate by fewer people.

Today the General Motors plant in Oshawa is the world leader in automotive manufacturing processes. The plant and its 10 000 employees utilize a manufacturing system called autoplex. Instead of a car or truck moving along a conveyor, automated guided vehicles, or AGVs, carry it to a work station. There a number of specialized tasks are performed by several employees. When this work is complete, the AGV transports the vehicle to the next work station. The system allows workers to correct any problems by stopping the AGV before it moves on. The production process is not affected by this delay because similar tasks are being performed at the same time in other

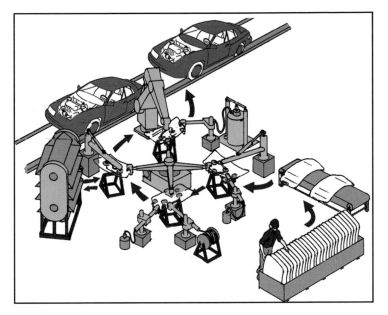

work stations. Thus the AGV system is more efficient and more effective than early assembly lines. In addition, these electric-powered AGVs have turned the once-noisy assembly plant into a quiet, clean, and more relaxed environment.

Many work stations at the GM Autoplex are equipped with computerized machines or robots. Figure 18.8 shows how a robot system installs windshield glass. An operator selects a pane of glass and places it on a conveyor; a robot transfers the glass to a fixture where sealants and other materials are added. The glass is then placed on a curing rack by another robotic arm. It is then installed by yet another robot. General Motors currently uses about 1000 robots at its Oshawa plant.

Figure 18.8
Robotic installation at GM *This illustration shows how windshield glass is installed by robots. The arrows indicate the work flow. What are the advantages of using robots for the employees? For the company? What are the disadvantages for both groups?*

11 Copy Figure 18.9 into your notebook. For the factory without mass production:
  a) Indicate the total costs for wages, raw materials, and the plant in column B.

Figure 18.9
Factory costs before and after mass production

A BEFORE MASS PRODUCTION	**B** COSTS PER WEEK	**C** PRODUCTION	**D** COST PER TRUCK
100 Workers Wages $700 each per week	Wages: _____		Number of trucks (10) ÷ Total cost: = _____ (cost per truck)
Raw Materials (metal, leather, glass) $8000 per week	Materials:_____	10 Trucks	
Plant (hydro, water, etc.) $20 000 per week	Plant:_____ Total cost:_____		

A AFTER MASS PRODUCTION	**B** COSTS PER WEEK	**C** PRODUCTION	**D** COST PER TRUCK
1000 Workers Wages $800 each per week	Wages: _____	1000 Trucks	Number of trucks (1000) ÷ Total cost: = _____ (cost per truck)
Raw materials $800 000 per week	Materials:_____		
Plant $100 000 per week	Plant:_____ Total cost:_____		

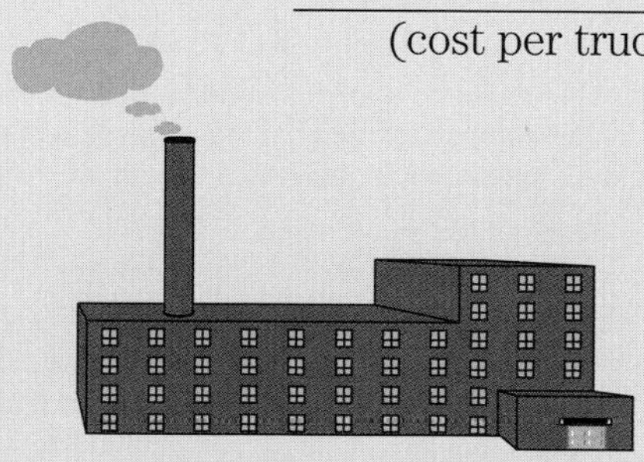

Add these figures together to get the total production cost and enter this in column B as well.

b) Find the cost per truck by dividing the total production cost from column B by the number of trucks produced in column C. Enter this figure in column D.

c) Repeat these steps for the factory after mass production is introduced.

d) What happened to the cost of manufacturing a truck once the company changed to mass production? Explain why the company, the workers, and the consumers would all benefit from mass production.

MATERIAL	1980 (kg)	1994 (kg)
Iron	219.5	185.0
Conventional steel	787.9	629.8
High-strength steel	79.3	119.2
Other steel	36.9	39.6
Aluminum	58.9	82.5
Copper and brass	15.8	19.0
Zinc	9.0	7.3
Glass	37.9	40.3
Plastic	88.4	111.4
Rubber	59.4	60.7
Other	131.9	143.1

Source: General Motors Canada, 1995.

Figure 18.10 Materials required for the average GM car a) Compare the materials used in 1980 with those used in 1994. What main changes have taken place? Suggest reasons for these changes. b) How will these changes affect companies doing business with General Motors?

Although General Motors makes many of its own automotive parts, it buys others from component companies located within 200 km of the plant. These companies specialize in manufacturing specific parts, such as lights, mufflers, steering wheels, and fenders. The current trend is towards manufacturing parts for a broad market. For example, a component company owned by General Motors may produce parts for both GM and non-GM cars. These parts may also be available for sale in service centres and other automotive retail outlets.

Instead of maintaining a large inventory, General Motors orders parts from its local suppliers as they are needed. This is part of the company's **just-in-time delivery and assembly system**. It usually takes no more than an hour and a half for shipments to arrive at the plant once an order has been placed—"just in time" for the workers to install them at their assembly stations! In the future, General Motors hopes to reduce delivery time to a matter of minutes through a computer connected to each supplier.

To add to the efficiency, the component parts are unloaded at docks located next to the work stations where they are needed. This is called **point-of-use delivery**. Some 900 delivery trucks and 100 rail cars bring parts to the GM plant every day. The finished cars, vans, and trucks are loaded onto 180 trucks and 225 rail cars. They are then shipped to dealerships across Canada and the United States. Over 85 per cent of the vehicles produced by GM Canada are bound for US markets.

12 a) What are the advantages for General Motors in having a just-in-time system?

b) Can you think of some disadvantages of not having parts in stock at the assembly plant?

c) How might just-in-time practices affect the operations of the component companies?

COMPANY	LOCATION
General Motors of Canada	Oshawa, ON Ingersoll, ON St. Thérèse, PQ Windsor, ON St. Catharines, ON London, ON Kapuskasing, ON
Chrysler Canada	Windsor, ON
Chrysler Canada	Brampton, ON
Ford Motor Company of Canada	Oakville, ON
Ford Motor Company of Canada	Talbotville, ON
Toyota Canada *	Cambridge, ON
Honda Canada *	Alliston, ON
Volkswagen Canada *	Barrie, ON
CAMI Automotive* (GM/Suzuki joint venture)	Ingersoll, ON
Hyundai Auto Canada *	Bromont, PQ
Volvo Canada*	Halifax, NS

*Foreign Manufacturers

Figure 18.11
Automotive plants in Canada

13 a) Design four symbols to represent car manufacturers in Canada—one each for General Motors, Chrysler, and Ford and one for all foreign manufacturers. On an outline map of Canada, use these symbols to plot the locations of the automotive plants in Figure 18.11. Include a legend.
  b) What can you conclude about the distribution of auto plants in relation to
     i) population distribution (markets);
     ii) exports to the United States;
     iii) access to labour; iv) access to transportation routes?

Tertiary industries

While primary and secondary industries employ thousands of Canadians, by far the largest number of people are employed in tertiary industries. Jobs that provide some type of service fall under this category.

People in both primary and secondary industries rely on the tertiary industry. From the time the iron ore is extracted to the time someone purchases an automobile, hundreds of services come into play. Some of these, like automobile dealerships and transportation services, are obvious; others, like law enforcement and insurance companies, are less so. What other tertiary industries would you associate with automobile manufacturing?

Case study: retailing

Retailers are people who sell products or services directly to consumers. They are the last link in the employment chain before a product reaches its final destination. Nearly 2.5 million Canadians work full time in the retail business; hundreds of thousands more are employed as part-time workers. Retail outlets vary by size, from department store chains employing thousands of workers to small corner shops run by two or three people.

The retail business is an important tertiary industry. It is a strong indicator of the state of our economy. When economic times are good, people feel confident and secure about their jobs. They spend their money more freely on consumer goods, especially expensive items like new cars. When the economy is poor, however, people are concerned about the future. They save their money rather than spend it. Instead of buying a new car, many people make do with their old one or buy a used car. When people stop buying cars and other products, however, manufacturers stop producing. This becomes part of the cycle that contributes to a slow economy.

How do Canadians spend their money? The majority of retail spending is on food and clothing. Automobiles and parts also account for a significant amount of our retail dollars. Figure 18.12 shows total retail sales by trade group in 1994. Figure 18.13 shows retail sales by province across Canada.

TRADE GROUP	SALES	$ MILLIONS
Food	Supermarkets and grocery stores	45 478
	All other food stores	3 333
Medical	Drugs and medicine stores	11 115
Clothing	Shoe stores	1 631
	Men's clothing stores	1 688
	Women's clothing stores	3 605
	Other clothing stores	4 120
Home furnishings	Furniture and appliance stores	7 861
	Household furnishings stores	2 132
Motor vehicles	Motor vehicle stores	43 152
	Gas stations	13 131
	Automotive parts stores	10 914
Other	General merchandise stores	19 709
	Other semi-durable goods stores	6 465
	Other durable goods stores	5 182
	Other retail stores	9 785
Total of all stores		**189 301**

Figure 18.12
Retail sales by trade group, 1994

Source: Adapted from Statistics Canada, Cat. No. 63-005, 1995.

14 Refer to Figure 18.12.
  a) Total the amount of money spent in each retail category.
  b) Calculate the total of each category as a percentage of the total spent across Canada ($189 301 billion).
  c) Draw a rectangle measuring 20 cm x 10 cm to represent a $10 bill. Divide the note into parts according to the percentage of money that is spent in each category. Label the parts. Which category accounts for the highest amount of retail spending by Canadians?
  d) If Canadians had to cut back on their spending, which category would be affected the most? Which category would be affected the least? Explain your answers.

15 Plot the information in Figure 18.13 on a bar graph.

  a) Draw a horizontal axis 22 cm long and label the provinces and territories along it.
  b) Draw a vertical axis 12 cm long; this represents billions of dollars spent. Using the scale 1 cm:$5 billion (2 mm:$1 billion), mark the intervals along the vertical axis. Don't forget to indicate the scale on your graph.
  c) Plot the retail dollar figures for each province/territory as a bar graph. Shade in each bar.

16 Compare spending in each province and territory with the provincial population. To discover retail spending per capita, divide the amount of money by the population. Rank the provinces and territories from highest spending per capita to lowest.

17 For each province, calculate i) the net growth in millions of dollars and ii) the

| PROVINCE/TERRITORY | $ BILLIONS | | POPULATION (000) |
	1986	1994	1994
Newfoundland	2.39	3.15	582
Prince Edward Island	0.57	0.80	135
Nova Scotia	4.79	5.99	937
New Brunswick	3.46	4.56	759
Quebec	34.68	46.09	7 281
Ontario	53.40	69.70	10 928
Manitoba	5.43	6.35	1 131
Saskatchewan	5.01	5.71	1 016
Alberta	14.19	19.94	2 716
British Columbia	15.32	26.33	3 668
Northwest Territories and Yukon	0.39	0.60	94

Source: Statistics Canada, Cat. No. 63-005, 1995.

Figure 18.13
Retail trade by province, 1994

percentage growth in retail sales
between 1986 and 1994. What conclusions
can you make about the retail business
during this period?

Quaternary industries

We live in an age of information. By the early twentieth century, there will be twenty times more information worldwide than there is today. At one time industries that involved the flow of information were classified as tertiary. Today, however, this rapidly growing industry has developed into a category of its own: quaternary industry. Some of the greatest employment opportunities in the future will be in these businesses.

Research and development, commonly called R and D, is a quaternary industry. People who work in R and D look for innovations to improve existing industries and create new ones. Canadian governments, colleges and universities, and industries invest large sums of money in R and D. In Canada, our vast and diverse geography has contributed to our need for innovative technologies.

The new information superhighway is rapidly emerging in Canada and around the world. (See pages 429–430.) Businesses, hospitals, schools, governments, libraries, and consumers will soon have links to billions of pieces of information through cable, telephones, modems, and satellite receivers. This information industry will create tens of thousands of jobs for Canadians. In 1994, Canada's major telephone companies committed to spending $9 billion on the Beacon Initiative over the next ten years. This will upgrade national phone lines and allow more information to be accessed by home and business computers. Consumers will be able to plug into information on such things as shopping, travel, weather, and business. They will also be able to renew a driver's licence, pay their bills, check home security systems from another location—even sit in on a rehearsal of the National Ballet of Canada! Eventually this technology will be in 13 million homes across Canada.

The construction and maintenance of the Beacon Initiative alone will produce 12 000 jobs for engineers, systems designers, programmers, and others. Thousands more will be added as the information superhighway expands around the globe.

18 List five jobs in the quaternary industry.

19 Research and development are important to all industries. Discuss how the geography of Canada may have been responsible for the following Canadian developments:
a) satellite communications
b) hydroelectric power dams
c) microwave and telephone communications
d) alternative sources of energy
e) hearty strains of wheat.

20 Why might Canada benefit more than other countries from the information superhighway?

Case study: financial institutions

Financial institutions, such as banks, trust companies, and credit unions, are tertiary industries that are being transformed into quaternary industries. Increasingly, daily banking transactions rely on computers. Billions of dollars are moved through the economy each day. Most of this movement takes place without a single piece of hard currency ever exchanging hands!

Canada has over sixty independent banking companies, with over 7700 branches employing over 180 000 Canadians. In 1994, the Canadian banking industry had nationwide assets of $771 billion!

In the past, an important location consideration for a business was to be close to a source of capital. In this age of computer technology, however, businesses can conduct complicated financial transactions on computers. They do not need to see or speak directly with a bank employee, even while they are transferring large amounts of capital from one account to another.

For the average consumer as well, computers perform many of the tasks once carried out by bank employees. Automated banking machines, or ABMs, have revolutionized the industry. Customers can transfer or deposit money, obtain cash, and pay certain bills from a simple-to-use computer system installed at their branch or another convenient location. The number of ABMs across the country is increasing almost daily. It is expected this trend will continue as banks offer even more services through these machines. Figure 18.14 shows the provincial distribution of banking services.

Direct banking, in which consumers can pay a bill in a store directly out of their bank accounts, is another innovation that is changing the industry. Simply by using

Figure 18.14
Number of bank branches in Canada and automated banking machines, 1994

PROVINCE/TERRITORY	BRANCHES	ABMS	POPULATION (000)
Newfoundland	138	141	582
Prince Edward Island	34	32	135
Nova Scotia	278	377	937
New Brunswick	200	251	759
Quebec	1 594	1 990	7 281
Ontario	3 206	5 579	10 928
Manitoba	329	456	1 131
Saskatchewan	377	339	1 016
Alberta	706	1 381	2 716
British Columbia	854	1 596	3 668
Northwest Territories and Yukon	28	18	94
Total	**7 744**	**12 160**	**29 247**

Source: Canadian Bankers Association, *Annual Report*, 1994.

TREND	1984	1994
Number of branches	7 060	7 744
Automated banking machines	2 279	12 160
Employees	147 776	180 000

Source: Canadian Bankers Association, *Annual Report*, 1994.

Figure 18.15
Canadian banking trends

their bank cards, customers can pay for their purchases without using cash or their credit cards.

21 a) Calculate the average number of people per bank branch in each province or territory.
   b) Which provinces have more than the average number of people per branch? Which provinces have less?
   c) Where would you recommend that more banking services be provided in Canada?
   d) Based on the average, how many bank branches should a city of 18 165 have?

22 Although the number of ABMs has increased six times since 1984, the number of bank employees has also increased. Why do you think this is so? What does this suggest about the types of jobs that are increasing in this industry? Identify other service industries that may be affected by increasing automation.

Sunrise and sunset industries

Advances in science and technology have revolutionized our lifestyle in the last fifty years. Before modern telecommunications, families gathered in their living rooms to listen to their favourite programs—on the radio! Now many families have communications centres equipped with televisions, video systems, multi-media computers, and telephone-answering machines.

Industries that are relatively new and increasing in number are called **sunrise industries**. Many industries associated with aerospace, communications, and computers, for example, fall into this category. Industries that are outdated as a result of changing technology or decreasing demand are declining in number or disappearing altogether. These are called **sunset industries**. The tobacco business is declining because of a decrease in demand for tobacco products; personal computers have led to the decline of typewriter manufacturing as the new machines offer a faster and more efficient means of written communication.

23 a) List three sunset industries that have declined or disappeared since your parents were teenagers.
   b) List three sunrise industries that have developed within the last ten years.
   c) What industries do you think might become sunset industries in the future? Why?

Canada's level of industrialization

Industrialization is the process by which countries manufacture products for consumption at home and abroad. Although Canada has a large natural resource base, we also have an important manufacturing sector. Canadian goods are produced for our domestic market and for foreign markets around the world. How industrialized is Canada compared with other countries? The appendix on page 466 lists selected countries by income level. The data provides a variety of information. Some of this can be used to measure and compare Canada's level of industrialization.

24 a) Select three categories that you believe are appropriate indicators of industrialization. Explain your choices.
   b) For one of the categories you chose, design an appropriate graph to show Canada's position relative to the other countries. Make sure that the graph is labelled correctly and gives a clear message to the reader. Show your finished graph to a partner and ask her or him what the graph shows.
   c) Write a conclusion describing what your graph reveals about Canada's level of industrialization.

Looking at one type of information for several countries is one way to make a simple comparison. But often we need to compare two or more types of information to see if there is a connection or relationship. To do this, we usually start with a **hypothesis**. This is an idea that we wish to prove. For example, we suspect that there is a connection between a country's wealth and its level of industrialization. We want to prove that a higher per capita income is found in countries with a high level of industry. How can we test this hypothesis?

A good method of determining if there is a relationship between two sets of information is to use a scattergraph. Figure 18.16 is a scattergraph. The two sets of data plotted are GNP per capita (the total wealth produced by a country divided by its population) and the percentage of people employed in agriculture. (We have assumed that the fewer number of people employed in agriculture, the more people there are employed in manufacturing.)

25 Create a graph similar to Figure 18.16. On it, plot the GNP per person and the percentage employed in agriculture for each country.
   a) Each axis of your graph should be 20 cm long. Label each axis as it is in Figure 18.16.
   b) To plot the data for each country, first find the GNP per capita. For example, in

Figure 18.16
A scattergraph to test a hypothesis

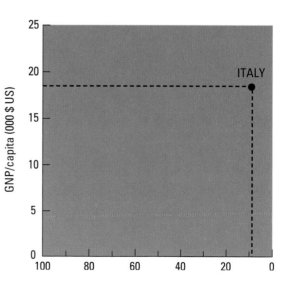

Italy this figure is 18 840. Find this point on the vertical axis. Now find the per cent employed in agriculture. In Italy, this is 9 per cent. Find this point on the horizontal axis. Mark the point at which the data intersect with a dot and label it Italy. (In the example, the broken lines are there only to show how to plot each country; do not include these on your graph.)

c) Once you have plotted all of the dots, study the pattern that has been created. Does it support your hypothesis? Explain.

Location factors in industry

Primary location factors

In establishing a business, many factors must be considered. People go into business to make a profit. Profit is the amount of money remaining once all the costs have been deducted from the company's income. To increase profits, companies need to keep costs down. Choosing an appropriate place for the operation of a business can help to reduce costs.

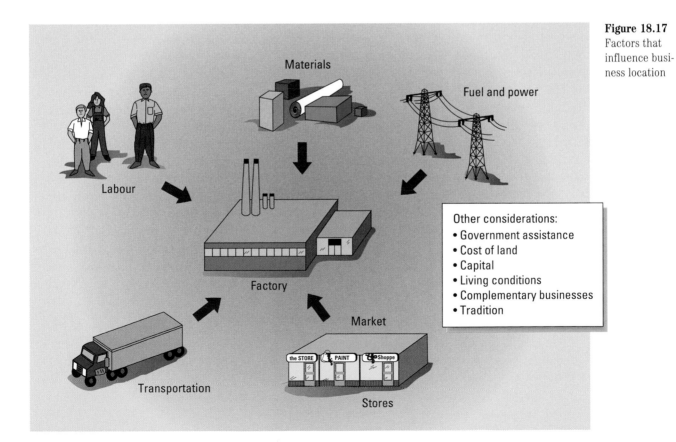

Figure 18.17 Factors that influence business location

Materials

Fuel and power

Labour

Other considerations:
• Government assistance
• Cost of land
• Capital
• Living conditions
• Complementary businesses
• Tradition

Factory

Transportation

Market

Stores

Businesses have a variety of needs that influence their choice of location: the availability of materials; a supply of skilled workers; a source of power, especially if manufacturing is involved; access to transportation; and an accessible market. Of course, some of these needs may be more important than others, depending on the type of business. Figure 18.17 illustrates factors that may influence business location.

Other location factors

Some manufacturers choose their locations for other reasons. They may wish to locate near their competitors because this tends to attract a larger number of customers for comparison shopping. Government incentives, such as grants, interest-free loans, and tax breaks, may be offered in order to stimulate economic growth and create jobs. Sometimes lower land costs attract businesses that need large areas of land. The quality of life, including housing developments, schools, and recreational facilities, may attract certain businesses. In other cases, tradition may dictate that certain businesses locate in a particular area.

26 Identify the factors that influenced the following decisions:
   a) a furniture superstore has moved next to a competitor
   b) a clothing designer has opened a design studio in the garment district
   c) a large engineering company has received an interest-free loan in a province where there is high unemployment
   d) a publishing company has moved to a spacious location on the outskirts of a city
   e) a company has renovated and expanded at its existing site because the staff prefer the present location.

Case study: a pulp and paper mill in La Baie, Quebec

Stone-Consolidated Corporation has a large pulp and paper mill in La Baie, Quebec. (See pages 173–174.) It is located near vast forests and close to a deep-sea port on the Saguenay River. An abundance of energy is available near the site. Figure 18.18 shows the factors that contribute to the mill's costs. Its tree harvest—over 766 t a year of mostly spruce and balsam—is collected from an average distance from the mill of 160 km. Logs are hauled to the mill by semi-trailers. Advanced technology is used in processing; computers control the mill's four paper machines and automatic rollers. The latest pollution controls have been installed. Over 600 employees produce an annual wage bill of over $40 000 000. Fifty per cent of the finished product—392 000 t of publisher-grade newsprint—is transported by rail, truck, and ship to the United States. Approximately 10 per cent remains in Canada. The rest is destined for countries around the world.

27 Locate La Baie on an atlas map of Quebec. Describe the advantages of this location in relation to i) the natural resources of the Canadian Shield; ii) a major transportation system; iii) its proximity to large urban markets.

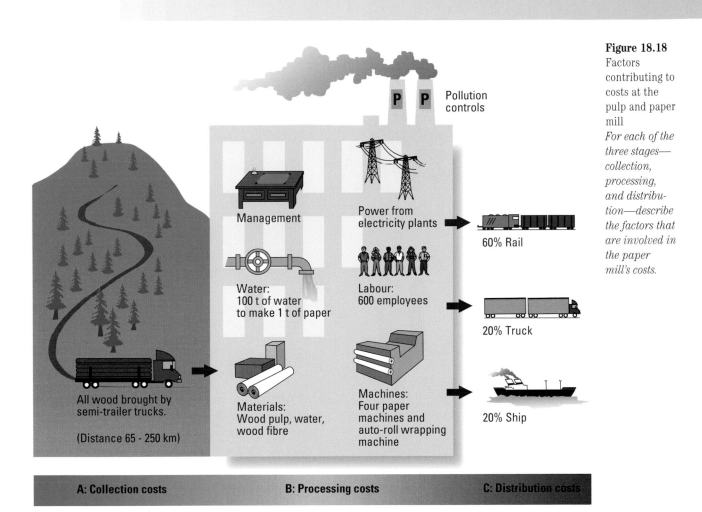

Figure 18.18
Factors contributing to costs at the pulp and paper mill
For each of the three stages—collection, processing, and distribution—describe the factors that are involved in the paper mill's costs.

Pollution controls

Management

Power from electricity plants

60% Rail

Water: 100 t of water to make 1 t of paper

Labour: 600 employees

20% Truck

All wood brought by semi-trailer trucks.

(Distance 65 - 250 km)

Materials: Wood pulp, water, wood fibre

Machines: Four paper machines and auto-roll wrapping machine

20% Ship

A: Collection costs   **B: Processing costs**   **C: Distribution costs**

28 Raw materials are important to the location of a fruit-canning business. Because fresh fruit bruises easily and spoils quickly, canning factories are usually located near fruit farm operations. Describe the location factors shown in Figure 18.19.

29 Bread needs to be consumed quickly, before it goes stale. It is also bulky, which means it can be costly if it has to be transported long distances.

a) Draw a diagram showing the important location factors for a bakery.
b) Is a bakery a primary manufacturing or a secondary manufacturing industry? Explain your answer.

30 Aluminum, produced from bauxite ore, is widely used in the construction industry. Canada imports bauxite from Guyana in South America. The production process requires a lot of energy. Large smelting

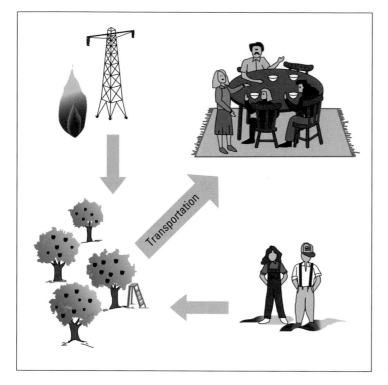

Figure 18.19
Fruit canning

operations are located at Arvida, Baie Comeau, Alma, Beauharnois, and Shawinigan in Quebec.

a) Draw a diagram showing the important location factors for the aluminum smelting industry.

b) Using an atlas, discover what necessary requirement each of the five smelting locations has.

c) Is a smelting operation a primary manufacturing or a secondary manufacturing industry? Explain your answer.

31 The computer industry requires highly trained technicians for the manufacturing of hardware and software. There is fierce competition to find people with the necessary skills and experience.

a) Draw a diagram showing the important location factors for a computer company.

b) What type of industry is a computer company?

32 Bulk commodities like grain require an inexpensive method of transportation. This is usually by water or rail. Consequently, flour mills tend to be located near water routes or major rail lines.

a) Draw a diagram showing the important location factors for a flour mill.

b) Is a flour mill a primary manufacturing or a secondary manufacturing industry? Explain your answer.

Footloose industries

Footloose industries are not influenced by any one location factor. They do not need to be near large markets or have access to vast amounts of energy. There is no demand for a large, specialized labour force. The raw materials and finished products are so small and of such high value that transportation costs are of little concern. So footloose industries can locate almost wherever they please! Computer software companies and jewellery manufacturers are good examples of footloose industries.

33 a) Give two examples of footloose industries. Explain why these industries can locate almost anywhere.

b) What type of industry is each of these examples?

Simulation: selecting an industrial location

Now it's your turn to find the best location for a manufacturing plant. Consider each of the following location factors:

Collection and distribution (transportation) costs

- Your manufacturing company will use a single raw material; this can be obtained at Rawville. (See Figure 18.20.)
- Your plant will manufacture a single product; it will be sold only in Marketville.
- Rawville and Marketville are 100 km apart by rail.
- The town of Semiville is halfway between Rawville and Marketville.
- Freight rates are $2.00 per tonne of raw material and $4.00 per tonne of finished product.
- 100 t of raw material can be converted into 100 t of finished product.

34 Consider each of the three centres, Rawville, Semiville, and Marketville as a possible site for your factory.
   a) Copy Figure 18.21 into your notebook. Calculate the collection-distribution costs as well as the total transportation costs to produce 100 t of finished product. For example, the collection costs of obtaining raw material for the Rawville location will be "$0" because the raw materials are already there. However, the distribution costs from Rawville to Marketville will be $400 (100 km x $4 per km). The total transportation costs for the Rawville location will therefore be $400 ($0 + $400).
   b) Based on collection and distribution costs only, which town would be the best location for your plant?

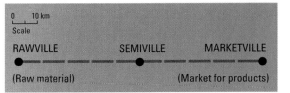

Figure 18.20
Selecting a site

Labour costs

Wages paid to factory employees are part of the process costs. They are another factor in determining where to locate a business because wage rates may vary from one community to another.

In this simulation, 100 h of labour are required to process 100 t of raw material into finished products. The number of labour hours is the same at each location,

POSSIBLE LOCATION	COLLECTION COSTS (raw materials)	DISTRIBUTION COSTS (to market)	TOTAL TRANSPORT COSTS
Rawville			
Semiville			
Marketville			

Figure 18.21
Transportation costs

Figure 18.22
Labour costs

POSSIBLE LOCATION	WAGES PER HOUR	x	NO. OF HOURS	=	TOTAL LABOUR COSTS	+	TRANSPORT COST	=	TOTAL COSTS
Rawville									
Semiville									
Marketville									

but the wage rates are different. In Rawville, workers earn $15.00 an hour; in Semiville, they earn $10.00 an hour; in Marketville, the hourly wage is $20.00 an hour.

35 Copy Figure 18.22 into your notebook.
   a) Calculate the cost of labour needed to produce 100 t of finished product in each location.
   b) Add the total cost of labour for each location to the cost of transportation.
   c) Considering labour and transportation costs only, which would be the best location for your factory?

Energy costs

The cost of energy needed in manufacturing is another process cost. The cost of energy to produce 1 t of finished product also varies in each of the three locations. The cost per tonne in Rawville is $4.00; in Semiville, it is $12.00; in Marketville, it is $25.00.

36 Copy Figure 18.23 into your notebook.
   a) Calculate the energy costs required to produce 100 t of finished product in each location.
   b) Add the total energy costs to the totals for transportation and labour for each location.
   c) Taking into account all three factors, which would be the best location for your factory?

Other influences

The government is concerned about high unemployment in Semiville. As a solution, it wants to attract new industries to the area. As an incentive, the government is offering to offset 50 per cent of the labour costs of any new industry locating in Semiville by reducing taxes. How might this influence your decision about the location of your plant?

37 Review your final cost chart from activity 36. Make the necessary changes to the

POSSIBLE LOCATION	ENERGY PER HOUR	x	100 t	=	ENERGY COSTS	+	TRANSPORT COSTS	+	LABOUR COSTS	=	TOTAL COSTS
Rawville											
Semiville											
Marketville											

Figure 18.23
Energy costs

Labour costs column based on the government incentive.

Exchange rates and business

Sometimes the international value of money can influence the success of a Canadian company, especially when much of its trade is with other countries. How does the value of the Canadian dollar influence the success of a business?

Case study: Mould Tech Ltd.

Mould Tech Ltd. is a mould manufacturing company located north of Toronto. It makes precision moulds for the manufacture of a variety of items in the automobile and arms industries. It has a workforce of thirty people and a total annual wage cost of $1.4 million. Other costs, for the factory lease, benefits, and transportation, are $800 000 a year. The company also imports a large number of engineered moulds from Halfo Ltd., of Manheim, Germany. The cost of these imports is approximately $1 million a year. The same products could be imported from the United States, but the cost would be $1.4 million.

So far Mould Tech Ltd. has been doing well. Its present income from sales to the auto industry is $2.1 million. Sales to the Department of National Defence are $1.4 million. Other domestic sales are worth $300 000.

38 a) What is Mould Tech's total revenue?
   b) What are Mould Tech's total costs?
   c) How much profit does Mould Tech make?
   d) Calculate Mould Tech's profit margin—that is, profits as a percentage of total costs. (Divide profits by total costs and multiply by 100.)

Mould Tech has been fairly profitable. During the past year, however, the company has faced a financial challenge. At the beginning of the year, 1 German deutchmark was worth 80 Canadian cents. But the German currency has increased in value. Now 1 German deutchmark is worth 1 Canadian dollar. This is a 20 per cent increase in its value. Now it costs Mould Tech $1.2 million to import mouldings from Halfo Ltd.

39 a) What is the new profit margin after the increase in the value of the German deutchmark?
   b) What other option is available to Mould Tech? How would this affect its profit margin?
   c) Based on these figures, do you think Mould Tech should change its foreign supplier of parts? Explain your answer.

40 a) Suppose the Canadian dollar increased in value by 25 per cent. How would this affect the profit picture for Mould Tech?
   b) If a Canadian company were selling materials to a German company during the period, who would benefit the most?

Manufacturing distribution across Canada

The manufacturing index indicates the distribution of manufacturing across the country. Each province's share of manufacturing is determined by dividing the percentage of manufacturing value by the percentage of population. For example, Newfoundland has a manufacturing value of 0.3 per cent and 2.1 per cent of the country's population. Therefore its manufacturing index is 0.14. If manufacturing were equally distributed across Canada, there would be 1 per cent of manufacturing for every 1 per cent of population in each province.

41 Refer to Figure 18.24.
   a) Rank the provinces according to their share of the value of manufacturing.

Indicate the percentage share of population beside each one.
   b) Calculate the manufacturing index for each province.
   c) Is manufacturing evenly distributed across Canada on a provincial basis? Explain your answer.

42 a) What are the advantages of having the majority of manufacturers concentrated in one area?
   b) What are the advantages of having a more even distribution of manufacturing across Canada?

43 a) Using an atlas, identify the types of manufacturing found in each province.
   b) Select one province that does not have a large manufacturing industry. Using various atlas maps, identify the factors that might account for this lack of manufacturing.

Figure 18.24 Provincial share of manufacturing and percentage of population, 1994

PROVINCE/TERRITORY	VALUE OF MANUFACTURING (%)	POPULATION (%)
Newfoundland	0.3	2.1
Prince Edward Island	0.2	0.5
New Brunswick	2.1	2.7
Nova Scotia	1.5	3.3
Quebec	23.9	25.3
Ontario	52.6	36.9
Manitoba	2.0	4.0
Saskatchewan	1.3	3.6
Alberta	7.1	9.3
British Columbia	8.8	12.0
Northwest Territories and Yukon	0.1	0.3

Source: Statistics Canada, Cat. No. 11-001E, 1995.

Destination of manufactured goods

Figure 18.25 shows what happens to products manufactured in Canada. Some are sold within the manufacturing province. The rest are exported to other provinces or countries. When products are sold outside the province, the people of the province benefit from the revenues received. This helps to maintain economic prosperity. The incoming money pays wages and makes jobs more secure. When people spend these wages, they create spin-off benefits for other businesses and people. On the other hand, if a province imports more manufactured products than it sells, more money leaves the province to pay for these goods. This means there is less money available for the province and the people who live there.

44 Create a graph to illustrate the information in Figure 18.25.
   a) Draw five columns, each 10 cm high and 2 cm wide. These represent the five regions. Label the regions along the horizontal axis. Label the percentage of production in 10 per cent intervals along the vertical axis.
   b) For each region, mark the bar graph to represent the amount of production that remains within the area. For example, in British Columbia, 42.6 per cent remains in the province. Colour these sections of the bar graphs.
   c) Calculate the percentages sent to other parts of Canada. To find this figure, add the amount remaining in the region and the amount exported, then subtract this total from 100. For example, in BC the figure is 14.1 per cent (42.6 + 43.3 = 85.9; 100 − 85.9 = 14.1). Using a second colour, add these figures to the appropriate bar graphs.
   d) Using a third colour, shade the remainder of each bar graph to show the percentage of manufactured goods exported to other countries. (This figure is 43.3 per cent for BC.) Don't forget to include a legend!

Figure 18.25
Destination of products as a percentage of production

TO \ FROM	BRITISH COLUMBIA	PRAIRIES	ONTARIO	QUEBEC (%)	ATLANTIC	EXPORTED
British Columbia	42.6	8.6	3.2	1.7	0.6	43.3
Prairies	6.8	66.5	7.0	6.2	1.0	12.5
Ontario	3.1	6.7	51.8	10.5	2.8	25.1
Quebec	2.2	4.5	17.0	51.8	3.3	21.2
Atlantic	1.2	2.3	8.4	8.6	47.1	32.4

Source: Statistics Canada.

45 Review the graph you just created.
a) Which regions consume the majority of their own manufacturing?
b) Which regions export the majority of their manufacturing?
c) Does a province's geographic location appear to influence the likelihood of products being exported to other countries?
d) Before you can determine which is the most important exporting province, what additional data do you need?

Regional economic differences

In a large country like Canada, there are differences in economies from one region to another. Some regions prosper; others do not. Wages and unemployment rates are good indicators of how well a province is performing economically. Figure 18.26 shows the average weekly earnings and the unemployment rate across Canada.

There are many causes of regional economic differences. Climate, for example, dictates that agriculture in southern Saskatchewan is quite different from that in Newfoundland. The distribution of natural resources means that some provinces, like British Columbia, have large metallic mineral resources, while others, like Nova Scotia, do not. Distance from the manufacturing base in southern Ontario and southern Quebec means that customers in Newfoundland and British Columbia may

PROVINCE/TERRITORY	AVERAGE WEEKLY EARNINGS ($)	UNEMPLOYMENT RATE (%)
Newfoundland	532	20.4
Prince Edward Island	453	17.1
Nova Scotia	497	13.3
New Brunswick	503	12.4
Quebec	544	12.2
Ontario	604	9.6
Manitoba	499	9.2
Saskatchewan	487	7.0
Alberta	552	8.6
British Columbia	577	9.4
Yukon	687	na
Northwest Territories	704	na
Canada	**553**	**10.4**

Figure 18.26 Economic indicators, 1995

na = not available
Source: Statistics Canada, Cat. No. 75-001E, 1995.

pay more for products because of transportation costs. Large concentrations of population in some parts of the country enable these places to enjoy services that are not available to those in less populated regions.

Regional economic problems may worsen through the **vicious circle**. When a region has slow economic growth, low wages, and high unemployment, other factors come into play. It becomes hard to attract highly trained people from other areas to the region. In fact, many local workers leave for better wages elsewhere, taking their skills with them. In turn, companies are less likely to move to an area with a declining population and a dwindling supply of skilled workers. Fewer people also means less tax revenue. As a result, social services like health care and education may suffer from a lack of funding. And so economic problems grow worse.

46 a) Which provinces rank above the national average in weekly earnings? Which provinces rank below the national average?

   b) Which provinces rank above the national average in unemployment? Which provinces rank below the national average?

   c) Which provinces rank above the national average in both average weekly earnings and unemployment? Which provinces rank below the national average in both categories?

   d) Design a visual technique to show average weekly earnings and unemployment, by province, on an outline map of Canada. Include a brief written summary of these regional differences.

47 Create a diagram to illustrate the vicious circle in a region experiencing economic difficulties.

The Canadian government, as well as some provincial governments, are decentralizing their operations. This means they are relocating some ministries outside of Ottawa or the provincial capitals to other places in the country or province. Sometimes this is to provide jobs in certain regions or to create equal opportunity for government positions. Sometimes, however, decentralization results in services being relocated to remote communities, far away from the majority of the population.

48 a) Discuss the arguments for and against decentralization.

   b) Suggest which regions of Canada should be selected for the relocation of each of the following federal departments, and explain why: Agriculture; Energy, Mines, and Resources; Fisheries and Oceans.

Equalization payments

The federal government helps all provincial governments pay for their social services. Less prosperous provinces receive a greater amount of money towards these costs. The additional funds are called **equalization payments**. This system is intended to ensure that Canadians in all regions of the country receive adequate social services. In 1994-95, six provinces qualified for equalization payments. (See Figure 18.27.)

Figure 18.27
Provinces receiving equalization payments, 1994-95

PROVINCE	$ MILLIONS
Newfoundland	964
Prince Edward Island	190
Nova Scotia	934
New Brunswick	948
Quebec	3900
Manitoba	918
Saskatchewan	605
Total	**8459**

Source: Atlantic Canada Opportunities Agency, 1995.

49 Compare the information in Figure 18.27 with the economic indicators in Figure 18.26. What connections can you make between these statistics?

Government assistance

Four agencies have been established by the federal government to provide economic development assistance. These are Western Economic Diversification Canada (WD), the Federal Office of Regional Development—Quebec (FORD-Q), the Atlantic Canada Opportunities Agency (ACOA), and Federal Economic Development in Northern Ontario (FEDNOR). The objective of these agencies is to promote new business opportunities in an effort to increase the economic base. The agencies focus on the development of small- and medium-sized businesses, providing low-interest loans and other incentives to entrepreneurs. They also try to eliminate the duplication of services between businesses and governments and encourage diversification of the economy. But as the federal government is forced to cut spending in an effort to reduce the deficit, funding for these agencies is becoming more limited. Figure 18.28 shows total reductions in regional assistance between 1994 and 1998.

Case Study: Atlantic Canada

The Atlantic region has been dealt some severe economic blows in recent years. In addition to the economic recession experienced across Canada, there were major cutbacks in the fishing, pulp and paper, and mining industries. The collapse of the fishing industry alone resulted in over 30 000 layoffs. The Department of National Defence also closed many military facilities in the region. As a result, unemployment in Atlantic Canada in 1995 was 15 per cent,

Figure 18.28
Regional agency funding, 1994-98

	1994-95	1995-96	1996-97	1997-98
Spending levels ($ millions)	1 138	1 313	798	576

Source: Atlantic Canada Opportunities Agency, 1995.

4 per cent higher than the national average of 11 per cent.

The problem in Atlantic Canada is a lack of economic diversity. The economy is largely resource-based, with limited secondary manufacturing. As a result, when the resource industries experience difficulties, there are few employment alternatives.

The Atlantic Canada Opportunities Agency (ACOA) was established in 1987. Its objectives are to promote small- and medium-sized business ventures that create jobs and diversify the economy. Headquartered in Moncton, New Brunswick, the agency has regional offices in the provincial capitals of Nova Scotia, Prince Edward Island, and Newfoundland.

In 1995, the federal government announced another economic assistance program for Atlantic Canada. The Atlantic Groundfish Strategy (TAGS) will spend $1.9 billion over five years to restructure the Atlantic fishery. This includes the renewal of fish stocks as well as retraining programs for those people forced out of the fishing industry. The federal government will also work with the provincial governments to create more business and job opportunities in aquaculture, tourism, and information technologies.

In Newfoundland, the government has also developed a Strategic Economic Plan to help overcome its fisheries crisis. New companies locating in the province will have a tax "holiday"—that is, they will be exempt from paying provincial corporate income taxes, payroll taxes, and retail sales taxes for ten years. They will also have the opportunity to purchase crown land (land owned by the government) at low prices.

50 Working with a small group, act as business consultants to the governments of the Atlantic provinces.
  a) Make five specific recommendations for new businesses in this region. For example, some fishing families have turned to tourism, offering attractions like whale-watching excursions.
  b) Share these recommendations with other groups. What similarities and differences do you notice?

We know that Canada is a huge country. It stretches 5140 km from its easternmost point at Cape Spear, Newfoundland, to its westernmost point at the Yukon/Alaska border. From north to south the country spans 4634 km from Cape Columbia on Ellesmere Island to Middle Island in Lake Erie. Because of its size, one of the greatest challenges Canada faces as a nation is connecting this vast land. How do people, resources, goods, and information flow across the country?

Systems

In a country as large as Canada, it is most efficient for people to control their immediate environment. Each province manages its own natural resources, health care systems, education, and other social services. The federal government is responsible for those things that are in the national interest, such as the economy and defence.

Whenever small working parts come together to form a whole it is called a **system**. Although each part of a system is separate, each is necessary in order for the whole to function. Think of an automobile. The transmission, engine, and wheels are all separate parts and each performs its own special task. But if one part doesn't work, the whole system of the car breaks down.

The Canadian settlers had little contact with people and places outside their own community. Communications systems did not exist. In fact, the main reason for completing the railway from coast to coast in the 1880s was to provide a system that would connect all of the people who lived in this vast land and to create a sense of a single nation. Today, however, a person in St. John's, Newfoundland, can communicate with someone in Victoria, British Columbia, within hours by plane, or within seconds by telephone or fax.

Systems are a common element of our daily lives. Consider the postal system. Canada Post Corporation delivers 29 million pieces of mail each working day! To make the process of sorting and delivering the mail as efficient as possible, Canada has a system of **postal codes**. These are a series of six letters and numbers that readily identify the destination of each piece of mail. The first letter in the code refers to a specific area of the region. The M in the code M5V 3E6, for example, indicates the destination is Metropolitan Toronto. The remaining five digits direct the mail to specific areas and delivery routes within the city.

Postal codes can be read by electronic scanners. This speeds up the sorting process and allows the mail to reach its destination much faster. Figure 19.1 shows the divisions of the Canadian postal code system.

One of the most common communications systems today is the telephone. In Canada, there are 85 telephones for every 100 people. In fact, Canadians make more telephone calls than any other people in the world—an average of 1300 calls per person each year!

To telephone people in other parts of the country or the world, we use another system called **area codes**. Each region or country has its own area code. This enables us to place most long-distance calls ourselves without the assistance of an operator. Direct long-distance calling is easy. We simply dial 1, the area code, and the telephone number. Area codes are listed in the telephone directory.

In Canada, we can find phone numbers in other parts of North America through Information. The Information telephone number across Canada and the United States is 555-1212. All we have to do is dial 1 and the area code before this number and we will be connected with the Information operator for that region.

1 Refer to Figure 19.1.
   a) Identify the region for each of the following postal codes: i) H3C 9Z7; ii) S4R 1A3; iii) C7V 9L2; iv) V6A 2X7; v) N2B 5L9.
   b) How have political boundaries been used to establish the postal code system?
   c) What other boundaries have been added? Why are these boundaries necessary?
   d) Certain letters of the alphabet have not been used in the postal code system. Can you explain why some letters have been omitted?

2 Identify the area codes for each of the following cities: i) Saskatoon; ii) Charlottetown; iii) Winnipeg; iv) Montreal; v) Vancouver.

Figure 19.1
Postal codes and telephone area codes in Canada

Area codes (in brackets)

A Newfoundland	J Quebec West	R Manitoba
B Nova Scotia	K Eastern Ontario	S Saskatchewan
C Prince Edward Island	L Central Ontario	T Alberta
E New Brunswick	M Metropolitan Toronto	V British Columbia
G Quebec East	N Southwestern Ontario	X Northwest Territories
H Metropolitan Montreal	P Northern Ontario	Y Yukon

Movement

In today's society, there is tremendous movement, or flow, of people, goods, and information from one place to another. The connections established by these movements are called **linkages**; the routes they take are called **pathways**. In selecting pathways to our destinations, we usually apply the **principle of least effort**. This means we choose the shortest, most convenient, and least costly means of transportation.

Networks

If we moved only between two points we would need only one pathway. But movement in today's society is not so simple. Often people, goods, and information move through a complex web of linkages and pathways. This is called a **network**.

3   In your notebook, draw five circles at random to represent five locations within a community. Link these locations with a network of roads. Try to design a network that uses the fewest number of pathways in the most efficient means possible.

One of the most common networks can be seen in the development of a community. In early Canadian settlements, people either travelled by horse or on foot.

Often they created their own pathways across fields instead of using the simple roads that were available. Eventually this created a network of local streets around the Central Business District.

As settlements developed and expanded, the distances people travelled increased. The introduction of streetcars expanded the transportation network in the community as people could now live further away from the business district. This is called the cascading effect: people are attracted to a fast, inexpensive pathway that satisfies the principle of least effort.

In the 1920s, mass production of the automobile meant that people could live beyond those areas serviced by streetcars. Roads called collectors were built to gather automobile traffic from local streets. From

Figure 19.2
Yonge Street in Richmond Hill, north of Toronto, circa 1900
This streetcar carried people back and forth from the suburbs to the CBD.

the collectors, arterial roads that carried traffic around the outskirts of the community were built. Highways were then added to link distant communities with one another; because they could accommodate large volumes of traffic, people and businesses moved to areas with easy access to highways.

The **grid** pattern in Figure 19.3 is the most common street pattern in Canadian towns and cities. Developed in the 1900s, this north-south/east-west pattern is most common in downtown areas. After 1945, in-filling began between arterial roads. This gave people the opportunity to live in quieter areas, but remain close to arterial roads that would take them downtown. New street designs of winding roads, crescents, and cul-de-sacs began to emerge. (See Figure 19.5.)

4 a) Copy Figure 19.3 onto a piece of paper. Shade in the areas that are likely to attract new development.
   b) Describe how the streetcar system changed the shape of the community.

5 Add a grid of arterial roads to Figure 19.3.
   a) Shade in the areas that would develop with the introduction of arterial roads.
   b) Draw highways connecting the area with other communities.
   c) Shade in areas around the highways that might attract development.
   d) Describe the pattern of this community.

6 On an overlay, trace the street pattern shown in Figure 19.5. How would you describe this pattern?

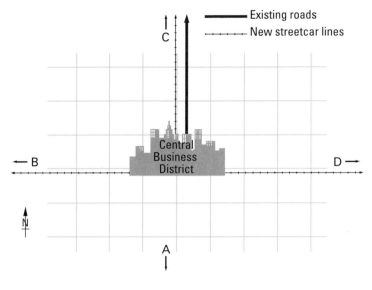

Existing roads
New streetcar lines

7 Find two city maps in an atlas.
   a) Describe the pattern or shape of each of these communities.
   b) How might these communities have been shaped by important pathways?
   c) How might the physical landscape have influenced the routes of these pathways?

Figure 19.3
Streetcar systems

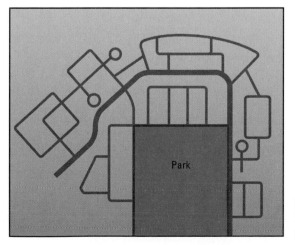

Figure 19.4
Irregular street patterns

Figure 19.5
A modern
subdivision

Pathway capacity

There is a limit to the number of vehicles a road can carry at one time. This is called the **carrying capacity**. Figure 19.6 shows the carrying capacity of different types of roads. If the number of vehicles exceeds carrying capacity, then traffic slows down.

Overload of the carrying capacity happens twice a day in most cities, during rush hour when the majority of people travel to and from work. Seventy-eight per cent of people travel to work by car. We might expect that most rush-hour commuting takes place between the suburbs and the Central Business District. But is this really true?

8 Figure 19.7 shows the travel patterns across a city. Measure the width of each arrow. Using the scale, calculate the percentage of work-related journeys:
   a) from home to work when both locations are within the CBD;
   b) from home in the suburbs to work in the CBD;
   c) from home to work when both locations are in the suburbs;
   d) from home in the CBD to work in the suburbs.

9 Figure 19.8 shows the time and number of vehicles that travel to and from the Toronto suburbs to the CBD.
   a) On a piece of graph paper, draw a horizontal axis 16 cm in length to represent the 1 h periods between 07:00 and 23:00

TYPE	WIDTH (m)	USE	CARRYING CAPACITY (vehicles/ lane/hour)	SPEED (km/h)
Highway	50+	Large volume of traffic, without journey interruption over long distances	1800	Max. 100
Arterial	25–45	Moderate to high volume of traffic travelling short to medium distances. Plenty of access. Links to collectors and freeways	700	60–80
Collector	20–25	Light volume of traffic from local to arterial roads	Small	Max. 50
Local	Up to 20	Very light volume of traffic from points of origin	Very small	Max. 40 or less

Figure 19.6
Carrying capacity of different roads

h. Each centimetre will represent 1 h. Label the line.

b) Draw a vertical axis 8 cm high. This represents the volume of people travelling to or from downtown within each 1 h period; 1 cm represents 10 000 people.

c) Plot the inbound figures at appropriate vertical points for each hour. Join these points with a continuous coloured line.

d) Plot the outbound figures in the same way using a different colour.

e) Label the rush-hour periods on your graph.

f) Review your graph. Is there any evidence of reverse commuting—that is, people living downtown and working in the suburbs? What are the implications of these commuter patterns for the city's transportation network?

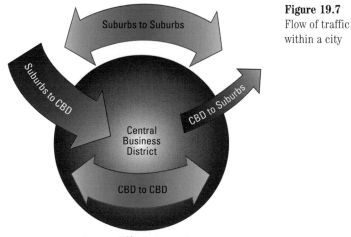

Figure 19.7
Flow of traffic within a city

1 mm = 3% of commuters

TIME	INBOUND	OUTBOUND
07:00—08:00	42 000	17 000
08:00—09:00	75 000	24 000
09:00—10:00	43 000	16 000
10:00—11:00	28 000	14 000
11:00—12:00	26 000	17 000
12:00—13:00	25 000	23 000
13:00—14:00	23 000	24 000
14:00—15:00	23 000	26 000
15:00—16:00	26 000	40 000
16:00—17:00	37 000	61 000
17:00—18:00	34 000	65 000
18:00—19:00	22 000	34 000
19:00—20:00	19 000	25 000
20:00—21:00	12 000	19 000
21:00—22:00	9 000	18 000
22:00—23:00	8 000	16 000

Source: Metropolitan Toronto Planning Department, 1994.

Figure 19.8
Hourly travel to and from the Toronto suburbs to the CBD

Simulation: solving the traffic problem in Clear River

Figure 19.9 is a map of the city of Clear River. Its population of 1.9 million people spreads inland as far as 25 km from the ocean. About 35 per cent of its rush-hour traffic flows from the suburbs to the Central Business District. This presents a traffic problem.

When the city first began to grow in the 1930s, it expanded to the northwest into an area north of Highway 50. In later years, commuting corridors to the downtown core were built. In 1950, an existing rail line into the city was supplemented by the Valley Expressway, which ran along the Clear River Valley. In 1958, a subway system was opened. It stretched from the CBD west along Highway 50 and then to the northwest into the suburbs.

In the last twenty-five years, the area south of Highway 50 has seen considerable development. The Crosstown Expressway links this part of Clear River to the subway line and the Valley Expressway. The entire area has an extensive grid system of arterial roads.

10 a) Describe the route you would take to get downtown if you lived in each of these areas: B5, F5, J5.
  b) Which of these areas has the best commuter links with downtown?

Clear River's population continues to grow. The existing transportation routes are at capacity during rush hour. Most commuters are frustrated by the traffic, especially those who live south of Highway 50. Many of these people believe they should have the same transportation network as exists north of Highway 50 instead of having to use the slow-moving arterial roads. Commuters north of Highway 50 believe a new expressway in the south will ease the load on their transportation facilities.

The Clear River Metropolitan Council is under pressure to do something about commuter traffic. Four alternatives are under consideration: an extended subway system; additional expressways; a new light rapid transit system; and better management of the arterial road system. The details of each alternative are given in Figure 19.10.

Select four groups of no more than four students to represent the planners. Each planning group is to submit a proposal for one of the alternatives in Figure 19.10.

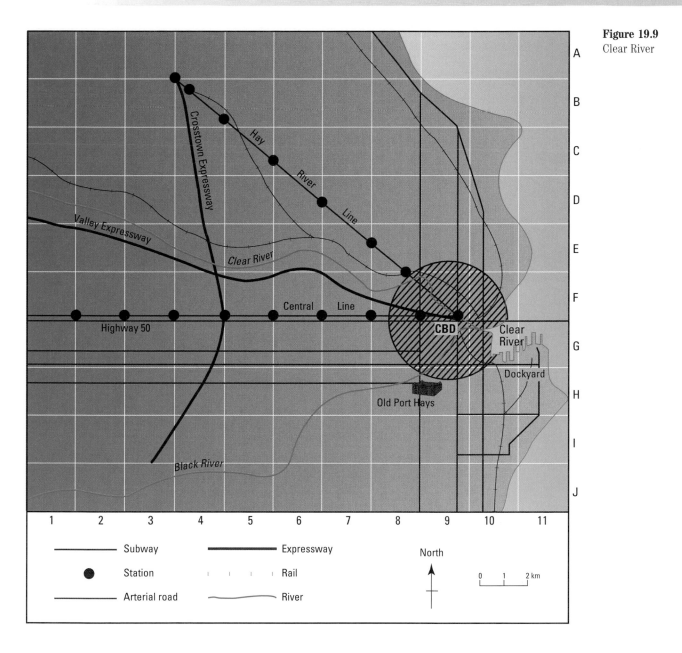

Figure 19.9
Clear River

The interest groups described in the briefing notes on page 409 will also present their positions. Assign these roles to other members of the class. The rest of the class will constitute the Clear River Metropolitan Planning Committee. One student should be chosen to chair the committee and maintain order.

Figure 19.10
Alternative
solutions to the
transportation
problem in
Clear River

Traffic Management of Arterial Roads
- cost: $2 000 000 per km
- carrying capacity: an additional 500 cars
- travel time: saves 10 min per trip
- street parking restrictions
- more computer-controlled lights
- more one-way streets
- better traffic policing
- reversible lanes (one-way traffic to CBD in the morning, reversed to the suburbs in the evening)
- more buses and private bus lanes
- fewer accidents than existing system
- increased revenue for downtown parking
- no extra personal costs

Additional Expressways
- cost: $35 000 000 per km
- carrying capacity: 1800 cars per lane per hour
- travel time: cuts 10 min from existing trip to the CBD
- convenient
- private
- increases land values near access points
- safer than driving on ordinary roads

Light Rapid Transit
- cost: $60 000 000 per km
- carrying capacity: 8000 people per hour in either direction
- travel time: saves 10 min each way
- surface rail line
- easy access through multiple stops
- affordable fares

An Extended Subway System
- cost: $175 000 000 per km (including stations)
- carrying capacity: 40 000 people per hour
- travel time: 20 min to the CBD
- completely underground
- quiet and non-polluting
- increases land values near subway stations
- downtown parking not needed
- few homes or businesses need to be demolished
- affordable fares
- subway stations link to bus routes

11 For members of the planning group:
  a) Create a large outline map of the present transportation network in Figure 19.9. Add the changes your group proposes.
  b) Present a **cost-benefit analysis** of your group's proposal based on the information in Figure 19.10. Under separate headings, list all the monetary costs and benefits and all the social costs and benefits of your proposal.
  c) Prepare a statement outlining your proposal to be read at the next meeting of the Clear River Metropolitan Planning Committee. NOTE: Do not distort the facts! These are available to the public.

12 For members of the interest groups:
  Study each transportation alternative. Prepare your arguments in support of the alternative you favour. Be prepared to explain why you object to the other alternatives. Be sure to use persuasive arguments to convince council members to see things your way!

13 For the committee members:
  Once the planning groups have prepared their proposals, hold the council meeting. Allow each planning group five minutes to make its presentation. Committee members must be prepared to question each group about its proposal. When all four presentations have been made, allow each interest group two minutes to present its position. The committee members should then evaluate the alternatives and weigh the opinions of the interest groups before voting for the proposal they feel is best for the community.

Briefing notes

- *A metropolitan councillor:* You represent the commuters of the southwest area, who want the problem resolved quickly.
- *A downtown retailer:* As a store owner, you want better transportation access to the CBD to attract more shoppers.
- *A representative of a downtown residents group:* Your group opposes an expressway because it would increase the number of vehicles on downtown streets. Instead, it favours some type of mass transit.
- *A member of the Clear River Historical Society:* The society is concerned that any extensive construction would mean that some historic buildings would be destroyed.
- *A business representative:* You and your business colleagues are concerned that many businesses would be forced to relocate if an expressway were built.
- *The chairperson of the Clear River Ratepayers Association:* The association believes that local taxes are already too high and you oppose any project that will increase taxes.
- *A real estate developer:* Your company favours a subway line because it offers the opportunity to develop prime land around the new subway stations.
- *A member of the Nature Conservation Society:* The society wants to preserve the natural state of the Black River Valley and its ravines in the south.

14 Prepare a front-page news story to announce the planning committee's decision in the *Clear River Tribune.* Your story

should contain highlights of the council meeting, including the statistics that support the plan. Include a map showing the new transportation routes as outlined in the winning proposal.

15 Write a letter to the editor of the *Clear River Tribune* explaining why you do or do not support the decision reached by the planning committee.

Road network planning

The price of land and materials used in construction makes roads and rail lines expensive to build and maintain. Since these permanent pathways affect the people who use and live near them, important decisions must be made before construction can begin.

Distance and size are two factors that influence highway design. The greater the distance between two places, the less traffic there will be travelling between them. On the other hand, the larger a city is, the more traffic there will be travelling between it and neighbouring cities.

16 a) On an outline map of your region, plot the cities with populations greater than 30 000.

b) Draw the highway network on your map. Use topographic map symbols to indicate the types of roads. What general pattern does this network create? How have size and distance influenced this pattern?

17 a) Add important railway lines between cities onto your highway map. Do the

rail lines follow the same pattern as the highways?

b) Are there other important pathways in your region? If so, mark these on your map.

c) Has the network of transportation in your region been affected by any physical features? Explain.

National transportation patterns

Canada is a huge country. Early settlers arriving on the east coast bound for the prairies may well have been discouraged when they discovered that after their long journey they still had thousands of kilometres to travel! Even today it takes several days to transport products by road or rail across the country. In addition to distance, the rugged Canadian landscape creates other transportation difficulties, as does our often harsh winter climate. As a result, Canada has developed a unique pattern of transportation linkages. Figure 19.11 shows Canada's road and rail routes as well as our air, water, and pipeline systems.

18 a) On an outline map of Canada, draw a grid like the one in Figure 19.11 and label it the same way.

b) For each square on the grid that represents land area in Canada, assign 1 point for each transportation use it contains. A square that contains four or more systems will receive 4 points. For example, square 3M contains two types of transportation, the Dempster

Figure 19.11
Transportation networks

Oil pipeline

Gas pipeline

▼ International airport

Main railways

Ferries

Trans-Canada Highway and other main roads

Great Lakes – St. Lawrence Seaway

Highway and a gas pipeline, so it will receive 2 points. Pencil in the total points for each square.

c) Now shade each square according to its intensity of pathway usage using the following legend: 4 points—dark red; 3 points—medium red; 2 points—light red; 1 point—medium yellow; 0 points—no colour.

In a small community, a **mainstreet** is always the busiest road. It is here that we find the most people, stores, and traffic. Canada's transportation pattern has been described as one long, linear mainstreet. When goods and people move across the country they usually make contact with this important corridor.

19 Refer to the map you created in the previous activity and to Figure 19.11.
a) On your map, draw a thick line along what you believe to be Canada's mainstreet.
b) Describe the general pattern of linkages in the corridor and explain the reasons for these.

20 a) On a tracing-paper overlay of your mainstreet map, plot Canada's twenty largest CMAs. These are listed on page 309.
b) What is the relationship between the distribution of these cities and Canada's mainstreet?

21 Refer to a map of climate regions in Canada in an atlas.
a) Describe the climate regions along the mainstreet from west to east. Which climate regions do not come into contact with the mainstreet?

b) Write a summary describing the relationship between Canada's transportation system and its climate.
c) What other physical factors may influence the location of the mainstreet? Use an atlas to find examples.

Linkages

Figure 19.12 shows the number of hours it takes to travel between the centres of the fifteen largest CMAs in Canada using the fastest means of transportation—usually air. For example, to find out how long it would take to travel from downtown Winnipeg to downtown Windsor, locate Winnipeg in the vertical column, then follow the horizontal line across until it meets Windsor's vertical line. The number of hours (four) is indicated at this point. We can use this data to determine which city is the most accessible from all other cities. If we add Windsor's vertical or horizontal column of figures, we get a total of sixty-five hours. This is Windsor's **accessibility index**.

22 a) Calculate the accessibility index for each CMA. Canada's most accessible city is the one with the fewest hours needed to reach it from all other cities.
b) Rank the CMAs from most accessible (1) to least accessible (15).
c) In which area of Canada's mainstreet are the most accessible cities found? Can you explain why?

The larger a place is, the more vehicles flow into and out of it. We might expect, therefore, that larger places have better transportation routes to and from

	CAL	EDM	HAL	HAM	KIT	LON	MON	OTT	QUE	STC	TOR	VAN	VIC	WDR	WIN
Calgary	—	2	7	6	7	7	5	5	7	7	5	2	3	7	3
Edmonton	2	—	7	6	7	7	5	5	7	7	5	2	3	7	3
Halifax	7	7	—	5	5	5	3	3	4	5	4	9	10	6	5
Hamilton	6	6	5	—	1	1	4	4	4	1	1	8	8	2	6
Kitchener	7	7	5	1	—	1	5	4	5	1	2	8	8	2	6
London	7	7	5	1	1	—	4	4	5	1	2	8	8	2	6
Montreal	5	5	3	4	5	4	—	2	2	4	3	8	8	5	4
Ottawa	5	5	3	4	4	4	2	—	3	4	3	8	8	4	4
Quebec	7	7	4	4	5	5	2	3	—	5	4	8	8	5	6
St.Catharines	7	7	5	1	1	1	4	4	5	—	2	9	9	2	6
Toronto	5	5	4	1	2	2	3	3	4	2	—	6	6	2	4
Vancouver	2	2	9	8	8	8	8	8	8	9	6	—	2	8	5
Victoria	3	3	10	8	8	8	8	8	8	9	6	2	—	9	6
Windsor	7	7	6	2	2	2	5	4	5	2	2	8	9	—	4
Winnipeg	3	3	5	6	6	6	4	4	6	6	4	5	6	4	—

Based on airline schedules at the time of publication.

Figure 19.12
Accessibility of Canada's top 15 CMAs by fastest route

them and are generally more accessible than smaller places. Is there a relationship between population and accessibility?

23 Compare each city's accessibility ranking with its population on page 309. Are larger cities more accessible (based on the index score) than smaller cities?

A city that has many different types of transportation routes leading into it is called a **transportation node**. It is possible to identify nodes by counting the number of important pathways that radiate from a city. Maps showing air routes are helpful for this.

24 a) Obtain a map of Winnipeg in your library resource centre. Count the number of important pathways that radiate from the city. Indicate these totals by category.

b) Repeat this exercise for Canada's ten most populated cities, then rank the cities according to their total number of important pathways.

c) Compare these rankings with those for the accessibility index. Are cities that are transportation nodes more accessible?

Canada's ports

A **port** is a place through which people and products enter and leave a country. The term applies to both airports and seaports. Canada has many important ports through which millions of people and products pass each year. Ports are vital links that allow both people and goods to flow between Canada and many international destinations. As we move towards a global economy and world travel increases, these ports will become even more important.

Airports

Air travel is important to a country as large as Canada. In 1893, the fastest way to travel from one side of the country to the other was by train. The trip took 115 h! Today we can fly from Halifax to Vancouver in about 8 h. Millions of people travel by air. In 1994, there were 9.4 million passengers flying within Canada; another 6 million passengers flew from Canada to other countries. Nine out of every ten of these travellers are flying on business. Therefore air travel is important to the Canadian economy.

Canada has several large international airports. These airports are part of the major flight routes in the country. They are the main gateways for people and products entering or leaving these regions. The flights that take off and land at these **transportation hubs** may be travelling across the country or around the globe.

International airports service not only the surrounding area, but the greater region as well. Smaller local flight paths radiate outward from the hub like spokes from a wheel. (See Figure 19.13.) Travel between the hubs and their surrounding centres is serviced by smaller commuter airlines. Figure 19.14 shows the hubs and spokes of airline routes in Canada.

25a) Count the number of routes that radiate outward from Vancouver i) to other hubs and ii) to smaller centres.
  b) Which cities would you consider to be the main hubs for Air Canada?
  c) Describe the flight path from i) Ottawa to Iqaluit and ii) Edmonton to Timmins.

Canada's busiest airport is Toronto's Pearson International. Over 175 000 aircraft land at Pearson each year. That's 480 flights a day! Figure 19.15 on page 416 highlights the twenty busiest routes in Canada during a typical three-month period.

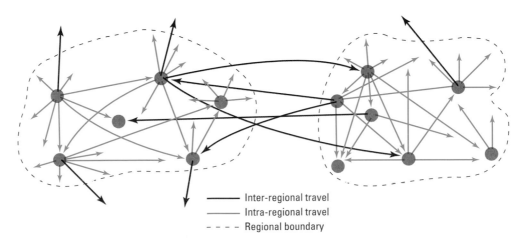

Figure 19.13
Inter- and intra-regional air travel

——— Inter-regional travel
——— Intra-regional travel
– – – Regional boundary

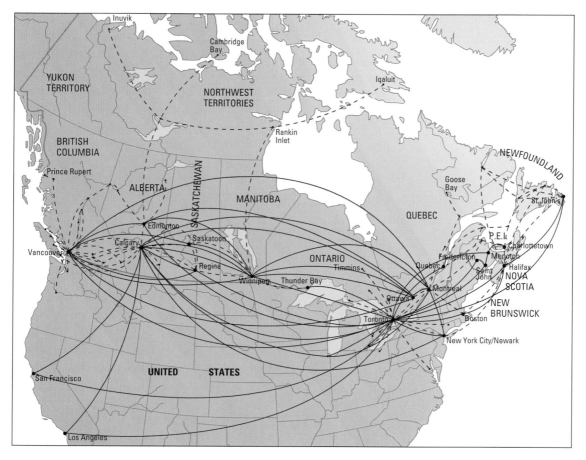

Figure 19.14
Hubs and spokes of airline routes in Canada

26 a) On an outline map of Canada, plot each city in Figure 19.15. Draw bars connecting the pairs of cities in each route. The width of each bar should be based on a scale of 1 mm for every 10 000 passengers. Do not shade in the bars until all of them have been drawn as some bars will overlap.

b) What are the five busiest transportation nodes?

c) Describe the pattern of passenger air travel that is created across Canada. How similar is this to Canada's transportation mainstreet?

d) There is a great deal of movement between Ottawa and Montreal. Why do you think this did not appear on a list of Canada's busiest air passenger routes?

RANK	CITY PAIRS	NUMBER OF PASSENGERS
1	Montreal-Toronto	261 000
2	Ottawa-Toronto	152 000
3	Toronto-Vancouver	107 000
4	Calgary-Edmonton	74 000
5	Calgary-Vancouver	73 000
6	Calgary-Toronto	65 000
7	Edmonton-Vancouver	55 000
8	Halifax-Toronto	52 000
9	Toronto-Winnipeg	48 000
10	Edmonton-Toronto	40 000
11	Thunder Bay-Toronto	34 000
12	Vancouver-Victoria	33 000
13	Montreal-Vancouver	30 000
14	Ottawa-Vancouver	28 000
15	Prince George-Vancouver	27 000
16	Calgary-Winnipeg	25 000
17	Vancouver-Winnipeg	24 000
18	Kelowna-Vancouver	24 000
19	Halifax-Ottawa	20 000
20	Halifax-Montreal	20 000

Source: Statistics Canada, Cat. No. 51-004, 1995.

Figure 19.15
Number of air passengers between cities in a typical three-month period

Most large ports handle a variety of cargo. Some ports, however, specialize in one or two products, such as grain, iron ore, or coal. Industries that rely on cargo shipments often locate near ports. Flour mills, for example, may be found around ports that handle grain shipments.

Seaports have changed a great deal over the years. Port authorities have had to keep up with new technology in both shipping and facilities in order to maintain their volume of traffic. As ships have become larger, the need for deep-water ports has increased. As a result, some piers, like the coal-loading facility at Robert's Bank near Vancouver, had to be extended into deeper waters. Ports have also had to equip themselves with specialized mechanical handling facilities for bulk materials and containers. They have also adapted to **intermodal transportation**. This container system allows cargo to be transferred easily to trains or trucks. (See page 424.) Container ports are easy to identify with their large stacks of containers, special hoists or cranes, and rail and truck lines that run into the container port.

27 a) Rank each of the ports in Figure 19.16 according to its importance for both domestic and international trade.
   b) Which are inland ports?

Seaports

Canada's major seaports are located along the southern part of the east and west coasts. They provide Canada with excellent gateways to international destinations, particularly for the trading of raw materials and manufactured goods. Canada also has inland ports. These are located primarily on the Great Lakes-St. Lawrence water system. While these ports may be well away from the open sea, they are able to accommodate many ocean vessels.

The St. Lawrence Seaway

In 1959, a major breakthrough in North American shipping was made when the St. Lawrence Seaway system was opened. This shipping pathway established a route from

PORT	DOMESTIC CARGO (000 t)	INTERNATIONAL CARGO (000 t)	PORTS TOTAL (000 t)
Vancouver, BC	2 547	56 330	58 878
Sept-Îles, PQ	4 366	16 653	21 019
Port Cartier, PQ	4 013	15 257	19 270
Saint John, NB	1 931	17 336	19 266
Montreal, PQ	5 089	10 718	15 807
Halifax, NS	2 885	11 293	14 178
Quebec City, PQ	3 670	9 508	13 178
Hamilton, ON	6 562	5 832	12 394
Prince Rupert, BC	110	11 256	11 328
Thunder Bay, ON	7 666	3 613	11 279
Canada Total	**99 951**	**121 985**	**324 111**

Figure 19.16 Canada's ten busiest ports, 1993

Source: Statistics Canada, Cat. No. 54-205, 1995.

the mouth of the St. Lawrence River at the Atlantic to the western edge of Lake Superior. It offered easy access to the massive markets of eastern Canada and the United States.

The St. Lawrence River, flowing eastward from the Great Lakes to the Atlantic Ocean, had long been used for transportation. Native peoples called the waterway "river without end." But for European settlers, the river did indeed have an end. When Jacques Cartier's ships moved upstream in 1534, they were forced to stop at the site of Montreal by what we today call the Lachine Rapids. Over the years, canals were built that enabled smaller vessels to cross these rushing waters. But it was not until 1955 that construction began on the most advanced waterway engineering project in the world. For the next four years, Canada and the United States jointly set out to replace the outdated canal system. The St. Lawrence Seaway system created seven locks that enabled large vessels to cross the rapids. The project opened up the Great Lakes to all sea traffic from the Atlantic.

Today, the St. Lawrence Seaway is one of the most important international water routes in the world. Before 1959, larger ocean-going vessels were not able to enter the Great Lakes. Most of the commodities shipped into and out of the heavily populated industrial region had to be transported through a combination of water and overland routes. The new system of locks and canals now allows ships up to a maximum of 222 m in length and 35 m in width to enter the Great Lakes. These large vessels, called lakers, can carry bulk cargo from Thunder Bay to European ports for less than the former overland transfer costs alone!

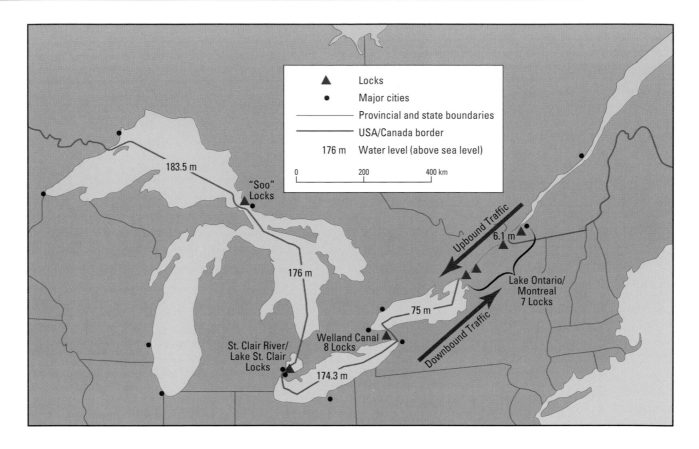

183.5 m

"Soo" Locks

176 m

Upbound Traffic

6.1 m

Lake Ontario/ Montreal 7 Locks

75 m

Welland Canal 8 Locks

Downbound Traffic

St. Clair River/ Lake St. Clair Locks

174.3 m

Legend:
▲ Locks
• Major cities
— Provincial and state boundaries
— USA/Canada border
176 m Water level (above sea level)

0   200   400 km

Figure 19.17 The Great Lakes–St. Lawrence Seaway system

The Seaway has made shipping in eastern Canada much more profitable. Shipping is now able to compete with the bulk handling capabilities of the railways. The Seaway has also increased the importance of the Great Lakes ports, and over the years has contributed to the region's industrial growth.

28 Refer to Figure 19.17.
  a) On an outline map of the Great Lakes–St. Lawrence region, label the bodies of water, major cities, and the Canadian provinces and American states that border the Great Lakes.
  b) The numbers on the map represent the height of the water above sea level. Indicate these water levels on your map.
  c) Using the scale, estimate the distance on the Seaway system between Thunder Bay and Montreal. What is the total drop of the water level between these two centres?

29 Refer to Figure 19.19.
  a) Draw two circles to represent the total amount of cargo upbound and downbound on the St. Lawrence Seaway. (You may want to make these circles proportional to one another.)

Figure 19.18
Lock operation of the St. Lawrence Seaway
Describe how a ship moves through a lock from one level of water to the next.

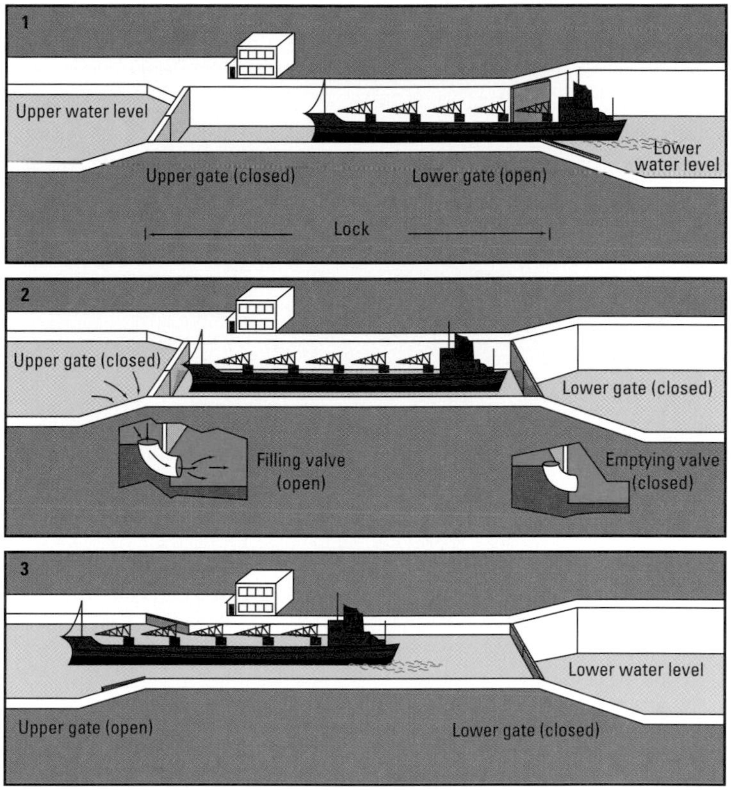

b) Divide each circle to show the proportion of each of the five main categories of cargo. To do this, calculate each category as a percentage of the total and multiply by 3.6 to obtain the number of degrees in a circle. For example, the number of degrees for mine products would be 12 930 603 ÷ 24 429 448 x 100 = 52.9 per cent x 3.6 = 190.5.

c) Explain why so much wheat is shipped down the Seaway.

d) Look at a map of the Great Lakes. Which Canadian port, situated closest to the Prairies, handles most of this wheat shipment?

TYPE OF CARGO	UPBOUND	(tonnes)	DOWNBOUND
Agriculture	60 991		13 823 057
Wheat	45 050		6 812 022
Animals	53		73 055
Mine products	12 930 603		22 148 570
Iron ore	11 353 627		12 624 897
Coal	0		3 641 745
Salt	43 894		1 822 118
Forest products	35		7 123
Manufactured products	11 437 766		12 839 301
Iron and steel	6 744 561		6 766 696
Total	**24 429 448**		**48 891 106**

Source. *St. Lawrence Seaway Authority Report*, 1994.

Figure 19.19
Seaway traffic by commodity, 1994

Figure 19.20
Port profiles:
tonnage
handled in
1993 (000)

THUNDER BAY		HAMILTON		MONTREAL	
1 Wheat	5 626	Iron ore	6 809	Machinery	2 883
2 Coal	2 290	Coal	2 977	Wheat	2 062
3 Canola	699	Iron and steel	1 058	Fuel oil	1 752
4 Oats and rye	588	Other ores	312	Gasoline	1 415
5 Potassium	518	Fuel oil	219	Lumber	1 116
6 Other	1 557	Other	1 018	Other	6 578

Source: Statistics Canada, Cat. No. 54-205, 1994.

e) What evidence indicates that the St. Lawrence Seaway system is used more to send goods to other countries than to receive them?

30 How does the information in Figure 19.20 show that:
a) a large volume of Canada's prairie grain is sent by rail to ports on the Great Lakes-St. Lawrence Seaway?
b) Hamilton is the steel capital of Canada?
c) Quebec is an important exporter of softwood lumber?
d) many manufactured products are shipped overseas from southern Quebec?
e) Great Lakes lakers transport grains to international ports with sea access for export to other countries?

31 The St. Lawrence Seaway is busiest from May to October. How would climate affect the operation of the Seaway? How would an Atlantic port like Halifax benefit from this?

32 The size of ocean vessels has been increasing. How will this affect the Seaway?

Simulation: the growth of a port

Stage 1
Figure 19.21 shows the site of a small port in the early 1800s. It consists of warehouses and storage sheds, merchants' and sailors' homes, banks, and a small military fort. The sailing ships anchor at a dockside that runs parallel to the land, close to the centre of town.

33 In a few sentences, explain i) why the port might have been established at this location and ii) why the storage sheds and warehouses are important.

Stage 2
The port is growing and more ships are using the docks. More dock space is needed.

34 Make a large copy of Figure 19.22.
a) Mark on an extension to the existing dock facilities.
b) What physical features might limit the expansion of the port?

Stage 3
The port is prospering. Larger ships are arriving loaded with cargo. These vessels

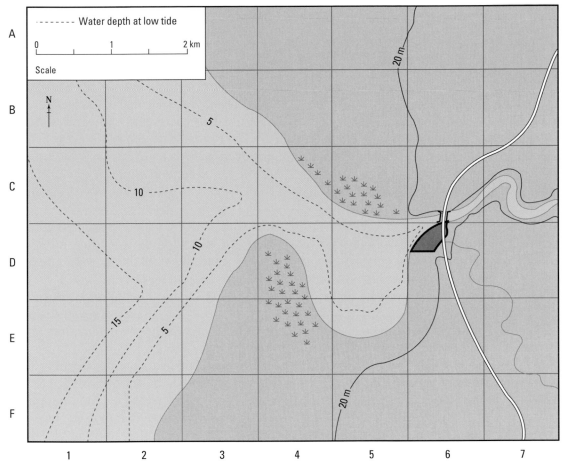

Figure 19.21
The site of a port

need a draft of at least 5 m; this is the depth of water a ship needs when it is fully loaded in order to clear the bottom. The only solution is to build piers out into deeper waters. This does not mean that the older dockside will not be used, as smaller ships will continue to dock there. The expansion of the town means that more transportation routes are needed inland as well.

35 a) Draw three piers on your map. Each one should be about 100 m long. Number them 1, 2, and 3.

b) Draw in the extended town limits.

c) Using topographic map symbols, draw a single-track rail line and roads connecting the new docks with the town and surrounding area.

Stage 4

By the mid-twentieth century, the port facilities can no longer meet the demands of modern shipping. The ships are getting longer; many have drafts up to 10 m. Piers 200 m long are needed to accommodate these vessels. The port also needs more dockside space.

36 Draw three new piers on your map. Label them 4, 5, and 6.

Stage 5

The port must now expand in order to handle bulk cargoes of wheat, oil, and iron ore. These arrive in large, specially constructed ships that need very deep water as well as specialized storage and transportation facilities. Large elevators are needed to store grain. The oil tankers are so long they are unable to turn in a normal port. They must remain at the end of a long jetty in waters 15 m deep. Pipes must carry the oil to storage tanks on land. Other cargo is being packed in containers that can be loaded and unloaded with special cranes. These containers require a lot of dockside space for storage. Truck and train facilities are also needed for intermodal transport.

37 a) On your map, indicate the location of the grain elevators, an oil jetty and terminal, and a container facility.
   b) Draw the rail and road facilities that link the new port areas to the existing network.
   c) Indicate any changes that may have been made to the older dock areas. (For example, part of the dock may have been converted to berths for pleasure crafts.)

38 Complete your map by outlining the five areas of growth and numbering each stage.

Moving people

Since most journeys are made within or between cities, the automobile and public transit are logical choices of transportation. There are 15.4 million passenger cars on Canadian roads and highways. Cars are the overwhelming choice of travel. They are expensive to own and operate, but people enjoy their convenience, comfort, and privacy. Some people, however, prefer to travel by mass transit. The cost is much less than owning a car. Transit riders don't have to worry about parking rates, gas prices, insurance hikes, or repair bills. In addition, they are not contributing to traffic congestion and air pollution. But buses and subways are usually crowded during rush hour and the journey may take longer than by car.

One of the growth areas in public transit is the use of buses for short journeys from rural areas to cities. Bus companies offer long-distance commuters non-stop service from a rural station to a central location. Buses are becoming more attractive for intercity travel, too. Over 43 000 000 Canadians travel on intercity buses each year!

39 a) Copy Figure 19.22 into your notebook. With a partner, discuss and note all the advantages and disadvantages of using cars and buses for travel within and to and from a city.
   b) Take a class vote to determine which method of travel students in your community would prefer.

CARS		BUSES	
ADVANTAGES	DISADVANTAGES	ADVANTAGES	DISADVANTAGES

Many business travellers enjoy the convenience of the Short Takeoff and Landing (STOL) aircraft for intercity travel. These small aircraft usually operate out of small airports located near city centres. This enables passengers to arrive and depart from the Central Business District. This means they can avoid the travel time, traffic, and expense involved in commuting to the CBD from a larger suburban airport. This method of transportation is not without its critics, however. Many say that it brings more noise to an already noisy downtown environment and adds to air pollution.

Intercity rail travel offers the same advantage as STOL aircraft for passengers wishing to arrive and depart from the CBD. But train travel is relatively slow in today's fast-paced world. Few business travellers choose to travel by rail. As a result, passenger service between many communities has been reduced or even eliminated. This in turn discourages other people from travelling by train because of the limited schedules.

40 If you were a business traveller, which method of intercity travel would you prefer? Why?

Moving freight

Trucking is the most common method of moving freight. Trucks offer convenience. They can deliver goods to out-of-the-way places and they provide door-to-door service. Their pick-up and delivery times are flexible and they can guarantee reasonably fast service. The variety of types and sizes of trucks ensures that loads of all kinds can be transported efficiently. The cost of truck transport is competitive with rail transport and much less expensive than air freight.

Rail is an excellent method of transportation for bulk freight. Specialized cars like container flatbeds, triple deckers, and refrigerated compartments accommodate a variety of products. While train transport is reasonably fast, it is confined to destinations along the rail system.

Water is the least expensive form of shipping; it is also the slowest. Specialized ships are able to carry several tonnes of freight, from iron ore to grain. While shipping is the only method of transport across oceans, within Canada it is restricted to the Great Lakes and the St. Lawrence Seaway system.

Air freight is the most expensive method of shipping. It is also the fastest, which makes it the only choice when next-day delivery is required. Cargo planes are limited in the number, mass, and size of the containers they carry. They are best suited to small shipments. They also serve only large airports in urban centres.

Pipelines are a highly specialized method of transport. Only liquids, gases, and certain solids that have been crushed and mixed with water can be shipped by pipeline. Pipeline service is limited to the pipeline system. In Canada, pipelines are most commonly used to transport oil and natural gas from northern drilling sites to southern markets. While shipping by pipeline is not too costly, building the pipeline in the first place is an expensive undertaking. Pipelines are also controversial because of their impact on the environment.

Intermodal transport

Freight is seldom carried by a single method of transportation from its point of origin to its final destination. More often goods are shipped by **intermodal transportation**, which involves more than one carrier. Intermodal transport uses standardized containers to carry freight. These are built to specific sizes that can be stacked and fitted together like building blocks. Containers are also designed to fit into a variety of transport vehicles, including the holds of ships, flatbed railcars, and trailer beds on trucks. They can be unloaded easily from one carrier and reloaded onto another using specialized equipment, such as container hoist cranes. While goods may be shipped via more than one type of transport, a single corporation may own all of the different transport companies.

41 Study Figure 19.24.
   a) Decide which method of transport you would use to move each commodity to its destination. Use Figure 19.25 to help you. For each commodity, enter the appropriate information in the organizer.
   b) Once you have decided the method of transport for each commodity, draw the appropriate pathways on an outline map of Canada. Be sure to label your map so that it clearly explains the decisions you have reached.

Figure 19.23
Intermodal train transport through British Columbia

COMMODITY	WEIGHT	SOURCE	DESTINATION	VALUE (per t)	SIZE
Wheat	Heavy	North of Regina	Leningrad	Low	Bulky
Computer terminals	Light	Ottawa	Lethbridge	High	Small
Machine parts	Heavy	Montreal	Thunder Bay	High	Medium
Fruit	Medium	Okanagan Valley	Saint John	Medium	Medium
Oil	Heavy	South of Edmonton	Sarnia	High	Bulky
Mail	Light	Quebec City	Vancouver	High	Small

Figure 19.24
Commodities to be transported

AVAILABLE ALTERNATIVES	CRITERIA		
	COST	SPEED	PATHWAY
Truck			
Rail			
Water			
Air			
Pipeline			

Figure 19.25
Decision-making organizer

Communications

A devastating hailstorm has just hit an area 65 km southeast of Brandon, Manitoba. It is early August and the farmers are preparing to harvest their grain crops. Although summer hailstorms are not uncommon here, the severity of this storm has taken everyone by surprise. Few farms in the 2000 km² area have escaped the fury of the storm. It is estimated that crop damage could exceed $400 million; damage to property is also extensive. Farmers who are already facing hard economic times are concerned that the storm may be the final straw. They are worried that they may be about to lose their farms.

42 a) Suggest five ways that news of this storm might reach communities beyond the affected area. How long would each method take?

b) If a similar storm had occurred 100 years ago, how might news have spread then? How long do you think this would have taken?

Even if you had not actually seen this hailstorm, you would have been linked to it by the flow of information that left the Brandon area and moved across the country. When information links people or places together, communication has taken place. The ways in which you found out about the storm are examples of the different methods of communication today. They are quite different from what they would have been 100 years ago, particularly in the speed that information travels.

There are three types of communication: personal, written, and telecommunication. Personal communication is the simplest linkage. It involves one person speaking directly to other people. When you tell your best friend about your weekend or when an executive outlines sales forecasts to a business meeting, personal communication is taking place. Written communication takes many forms. Letters in the mail, articles in newspapers, and advertisements in magazines are all forms of written communication. Telecommunication is information transmitted through wire and cable or across airwaves. Television and radio programs, telephone calls, computer messages, and electronic mail are all methods of telecommunication.

43 Give two examples of each type of communication—personal, written, and telecommunication—that you have experienced in the last 24 h.

Communications networks

How an important news story spreads across the country tells us a great deal about our communications network. *Network* is an appropriate term here, since information may be transmitted through many different methods before it is linked with its final destination. Let's see how the story of the hailstorm spread across the country.

Telecommunications is the fastest way to transmit information. When the storm broke, a television station in Brandon dispatched a reporter and camera crew to the area. They interviewed farmers and recorded scenes of the damage. They produced 25 min of videotape. This was rushed back to the television station, where it was edited into a 3 min news report. The Brandon station fed the story to an affiliate in Winnipeg.

Since the story was of national interest, it was sent to the CTV Daily News Service (DNS) in Toronto. This agency collects news for all television stations in Canada that are part of the CTV network. The tape was transmitted from Winnipeg to Toronto using a **microwave transmission**. The microwave system is a network of communication towers and dishes. It contains three pathways, two owned by Stentor Canadian Network Management and the third by CNCP Telecommunications. When one line of transmission is busy, switching stations automatically switch the signal to another line.

Stentor Canadian Network Management is an association of ten affiliate members. Nine provincial telephone companies have joined forces to operate this national system. The tenth member is Telesat Canada, the country's domestic satellite carrier. The system provides links for most cross-country TV, radio, telephone, and computer transmissions. Most Canadians know Stentor by the name of their telephone company.

Stentor operates two coast-to-coast digital phone routes. They run parallel to each other. One is fully fibre optic and the other is a mix of fibre and digital radio wire. They provide a back-up for one another and cross paths every 400 km. If cable damage occurs, telephone conversations can be switched automatically to the other line. It takes 50 ms to make the switch—so fast we would not even notice. These lines handle over 4 billion calls each year.

All stations belonging to the CTV network receive updates on news items available at the Daily News Service. If the CTV affiliate station in Halifax wants to show video of the storm, for example, it asks to have it transmitted through the microwave system. Once the station receives the signal, it can be transmitted via airwave or cable to televisions in the Halifax area. The entire process of transmitting the video from Toronto across almost 2000 km and into Halifax homes takes only a couple of seconds!

It is also possible to use microwave pathways to transmit live events, like an on-the-scene update on the storm. A signal can be transmitted via a mobile dish mounted on a special truck. The signal is aimed at a nearby microwave tower, which in turn transmits images of the scene to stations requesting the feed.

44 Using Figure 19.26, draw a flow diagram showing the route that the videotape would take from the scene of the storm to the Halifax television station and into a viewer's home. Name each part of the electronic pathway the signal would follow.

Satellite transmission

In 1969, the federal government created a company called Telesat Canada. (Today it is privately owned by Alouette Telecommunications, an association of provincial telephone companies, and Spar Aerospace Ltd.) The purpose of Telesat was to improve telecommunications across the country through a system of space satellites. In 1973, the Anik A1 satellite was launched, making Canada the first country to use satellites for domestic rather than military purposes. The life of a satellite is no more than twelve years. Since 1973, four series of satellites have been launched, including the latest Anik E1 and E2 series. (In 1993, the E2 satellite was lost when a huge solar flare caused it to spin out of control.) All satellites are controlled from a single operations room in downtown Ottawa.

There are many different users of satellites. Telephone companies use satellites to transmit thousands of telephone conversations at the same time and to hold teleconferences in which several people engage in one conversation. Satellites are used by oil and mining companies to relay data from exploration camps and remote ocean rigs.

Most of Canada's national television broadcasters, including CBC, CTV, and Canwest-Global, use Telesat to distribute their programs across the country. So how would news of the Brandon storm have reached Halifax via satellite? Once the video is recorded, the television station in Winnipeg transforms it into an electronic signal. This is beamed from a dish on the ground up 35 800 km into space to a satellite positioned in a **geostationary orbit**. This means that its orbit around the earth is fixed at a speed that keeps it exactly above a certain position on the ground. The transmission from the dish to the satellite is called the **uplink**. The signal is then

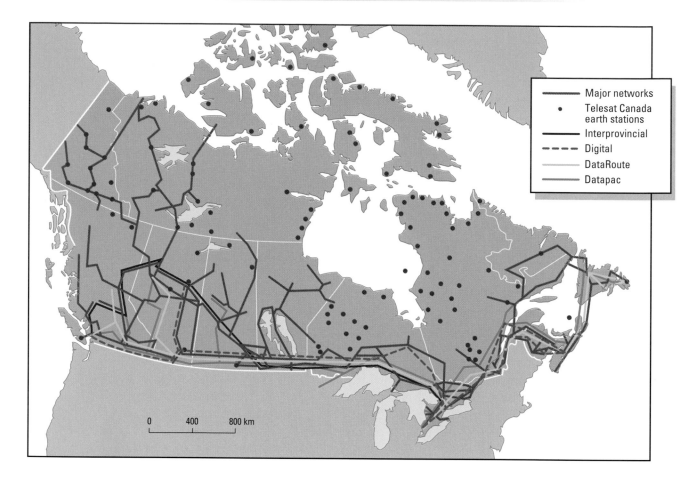

Figure 19.26
Microwave routes and telesat earth stations

transmitted from the satellite down to a receiving dish in Canada. This is called the **downlink**. The receiving dish must be located in an area that can receive a clear signal. This area is known as the satellite's "footprint." (See Figure 19.28.) It takes only a quarter of a second for a signal to travel between two points in Canada.

Telesat owns more than 152 ground-receiving stations; hundreds more are owned by other communications companies. These stations are linked to a network of major satellite earth stations called **tele-ports**. These are satellite communications centres capable of transmitting voice, image, and data communications to and from any location in a split second. Most major cities in the world have or will soon have a teleport. In Canada, Telesat operates teleports in Vancouver, Edmonton, Calgary, Toronto, and Montreal.

Satellite technology has also paved the way for pay-tv stations such as TSN, MuchMusic, and the Family Channel. In 1995, direct-to-the-home satellite television transmission was introduced. This service enables monthly subscribers to receive up to 150 channels via a home satellite dish not much bigger than a large pizza! New satellite networks, such as the Iridium Global Personal Communications System, will use low-level geostationary satellites to transmit conversations around the globe.

45 a) Refer to Figure 19.27. Describe how the video of the storm in Manitoba reaches Halifax televisions via satellite.

b) How do you think satellite communications have affected communities in the far North?

46 Examine the pattern of Canada's microwave lines and satellite ground stations in Figure 19.27. What relationship is there between this pattern and Canada's transportation and communications mainstreet?

47 *Anik* is an Inuit word meaning "brother." In what way has satellite technology enabled Canadians to become more united?

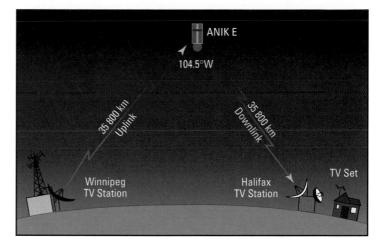

Figure 19.27
Anik E satellite system

The first step on the information superhighway is E-mail, or electronic mail. This allows the user to type a message on the computer and distribute it to someone else with access to E-mail. The same message can also be sent to many people at the same time.

Figure 19.28
"Footprint" of Anik E satellite

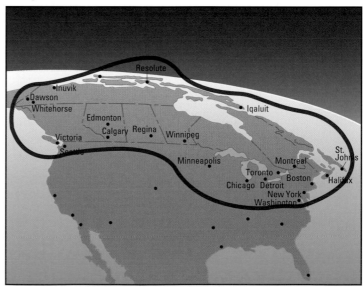

The information superhighway

The **information superhighway** has revolutionized the way in which information is transmitted across Canada and to other parts of the world. The superhighway is a vast network of computers that can communicate information with the touch of a keyboard. Statistics Canada estimates that 2.4 million Canadian homes (23 per cent of the total) have at least one personal computer. Of these, 500 000 have modems, which connect personal computers in a network with other computers.

Computer networks allow people to access information across the superhighway. There are two main Canadian networks—CRS On-line based in Toronto and the National Capital FreeNet based in Ottawa. Together, they have over 30 000 subscribers. This number will continue to grow as more networks emerge.

The world's largest computer link is the international network called Internet. In 1996, the Internet linked over 2 million computers and more than 20 million users in sixty countries. It allows huge volumes of information to be transferred between neighbours or across continents. Internet is controlled by a group called the Internet Engineering Task Force in the United States and Europe. The Canadian branch of Internet is controlled by the University of Toronto and IBM.

Network subscribers can post or read messages on bulletin boards. These are usually arranged according to specific topics. In many ways, it is similar to reading a specialty newspaper or magazine. Bulletin boards may be open for everyone to access or they may be designated as private conferences; in the latter case, access is limited to those who have been accepted as a member of the conference. These conferences are collections of information that are stored in huge reference files, much like traditional reference sources in the library. Anyone can use the files, whether you are a student writing your geography report or a professor looking for details on a scientific breakthrough!

48 Explain how each of the following users would benefit from the information superhighway:

a) a doctor seeking information about a new treatment
b) a humanitarian organization seeking aid following a natural disaster
c) a political party planning its national strategy for an upcoming election
d) a student wanting to complete an important geography assignment.

49 What traditional methods of communication has the information superhighway replaced?

Fibre optic cables

Most telecommunication uses **fibre optics**. Thin glass fibres, about the width of a human hair, allow light to be transmitted within the cable. This light can be converted into an electrical signal. A single glass fibre can carry over 4000 voice channels. The glass fibres are so thin that hundreds of them can be placed into a single cable. This enables the cable to carry hundreds of thousands of telephone conversations at the same time. In addition, the glass cables are inexpensive to produce. A couple of millimetres of silicon produces a kilometre of glass fibre. At present, these fibres can transmit some 3.4 billion bits of information per second! And it is believed that this is only 1 per cent of future capability.

Videotext

Videotext transmits information from a central databank to an ordinary television at home or at work. The information could be about the stock market, the weather, sports results, airline schedules, shopping prices, and so on. Telidon is a videotext system operating in Canada. Eventually, most homes in Canada will probably receive Telidon for a small fee. By using a home computer with the televised information, it will be possible to shop, bank, and take courses in the comfort of your own home. Your only task will be to enter the necessary signals through the computer into the system. The reaction to your request will be instantaneous. The Canadian Telidon system is considered one of the best in the world and is being used as a model for other countries.

New technologies

Computers are becoming increasingly powerful. In fact, it is estimated that within ten years, they will be 500 times more powerful than they are today! When computers are combined with fibre optic technology, the future of the information superhighway seems incredible.

In 1997, Canadians will experience the first two-way information superhighway. A business consortium will launch a system that will allow homeowners to receive and transmit signals to order movies and television programs at any time from a computer "jukebox," or central library. Viewers will be able to pause, reverse, or fastforward just as they do with a videotape in their VCRs. Information about shopping, travel, library books, or the weather will be available on request. The system will allow viewers watching a sporting event to switch to different cam-

era angles. Banking, postal delivery, and business purchases will also be possible. This communications network will operate either through a home computer or a television set. Canada's provincial telephone companies are spending $8 billion over the next ten years to upgrade phone lines to link 13 million homes to the service.

These telecommunications services will also enable more people to conduct business from their homes. In 1994, 1.4 million Canadian households (14 per cent of the total) were the operating base for a business. Many corporations view home work places as a means of reducing the cost of office space and eliminating the time and frustration of commuting to and from work.

50 Explain how any of these new technologies might affect:
a) you as a student
b) a travelling salesperson
c) a banker
d) a reporter
e) your leisure activities.

51 Experts suggest that it will be necessary to have a media room in our homes to accommodate all of our communications machines. Draw a sketch of your ideal media room, labelling all of the items it would contain.

52 Many Canadians are concerned that instant access to programming from around the world is a threat to Canadian culture. Do you agree with this evaluation? What steps, if any, should be taken to protect our culture?

Unit 6

WORLD CONTACT

Interdependence is the dominant fact of life in our era—that we are all responsible for each other's well-being, and that we must learn to live together or face the prospect of perishing together.

Pierre Elliot Trudeau, in the Foreword to *Dangers & Options: The Matter of World Survival* (1982) by Willy Brandt.

Shadow Man with Wreath by Wanda Koop/Courtesy Wanda Koop

Linkages occur whenever places are connected by the movement of people, goods, or information. We have a great number and variety of linkages in our lives. Most of these occur within our community, region, or country. But as we move towards a **global economy**, the links between Canada and the rest of the world will increase substantially. Trade is one of the most obvious and important international links a country has with the world around it.

1 a) **Working in groups of four to six students, brainstorm ways in which Canada is a member of the global community.**
   b) **Organize your responses by category. For example, you might record all the responses that deal with cultural links under Culture. List at least five responses under each category.**
   c) **Create a diagram to illustrate your group's impressions of Canada's role in the global community.**

International trade

Figure 20.2 shows three fictional countries, Mineraland, Foodland, and Factoryland. Each country has about the same area and population. But, as their names suggest, each produces wealth in a different way. Mineraland has large amounts of natural resources, such as oil, gas, and metals. Foodland has a climate and soil that are excellent for agricultural products, such as wheat, vegetables, and fruit. Unlike Mineraland and Foodland, Factoryland has few natural resources, so it specializes in manufacturing trucks, cars, and machinery.

Figure 20.1
Trade activity in the port of Vancouver

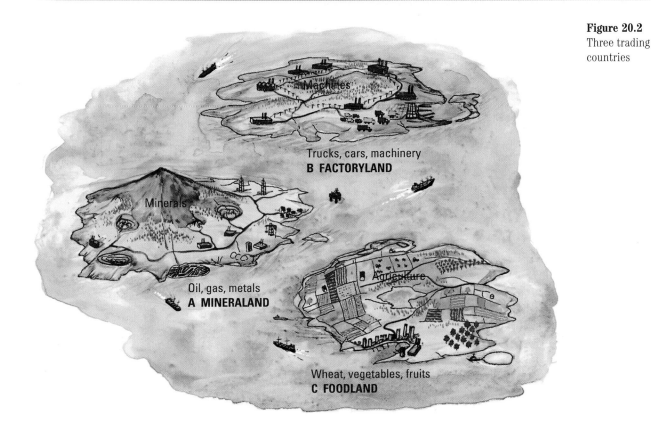

Figure 20.2
Three trading countries

These three countries cannot exist on their own. Each one needs something from the other two. In order to meet these needs, Mineraland, Foodland, and Factoryland must trade among themselves. Trade is the buying and selling of goods. Factoryland, for example, buys oil from Mineraland to fuel its manufacturing industries. This oil is called an **import**. Factoryland's manufactured goods are then sold to Mineraland to pay for more oil. These goods are called **exports**.

Figure 20.3
Imports/ Exports

COUNTRY	IMPORTS	EXPORTS
Mineraland		
Foodland		
Factoryland		

2 a) Copy Figure 20.3 into your notebook. For each country, list the items that it imports and exports from the other two countries.

   b) How does this information show that these countries are interdependent? What might happen to this relationship if Factoryland discovered enough oil to supply half its needs?

Canadian trade

International trade is the lifeblood of the Canadian economy. In fact, Canada is one of the world's largest trading nations. We have many resources and products that are in demand throughout the world. Yet we also require the resources and products of other countries. What is the nature of Canadian trade?

3 **Figure 20.4 lists Canada's top imports and exports.**

   a) List each of Canada's imports by product and total dollar value under one of the following categories: Food and beverages (for example, fish products);

IMPORTS CATEGORY	VALUE ($ millions)	EXPORTS CATEGORY	VALUE ($ millions)
Fruits and vegetables	3 641	Wheat	3 513
Cocoa, coffee, tea	2 079	Fish and fish products	2 947
Other agricultural and fish prod.	6 847	Live animals	1 347
Crude petroleum	4 760	Meat and meat preparations	1 518
Coal and other energy products	7 349	Misc. agriculture and fish	8 270
Forestry products	1 809	Crude petroleum	7 428
Metals and metal ores	9 629	Natural gas	6 849
Chemicals and plastics	13 722	Coal	2 120
Other industrial	15 352	Other energy products	5 316
fabricated products		Lumber and sawmill products	14 055
Industrial machinery	15 555	Woodpulp and other wood prod.	6 712
Agricultural machinery	2 390	Newsprint and paper	10 374
Aircraft and transport equip.	5 694	Metal ores	3 671
Office machines and equipment	11 411	Chemicals, plastics, fertilizer	11 539
Other machinery	30 532	Metals and alloys	15 899
Passenger cars	13 583	Other industrial materials	8 310
Trucks	6 225	Industrial machinery	8 652
Motor vehicle parts	28 008	Agricultural machinery	1 077
Clothing and footwear	4 681	Aircraft and transport equip.	8 015
Other consumer goods	18 753	Televisions, telecommunications	6 974
Total	**202 020**	Other machinery	18 327
		Passenger cars	31 899
		Trucks	12 272
		Motor vehicle parts	14 278
		Other consumer goods	17 178
		Total	**226 630**

Figure 20.4 Canada's top imports and exports, 1994

Source:Statistics Canada Cat.65-001, 1995

Natural resources (for example, crude petroleum); Fabricated products (for example, newsprint and paper); Finished products (for example, passenger cars). For each category, add the total dollar value of imports, then calculate this figure as a percentage of total trade.

b) Repeat the process in a) for Canada's exports.

c) Is Canada primarily an importing or exporting nation? Use the figures you have calculated to explain your answer.

4 a) Look at the products you use in your own home every day. List twenty items that were *not* produced in Canada. (In some cases, such as your CD player, the product may be labelled with this information. In other cases, such as fresh fruit, you may have to check the signs in the store where you made the purchase.)

b) On an outline map of the world, label the countries where the products on your list were produced. Alongside each, list the number of times the name of that country appeared on your list. What conclusions can you draw? Were you surprised by the results? Explain your answer.

5 One method of comparing quantities is a **comparative**, or multiple, **bar graph**. This allows us to compare two or more things, in this case, imports and exports.

a) Draw a graph similar to Figure 20.5. (NOTE: Do not include the bars in the figures. These are shown only as an example for constructing this graph.)

b) Using the import and export totals from activity 3, draw a multiple bar graph to show the four categories. How do the

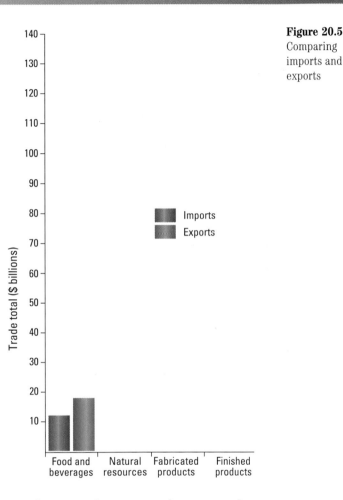

Figure 20.5 Comparing imports and exports

import and export totals compare in each category?

c) Describe the nature of Canada's exports and imports. What is Canada's overall trade pattern?

Exporting primary products

Canada is rich in mineral, forest, and agricultural resources. As a result, we are able to harvest far more of these natural resources than we consume as a nation.

This surplus production is sold and exported to other countries. This gives Canada the distinction of being one of the world's largest exporters of minerals and grains. The money earned from these exports helps to pay for those products we must import. For example, while we grow more wheat than Canadians can consume, we must import other foods, such as rice, tea, and oranges.

Mining exports

Canada has one of the most diverse mining industries in the world. Almost every important mineral is produced in this country. Canada ranks first in world production of zinc, second in nickel, gypsum, potash, cobalt, and asbestos, third in copper and cadmium, fourth in lead, and eighth in iron ore. In addition to this treasure chest, Canada has an enviable location next door to the world's largest industrial nation, the United States. This provides the mining industry with ready access to a huge market. The revenues generated from these export sales help to pay for further exploration and development of these resources.

About 80 per cent of all minerals produced in Canada are exported. The major destination is the United States, which receives 60 per cent of our mineral exports. Japan accounts for 15 per cent, while another 12 per cent is destined for the European Union.

Mineral exports are important to the Canadian economy. In fact, exports can bring new life to resources that may be in decline in our own country. An example is coal. After being the dominant fuel in the

COUNTRY	TOTAL (000 t)
Japan	17 409
South Korea	5 689
Brazil	1 530
United States	1 235
United Kingdom	941
Taiwan	824
Italy	758
Spain	497
Mexico	417
Denmark	309
Portugal	300
Netherlands	281
Chile	254
Egypt	229
Turkey	218
Belgium	189
Sweden	155
Pakistan	144
Yugoslavia (former)	91
France	54
South Africa	49
Algeria	45
Germany	10
Canada total	**31 629**

Source: Canada Minerals Yearbook, 1994.

Figure 20.6
Canada's coal exports, 1993

Figure 20.7
Robertsbank
Coal Terminal,
Vancouver

Large unit trains carry coal from the mines to coal-exporting ports like this one at Robertsbank, south of Vancouver. Here ships destined for Japanese and South Korean steel mills load coking coal. Canadians buy many Japanese and Korean cars, motorcycles, and other products that are made from the steel produced using Canadian coal.

first half of the twentieth century, coal mining began to decline after 1950. (See page 213.) Large coal deposits in Alberta and British Columbia remained largely untapped. In the 1970s, however, the rapidly growing steel industries of Japan and South Korea began buying large quantities of this high-quality coking coal. This launched a new coal-mining boom in the Canadian West. (See Figure 11.25 on page 231.) Today, over 40 per cent of the coal mined in Canada is exported. (See Figure 20.6.)

6 a) On an outline map of the world, shade in and label the countries that buy Canadian coal. Use dots or squares in different sizes to symbolize the amount of coal each country imports. Which continent receives most of Canada's coal?

b) What percentage of total coal exports go to Japan? Why do you think Japan buys so much Canadian coal?

c) In what forms does the steel manufactured using Canadian coal come back to Canada? Is this to our advantage or not?

7 Using an atlas, locate three sites in Canada that might provide coal for export to Japan. Identify these sites on an outline map of the world. Indicate how coal from Canadian mines reaches Japan. Include shipping ports, transportation methods, and routes. Make sure your map is labelled and titled.

Wheat exports

Canada's leading agricultural export is wheat. Saskatchewan is the largest wheat-producing province, followed by Alberta and Manitoba. The spring wheat grown in the cool northern climate of the Prairies is among the finest in the world.

Prairie wheat is moved by rail to export terminals on the Pacific coast at Vancouver and Prince Rupert and on the Great Lakes at Thunder Bay. Most wheat exported from Vancouver is destined for markets on the Pacific Rim and the Indian Ocean. From Thunder Bay, the wheat is moved by lake freighter to Montreal, Quebec City, and other ports along the lower St. Lawrence River. At these deepwater ports, the wheat is transferred to ocean freighters for shipment overseas. East coast ports ship to markets on the Atlantic Ocean and the Mediterranean Sea. Wheat sold to the United States is shipped by rail.

8 On an outline map of the world, construct a **flow map** to show the data in Figure 20.8.
   a) Group the data into three divisions: Pacific and Indian Ocean countries, Atlantic Ocean and Mediterranean Sea countries, and the United States.
   b) Within each division, group the countries by region according to continent. (For example, Brazil is in the Atlantic-Mediterranean division and should be grouped with other countries from South America in that list. Use an atlas to help you.) Total the wheat exports for each region.

Figure 20.8
Wheat export destinations, 1995

COUNTRY	TONNES (000)	% OF TOTAL WHEAT EXPORTS
China	5 173	25.3
Iran	1 996	9.8
Algeria	1 893	9.3
United States	1 499	7.3
Japan	1 458	7.1
South Korea	1 048	5.1
Brazil	930	4.5
Indonesia	737	3.6
Mexico	572	2.8
Italy	505	2.5
Venezuela	449	2.2
Colombia	378	1.8
Pakistan	362	1.8
Belgium and Luxembourg	361	1.8
Chile	334	1.6
Libya	228	1.1
Tunisia	192	0.9
United Kingdom	190	0.9
Malaysia	164	0.8
South Africa	163	0.8
Philippines	161	0.8
Ecuador	155	0.8
Bangladesh	128	0.6
Peru	126	0.6
West Africa	120	0.6
Thailand	104	0.5
Uzbekistan	97	0.5
Yemen	90	0.4
Bolivia	56	0.3
Guatemala	55	0.3
Israel	53	0.3
Ethiopia	51	0.3
Russia	na	na
Other	621	3.0
Total	**20 449**	**100.0**

na = not available
Source: Canadian Grain Commission.

c) Draw arrows showing the export route by water from Canada to each region and by land to the United States. Use a scale of 1 mm to 500 000 t of wheat exports to determine the width of each arrow. Label each arrow with the name of the region to which the wheat is destined.

d) Label the Canadian port cities through which the wheat must pass to reach its markets.

Selling primary products

An export economy that depends on primary products has its advantages. Surplus goods earn income, create jobs, and contribute to economic growth. Money from these exports helps to pay for imports from other countries. There are disadvantages as well, however. Prices paid for primary products can fluctuate over short periods due to changes in supply and demand. An increase in the value of the Canadian dollar may reduce exports if this increases the price of our products above that of our competitors. Countries with large surpluses of similar products may cut their prices, launching a trade war. But if we cut our prices to compete, we could bankrupt our producers at home. Changes in tariffs and quotas may also endanger exports. All of these uncertainties make resource investment risky.

Some of these disadvantages can be offset, however. To protect against fluctuating prices, governments may subsidize crop prices or stockpile products until they can be sold at a higher price. Maintaining

Figure 20.9 Ship loading grain at terminal elevator, Vancouver

quality may offset currency increases as consumers are often willing to pay more for a superior product. Establishing a mutually beneficial trading relationship in which we buy products from countries that buy our products may keep tariffs and quotas steady. Trading with a variety of countries ensures that if one market is lost for any of these reasons, other markets are there to cushion the blow. All of these strategies help to overcome the ups and downs in the prices of primary products.

9 In an organizer, list the advantages and disadvantages of exporting primary products.

10 Use your resource centre to research current world events that may affect world trade in minerals and agricultural products in general and Canada's trade in minerals and agricultural products in particular.

The balance of trade

If you were to add up all the money you earned last year, the result would be your yearly income. You could also add up all the money you spent last year. This would be your yearly expenditure. If you found that you were spending more money than you earned, you would find yourself in debt and in financial trouble! But if you were earning more money than you were spending, you would have some money in reserve and you would be financially stable.

In a similar way, we can see how well Canada is doing in its trade with the rest of the world. The money Canada receives for selling goods and providing services to other countries (exports) is income. (Services include such things as tourism, transportation, and banking, sometimes called invisible trade.) All the money Canada pays out to buy goods and services from other countries (imports) is expenditure. Comparing these two totals reveals Canada's balance of trade—that is, whether more money comes into the country or leaves it.

11 a) Figure 20.11 shows the total amount of money received for exports and paid for imports from 1975 to 1994. In your notebook, complete the balance of trade column by subtracting the import figure from the export figure for each year. The first one has been done for you.

b) What do you think would happen if Canada always had a trade deficit? A trade surplus?

12 a) Total Canada's imports and exports for 1994. Assuming Canada had a population of 29 million, what was the country's total trade per person? How does this figure compare with the countries in Figure 20.12?

b) What conclusions can you make about Canada's place in world trade and the importance of trade to the country?

13 a) Create a graph to illustrate trends in Canada's exports and imports. Draw a vertical line 15 cm high to represent the money value; each centimetre represents 10 billion (1000 million) dollars. Draw a horizontal line 18 cm long to represent the years; each centimetre represents one year.

b) Plot a red line to represent the annual import total and a green line to represent the annual export total. There will be a space between the lines. When the green line is above the red line, shade the space green. This represents a trade surplus—that is, more money is coming into Canada than leaving it. When the red line is above the green

Figure 20.10
Balancing imports and exports

YEAR	EXPORTS	IMPORTS	BALANCE
1975	33 616	33 962	-346
1976	38 166	36 608	
1977	44 495	41 523	
1978	63 361	49 048	
1979	65 581	61 157	
1980	76 681	67 903	
1981	84 432	77 140	
1982	84 393	66 738	
1983	90 556	73 098	
1984	111 330	91 493	
1985	119 061	102 669	
1986	120 318	110 374	
1987	126 340	115 119	
1988	137 780	128 862	
1989	141 514	135 455	
1990	145 555	136 859	
1991	140 220	136 617	
1992	155 794	149 101	
1993	181 342	171 827	
1994	226 630	202 070	

Source: Statistics Canada.

Figure 20.11
Canada's trade balance

COUNTRY	TRADE PER PERSON ($)
Singapore	48 376.07
Hong Kong	26 496.21
Germany	10 383.70
France	8 183.82
United Kingdom	7 130.43
Japan	4 582.06
Australia	4 582.00
Saudi Arabia	4 400.95
United States	3 807.37
Mexico	882.86
Russia	516.11
Brazil	383.83
China	142.42
India	47.90

Source: *World Development Report*, 1994.

Figure 20.12
Trade per person, selected countries, 1994

line, shade the space red. This represents a trade deficit—that is, more money is leaving Canada than entering it.

c) Describe Canada's balance of trade since 1975. Why might this balance change from year to year?

14 Like all currencies, the value of the Canadian dollar fluctuates. Why would a lower Canadian dollar help exports and discourage imports? What other effects would a low Canadian dollar have?

The importance of trade

In our everyday world, trading activities occur all around us. Friends trade sports cards and comic books. Trade shows cater to collectors hoping to trade their surplus items for those that will fill the gaps in their collections. The end result is that both traders win. They gain items they want and get rid of items they don't need.

International trade works much the same way. Countries trade what is surplus to their needs for other things that they need or want. Canada, for example, exports its surplus coal and wheat to Japan and uses the money to import Japanese electronic goods. Both countries win. Trade

Figure 20.13
Why do we trade?

Why export?

- *Revenue:* Anything we sell means that money and goods end up in Canada.
- *Jobs:* One in five jobs in Canada is linked to exports. The greater our exports, the more jobs for Canadians.
- *Expanded markets:* Canada has a limited market. We need to take advantage of large markets in other countries to keep our businesses profitable.
- *Lower prices:* A larger market means businesses can produce more, thereby lowering the cost per unit. This leads to lower prices at home and abroad.
- *Quality:* Competition from other countries means that we have to maintain quality products.

Why import?

- *Product needs:* There are many products Canada does not have or may not produce, so we must obtain these products elsewhere.
- *Quality:* Sometimes other countries, as a result of tradition, market size, or research spending, produce better products than we do. Competing with these quality imports means that Canadian companies must improve their products to remain competitive at home.
- *Cost:* Some countries can produce goods at lower cost than Canadian companies. This benefits Canadian consumers.
- *International development:* Buying products from other countries helps their economies and in turn provides them with funds to purchase Canadian goods.

also enables countries to specialize in what they do best. This means a country with expertise in a certain area can continue to develop this know-how and use it to produce better products. Canada, for example, is a leader in telecommunications and we market this technology around the world.

Trade also gives small countries access to large markets. Mass producing larger quantities of a product reduces the cost of production per item. Called the **economy of scale**, this benefits the producing country as well as consumers, who can buy these products at lower cost. Economy of scale is one of the advantages of the Canada-US Auto Pact, which established a single North American car market. Instead of producing many different cars for our small market, Canada specializes in making certain models that are sold across North America. In return, models made only in the US are imported duty free into Canada.

Competition is another factor in trade relations. If one country finds a way to produce a product at less cost, this benefits world trade. To keep their markets, countries have to maintain a competitive edge. This inspires creativity as companies look for new and better ways of doing things. For example, North American car makers were forced to improve the quality of their cars and the efficiency of their factories in order to compete with cars from Japan and Korea.

Today's global economy is based entirely on the growth of world trade through the elimination of trade barriers. In the past, most countries placed tariffs, quotas, and other restrictions on trade to protect their own industries from foreign competition. Over the last twenty-five years, however, these barriers have slowly been coming down. As a result, the value of goods and services in world trade has increased. (See Figure 20.14.) Figure 20.15 shows how Canada has shared in the growth of the global economy.

15 Using Figure 20.15, draw a line graph to show the increase in the total amount of Canadian trade from 1960 to 1993. What trend does your graph show? Is it the same or different from the trend shown in Figure 20.14? Suggest why.

16 You have read a letter in your local newspaper suggesting that Canada stop importing products from other countries. Write a reply to the editor of the newspaper in which you express your views about Canada and world trade.

17 Working with a group, write the script for a two-minute television commercial that focuses on the need for Canada to increase its exports. Produce your script as a skit to be performed in class or as a video presentation.

Trade barriers

Importing foreign products can create problems for domestic industries. Canada's high standard of living means that many of our products cost more to produce than those manufactured in other countries. Canadian consumers may be pleased that they can buy the foreign product for less. But the Canadian company may not be able to compete with lower foreign prices. As a result, it could be forced to close, eliminat-

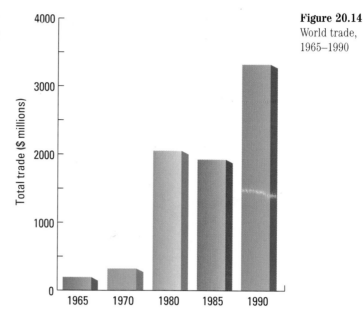

Figure 20.14
World trade, 1965–1990

ing jobs for Canadians in the process. To equalize the cost of foreign and domestic products, governments sometimes impose a **tariff**, or import tax, on products entering the country. This allows domestic products to be more competitive.

18 The two training shoes in Figure 20.16 are identical in style and quality. The only difference is price. The shoes made in South

YEAR	TOTAL TRADE ($ millions)
1960	5 386
1970	16 820
1980	76 159
1985	119 241
1990	148 170
1993	176 757

Source: Statistics Canada.

Figure 20.15
Canada's trade with the world

Figure 20.16
Tariffs and trade

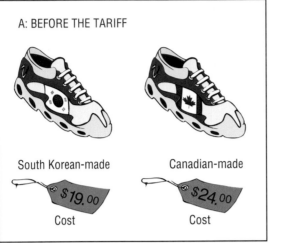

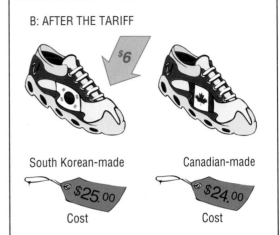

Korea cost $19.00. The shoes made in Canada cost $24.00.

a) **Which shoe would you buy? Why? How would your decision affect:**
   i)   **you personally?**
   ii) **workers in the Canadian shoe factory?**
   iii) **workers in the South Korean shoe factory?**
   iv) **workers in a mine that sells coal to a South Korean steel mill?**
   v)   **workers in a South Korean steel mill that depends on Canadian coal?**
   vi) **the future plans of the Canadian shoe company?**
   vii) **the future plans of the South Korean shoe company?**
   Summarize your answers in a three-column chart. List the seven situations down the left side of the chart and record the affects of your decision in column 1.

b) **Which shoe would you buy if the Canadian government raised the tariff on imported training shoes by $6.00?**

Why? How would your decision affect the seven situations in part a)? Record your answers in column 2.

c) **In retaliation for the Canadian tariff, South Korea stops buying Canadian coal for its steel mills. How would this affect the seven situations in part a)? Record your answers in column 3.**

Another way to limit imports is through **quotas**. A quota limits the number or the monetary value of products entering a country. In the late 1980s and early 1990s, Canada was concerned that the growing number of imported cars from Japan threatened the survival of Canadian auto plants. In response, a quota was established for imported cars. To maintain their share of the Canadian market and to gain access to the US market, Japanese car makers then set up auto plants in Canada. In this case, both sides won. The new Japanese car plants created jobs for Canadians, and the Japanese auto makers were able to protect their share of the North American market.

Imposing tariffs and quotas is called **protectionism**. In general, trade restrictions offer short-term benefits but have long-term disadvantages. In the short term, they keep jobs in Canada, generate revenue for the government, and give industries time to increase their efficiency and productivity. They also prevent foreign companies from flooding the market with lower-priced goods in order to eliminate domestic competition and give countries bargaining power in trade negotiations. On the other hand, protectionist policies create artificially high prices for imported goods and reduce selection. A lack of competitive incentive to produce higher quality products leads to outdated methods of production. Without new ideas and new inventions a country and its industries fall behind the rest of the world.

The opposite of protectionism is **free trade**. Under this policy, there are no tariffs or quotas. Trade is limited only by basic laws and regulations that apply to all traders inside and outside the country. Most countries, like Canada and the United States, have trade policies somewhere in between these two extremes. There are tariffs and quotas on some imports, but many goods are free to move across borders with few restrictions. The tariffs that do exist are used to protect newly developing industries or industries that are important to the nation, such as computers, biotechnology, automobiles, and military equipment.

19 a) List three advantages and three disadvantages of protectionism.
b) Under what conditions are tariffs and quotas useful?

Trading partners

Mineraland, Foodland, and Factoryland on page 435 had established perfect trade harmony. Each country specialized in a product, and each had something the other two needed. Specialization allows a country to focus its skills and research in areas in which it has special interests, abilities, and advantages. In Canada, most of our trade involves the buying and selling of automobiles and the exporting of natural resources.

To sell these products and to get what we need in return, Canada has trade relationships with most countries of the world. However, we trade more with some countries than with others. Need, of course, is one of the key factors in any trade relationship. Location is another. Figure 20.17 shows Canada's major trading partners by percentage of total trade and dollar value.

20 a) Identify Canada's leading trading partner. Suggest reasons why this is the case.
b) What countries are the second- and third-ranked trading partners for exports? For imports? Suggest reasons why.

21 a) Draw two line graphs to show the changes in the per cent of Canadian exports to and imports from i) the United States and ii) western Europe.
b) Summarize the trends in your graphs. How does the old saying "Don't put all your eggs in one basket" relate to the trends in Canadian trade?

22 Using yearbooks, encyclopaedias, almanacs, and atlases in your library

IMPORTS REGION/ COUNTRY	1960	1970	1980	1985 (% of total)	1990	1994	1994 ACTUAL VALUE ($ millions)
United States	67.2	71.1	70.2	70.9	64.6	67.6	136 624
Japan	2.0	4.2	4.0	5.8	7.0	5.6	11 343
Asia (excl. Japan)	1.8	2.0	3.3	4.9	6.0	7.7	15 474
Western Europe	17.5	14.0	10.0	12.0	12.0	11.0	22 139
Eastern Europe	0.3	0.5	0.4	0.3	0.4	0.4	885
Central America	2.6	1.5	1.5	2.0	1.5	2.7	5 373
South America	5.1	3.2	4.4	2.3	1.4	1.3	2 559
Middle East	1.9	0.7	4.4	0.4	0.8	0.5	1 015
Africa	0.6	1.1	0.8	1.0	0.6	0.8	1 538
Australasia	0.9	1.4	1.0	0.6	0.8	0.7	1 479
Total ($ millions)	**5 483**	**13 952**	**67 903**	**102 669**	**136 859**	**202 020**	

Source: Statistics Canada.

EXPORTS REGION/ COUNTRY	1960	1970	1980	1985 (% of total)	1990	1994	1994 ACTUAL VALUE ($ millions)
United States	56.4	64.8	63.3	78.0	75.0	81.7	185 217
Japan	3.3	4.8	5.7	4.8	5.5	4.3	9 652
Asia (excl. Japan)	2.3	2.9	4.1	3.7	4.0	4.0	9 064
Western Europe	28.3	18.6	14.8	6.8	8.6	6.1	13 794
Eastern Europe	0.7	1.0	2.8	1.6	0.9	0.2	453
Central America	2.5	2.3	2.1	1.2	0.6	0.8	1 712
South America	2.3	2.2	3.2	1.2	0.9	1.2	2 791
Middle East	0.5	0.7	1.5	1.1	0.7	0.8	1 795
Africa	1.4	1.0	1.4	0.9	0.6	0.4	1 001
Australasia	2.3	1.5	1.1	0.4	0.7	0.5	1 097
Total ($ millions)	**5 386**	**16 820**	**76 681**	**119 061**	**145 555**	**226 630**	

Source: Statistics Canada.

Figure 20.17
Canada's imports and exports by world region

resource centre, identify the most important products that Canada imports from and exports to any *two* regions/countries in Figure 20.17. Describe your findings in chart form.

Case study: exporting high technology

Innovation, business skills, and entrepreneurial spirit are the key ingredients in a growing number of small but highly successful Canadian companies selling high technology to the world. Wescam, Inc. is a high-tech company in Hamilton, Ontario. It manufactures camera systems designed to capture the dramatic action sequences seen in many Hollywood movies. The company was launched in 1987 with seventeen employees. By 1995, over 250 people were employed in this exciting business. Wescam has earned worldwide recognition for its technical excellence, along with an Academy Award and five Emmy Awards!

In Halifax, Nova Scotia, a marine geophysicist and computer wizard quit his government job to form Xon Digital Communications. Among the products of this computer hardware and software design company is an innovative pay-per-view television system to be installed in 200 000 hotel rooms across Canada and the US, ringing up sales of $20 million.

In Stoney Creek, Ontario, Dynamic and Proto Circuits, Inc. manufactures custom-made circuit boards for use in telecommunications, medical, scientific, and military industries. Sales in the US have risen steadily since 1993. Total sales

in 1995 reached $20 million. The company invests an average of $1 million a year in equipment, product testing, and research to improve its product, increase its efficiency, and expand its market.

23 What are the characteristics of Canada's new high-tech industries? Why are these companies so important to the Canadian export economy?

24 Find a new business venture in your city, region, or province. Describe its products, growth, and export markets. Look for newspaper and magazine articles, particularly in business publications, to research this information. You might also contact your local chamber of commerce.

Future trade options

In the new global marketplace, **trading blocs** are becoming increasingly powerful. These organizations are groups of countries that share special trading links and privileges among themselves. Usually, there are no tariffs among members, but collectively the bloc places common tariffs on goods from other countries. The European Union (EU) is the largest single trading bloc in the world. Its members include Belgium, Denmark, France, Germany, Greece, Ireland, Italy, Luxembourg, the Netherlands, Portugal, Spain, Great Britain, Austria, Finland, and Sweden. With a population of 369 million people, the EU accounts for approximately 42 per cent of world trade.

As the European Union strengthened its ties, Canada's trade with EU nations diminished. (See Figure 20.17.) As a result, in 1989 Canada entered into a free trade agreement with its major trading partner, the United States. In 1992, the original pact was replaced by the **North American Free Trade Agreement** (NAFTA), which brought Mexico into the agreement. In 1995, NAFTA accounted for 18 per cent of world trade, making it the world's second largest trading bloc.

NAFTA calls for the lowering of tariffs and quotas among members. It gives Canadian industries access to markets that are many times larger than our domestic market. After an initial period of adjustment, it is expected that Canadian industries will be able to compete successfully with their American and Mexican counterparts and that they will reap the benefits of free trade. NAFTA is the only free trade zone that possesses all of the ingredients for continued economic growth and prosperity: advanced businesses and technology, abundant food and natural resources, and a growing supply of new workers.

In the mid-1990s, talks were under way with Chile to join the free trade agreement. In 1996, Canada launched an independent round of negotiations with Chilean representatives. The United States chose not to participate. It is expected that if Chile is allowed to join NAFTA, many other Latin American nations will also apply. If this free trade area is expanded to include all of Latin America, it would enlarge the market from its present size of 368 million to 730 million people, making it much larger than the EU.

25 a) On an outline map of the world, colour in and label the members of the
European Union and NAFTA. Use different colours to represent each trading bloc.

b) Japan and other Asian countries are considering forming their own trading bloc. Why would they want to do this? Which countries might joint this trade alliance?

26 What would happen to world trade if the EU and NAFTA placed such high tariffs on products from non-member countries that these countries could not sell their products in these markets?

27 Review the Canadian-Japanese trade figures in this chapter. How important is Japan to Canada as a trading partner? Do you think Canada should expand its trade with Japan and the Pacific Rim despite its membership in NAFTA? Explain your answer.

Canada's trading options

The decision to join in a free trade alliance was a controversial one in Canada. Figure 20.18 highlights the four options in the debate.

28 a) In groups, suggest why Canada chose Option 1 over the other three.

b) What opportunities would be open to Canadian companies in NAFTA that would not be available outside of this association?

c) How might NAFTA affect our domestic politics and our ability to preserve a distinct Canadian culture?

Option 1: Stronger trade links with the United States

- Over 78 per cent of Canadian exports are sold in the US.
- The US and Canada have the largest trade partnership in the world.
- The US is Canada's closest neighbour and ally.
- The two countries share a similar culture and language.
- The American market is ten times larger than the Canadian market.
- Many US companies are already located in Canada.

Option 2: Stronger trade links with the European Union

- Canada has close historic ties to Europe, especially Britain and France.
- There are many ethnic and cultural links between Canada and Europe.
- Existing trade between Canada and the EU is small.
- Europe needs high-tech products.
- Europe has few natural resources.

Option 3: Stronger trade links with the Pacific Rim

- The Pacific Rim is the fastest-growing economic region in the world.
- Japan and South Korea are trade giants.
- Pacific Rim countries lack many natural resources.
- Pacific Rim countries want greater access to Canadian markets.
- Geographically, Canada is also a Pacific Rim country.

Option 4: Stronger trade links with non-traditional partners

- Russia and the former communist countries of Eastern Europe offer a large market.
- These new democracies want increased trade with and technical assistance from North America, Europe, and Asia.
- Russia and Eastern Europe need economic aid as they adjust to a free market system.
- Developing countries are becoming more industrialized and offer market opportunities for the future.
- The large populations in countries like China and India offer huge markets.
- Many developing countries need the type of goods Canada produces as well as development assistance to increase their standard of living.

Figure 20.18 Canada's four trade options

29 Some experts have suggested that the best trade policy for Canada would be to pursue all four trade options. Do you agree? Do you think such a policy would work? Explain your answer.

Canada cannot exist in a state of isolation in the world. As a nation, we are in constant contact with other countries. In a global marketplace, we need to import and export resources, manufactured goods, technology, and information. We interact with other nations through humanitarian efforts, development programs, and peace-keeping missions. Our multicultural heritage also ensures close bonds between Canada and countries around the world.

Cultural links

Canada maintains cultural links with many countries in the world. These ties may be informal ones, such as the bonds that are created when immigrants come to live in Canada. But there are formal cultural links, too. These involve membership in organizations whose members share a common interest. Our strongest formal cultural bonds, the Commonwealth and la Francophonie, reflect Canada's bilingual and bicultural heritage.

The Commonwealth

The **Commonwealth** consists of fifty-one independent countries representing 25 per cent of the world's population—some 1.4 billion people! Members of the Commonwealth share a background rooted in the history of the British Empire. Today, however, the association promotes racial harmony and understanding, equal educational opportunities, improved health care, and greater eco-

nomic well being for all of its members. These principles were set forth in the Singapore Declaration, which was signed at the annual meeting in Singapore in 1971. If members fail to meet the standards set out in the declaration, their membership may be suspended, or they may be expelled. In 1961, South Africa withdrew from the Commonwealth in the face of criticism of the government's policy of **apartheid**, which segregated South Africans by race. The country was readmitted in 1994 following free elections and the dismantling of apartheid. In 1995, Nigeria was suspended after the government executed several political prisoners, including a famous writer.

Not all Commonwealth countries share the same standard of living. Some members, like Canada, are developed countries. They have high incomes, an abundance of food, comfortable housing, good health care, educational opportunities, and modern transportation services. Developing countries are those that are trying to attain these standards for their citizens. Only a few Commonwealth countries are developed nations. Most are developing countries. Many programs of the Commonwealth, such as the Commonwealth Fund for Technical Co-operation, the Commonwealth Science Council, and the Commonwealth Youth Council, focus on development in these countries.

1 a) Select six Commonwealth countries from the appendix on page 466. Include Canada and Australia, two countries

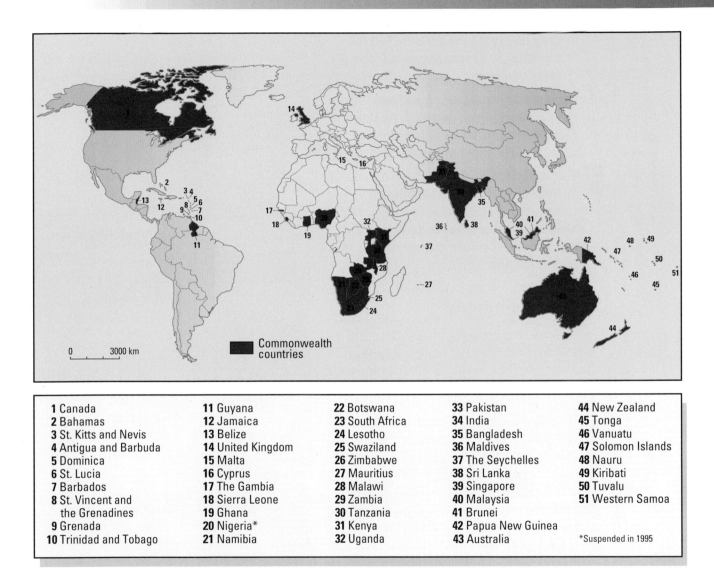

1 Canada	**11** Guyana	**22** Botswana	**33** Pakistan	**44** New Zealand
2 Bahamas	**12** Jamaica	**23** South Africa	**34** India	**45** Tonga
3 St. Kitts and Nevis	**13** Belize	**24** Lesotho	**35** Bangladesh	**46** Vanuatu
4 Antigua and Barbuda	**14** United Kingdom	**25** Swaziland	**36** Maldives	**47** Solomon Islands
5 Dominica	**15** Malta	**26** Zimbabwe	**37** The Seychelles	**48** Nauru
6 St. Lucia	**16** Cyprus	**27** Mauritius	**38** Sri Lanka	**49** Kiribati
7 Barbados	**17** The Gambia	**28** Malawi	**39** Singapore	**50** Tuvalu
8 St. Vincent and the Grenadines	**18** Sierra Leone	**29** Zambia	**40** Malaysia	**51** Western Samoa
9 Grenada	**19** Ghana	**30** Tanzania	**41** Brunei	
10 Trinidad and Tobago	**20** Nigeria*	**31** Kenya	**42** Papua New Guinea	*Suspended in 1995
	21 Namibia	**32** Uganda	**43** Australia	

from Africa, one from the Caribbean, and one from Asia.

b) Choose four factors that might be used to determine the level of development of Commonwealth countries. Using the data for each of the six countries, assemble a matrix to compare levels of development. List the countries along the vertical axis and the indicators along the horizontal axis.

c) Once you have recorded the data, rank each country by factor. For example, assign 6 points to the country that is the most developed and 1 point to the country that is the least developed. When all data have been ranked, total

Figure 21.1

Members of the Commonwealth

the scores for each country. List the countries in descending order from the most developed to the least developed.

2 Consider the terms *developed country* and *developing country*. Do you think the term *Commonwealth* is appropriate for this organization? Explain your answer.

3 Assume you are a member of the youth delegation to the next Commonwealth Conference. Suggest three issues that should be included in the conference agenda. Give reasons to support your recommendations.

La Francophonie

The French language and culture is an important part of our Canadian heritage. In Quebec, 80 per cent of the population speaks French. Montreal, the largest city in Quebec and the second largest city in Canada, is the largest French-speaking city after Paris. In New Brunswick, 34 per cent of the people are of Acadian, or French, descent. In Ontario, half a million people speak French as their first language. Indeed, French-speaking Canadians can be found in provinces across the country.

La Francophonie is an association of countries like Canada in which French is an official language or is widely spoken. It includes countries like Morocco, for example, in which Arabic is the official language but 5 million of the country's 26.2 million people speak French. In total, over 450 million people in forty-six countries are linked through this association.

Figure 21.2

Members of la Francophonie

Founded in 1960, the objective of la Francophonie is to protect the French heritage of its members. This is accomplished through economic and political co-operation and cultural exchanges. Like the Commonwealth, developed countries in la Francophonie assist developing members through educational, health, agricultural, and other social and scientific programs.

While Canada is a member of la Francophonie, Quebec and New Brunswick, the two provinces with the largest French-

Belgium	Laos
Benin	Lebanon
Bulgaria	Luxembourg
Burkina Faso	Madagascar
Burundi	Mali
Cambodia	Mauritania
Cameroon	Mauritius
Canada	Monaco
Cape Verde	Morocco
Central African	New
Republic	Brunswick
Chad	Niger
Comoros	Quebec
Congo	Romania
Cote-d'Ivoire	Rwanda
Djibouti	St. Lucia
Dominica	Senegal
Egypt	The Seychelles
Equatorial Guinea	Switzerland
France	Togo
Gabon	Tunisia
Guinea	Vanuatu
Guinea-Bissau	Vietnam
Haiti	Zaïre

Source: Department of Foreign Affairs and International Trade, 1995.

speaking populations, have official status as "participating governments." This means they occupy their own places at the discussion table and cast individual votes on matters of co-operation and development. On political issues, however, only the national Canadian delegation has voting rights.

4   On an outline map of the world, shade and label the members of la Francophonie as listed in Figure 21.2.

5   In an organizer, compare the Commonwealth and la Francophonie under the following headings: Language; Objectives; Levels of development; Geographic distribution.

6   Why do you think Quebec and New Brunswick have separate membership in la Francophonie? Do you agree with this? Give reasons for your answer.

7   Research a francophone community in your province. Where is it located? How large is it? What is its history? In what ways does it maintain its cultural heritage? Prepare a brief report of your findings.

8   a) Select one member of la Francophonie. Research this country and write a profile of it. Include such things as language, ethnic groups, government, economic base, and trading partners.
    b) Describe the similarities and differences between this country and Canada.

Strategic links

Throughout history the world has been plagued by political turmoil and war. Countries have forged strategic alliances with other nations to protect their mutual interests. Since the Second World War, the most important strategic links for Canada have been with the United Nations and the North Atlantic Treaty Organization.

The United Nations

The United Nations was first established at the end of the Second World War to "save succeeding generations from the scourge of war." Canada was one of its founding members. The main objective of the United Nations is to maintain international peace

Figure 21.3
Canadian peacekeepers

The uniforms worn by Canada's first peacekeepers were the same as those worn by the British in the conflict in the Middle East in 1956. To distinguish themselves as a neutral force, the Canadian troops obtained thousands of surplus helmets from US forces in Europe and spray-painted them blue. Thus the blue helmets, and the blue berets worn off the battlefield, became the symbol of the United Nations peacekeepers!

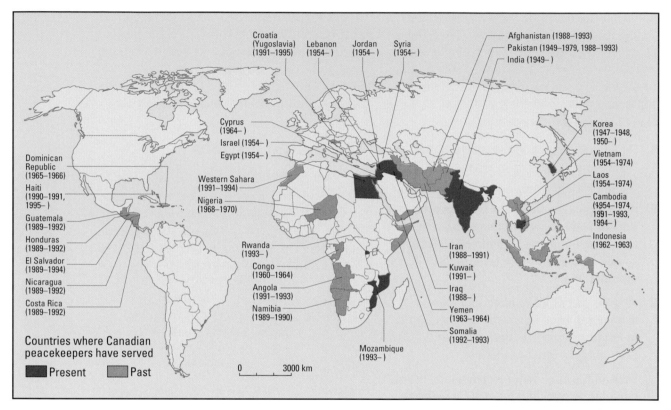

Figure 21.4
Deployment of Canadian troops on behalf of the United Nations

and security, and Canada has been a key player in fulfilling this goal.

Former Canadian prime minister Lester B. Pearson received the Nobel Prize for Peace in 1957 for his role in creating the first formal UN peacekeeping force. Pearson devised a plan to send troops to keep peace between Egypt and invading forces from Britain, France, and Israel in 1956. This marked the beginning of Canadian involvement in peacekeeping missions around the globe. Since then, over 90 000 Canadian soldiers have served in at least twenty-five UN operations. They have been joined by over 600 000 soldiers from seventy countries. But Canada holds the distinction of being the only country to have contributed to every

peacekeeping force in UN history. Figure 21.4 shows the deployment of Canadian forces on behalf of the United Nations.

9 Canada participates in many UN agencies. Using your library resource centre, identify the following agencies and write a brief description of their roles: GATT; WHO; FAO; UNICEF; UNESCO; UNEP.

10 Monitor your daily newspaper for reports of new conflicts in which Canadian peacekeepers may be called to serve. Keep a clippings file of any of these hot spots.

11 Some people believe that a permanent United Nations peacekeeping force should be established to react quickly to

trouble spots anywhere in the world and that Canada should be a founding member of this force. Discuss this idea in class.

The North Atlantic Treaty Organization

The **North Atlantic Treaty Organization** (NATO) was established in 1949. Its creation was the result of the Cold War between the United States and its Western allies and the Soviet Union and its allies in Eastern Europe. NATO joined together sixteen nations—Belgium, Canada, Denmark, France, Greece, Iceland, Italy, Luxembourg, the Netherlands, Norway, Portugal, Spain, Turkey, the United Kingdom, the United States, and West Germany—in a common defence pact. Members agreed to treat an armed attack on any one of them as an attack against them all. It also united the members to solve political problems and disputes amongst themselves through peaceful means.

Over the years, Canada has contributed troops and military equipment to NATO bases in Europe. Today, however, the role of NATO is changing. The once powerful Soviet Union has collapsed. Russia and the independent republics of the former USSR no longer pose a serious threat to the security of NATO members. The need for a powerful weapons arsenal and thousands of troops poised for action in Europe has disappeared.

In light of this new political order, NATO must carve out a new role for itself. Some have suggested that role should be as peacemakers and peacekeepers. NATO troops are currently stationed in Bosnia to enforce the 1995 peace treaty intended to end the conflict in the former Yugoslavia. This was the first war fought on European soil since the end of the Second World War in 1945. It served as a reminder that nationalism is still a powerful force in many countries. This fact alone suggests that NATO should not be abandoned altogether.

12 On an outline map of the world, shade and label the member countries of NATO.

13 "The main problem facing NATO is the problem of success. Peace has been kept for thirty-eight years. The generation now being elected to the parliaments of Western Europe and North America has not known war. But the very extent of this achievement can make it more difficult to demonstrate the need for continuing effort." *The Secretary-General of NATO*

Why can NATO be called a success? Why might this success be considered a problem?

14 In your library resource centre, research three other international organizations in which Canada is a member. In chart form, compare these organizations under the following headings: Purpose; Goals; Member countries; Canada's role.

Humanitarian links

One of the strongest links between Canada and developing countries is through international aid. This takes many forms, from providing medical care to building roads and schools. The Canadian government allocates billions of dollars each year in

Official Development Aid (ODA). This is distributed to development projects around the world.

The Canadian International Development Agency

The **Canadian International Development Agency** (CIDA) was created by the federal government in 1968. Its main objectives are to establish long-term development strategies and to provide short-term humanitarian relief. Canadian doctors, nurses, teachers, farmers, foresters, and technicians contribute their knowledge and skills to improving the qualify of life in places around the world. In emergencies, such as floods, droughts, hurricanes, and earthquakes, CIDA supplies money, materials, and human resources to relieve the hardships these disasters inflict.

CIDA's development policy is to provide aid to the neediest countries first. Its objective is to help people in these countries solve their problems themselves and to create long-term sustainable development.

Nongovernmental organizations

Canada also establishes humanitarian links through **nongovernmental organizations** (NGOs). These agencies raise millions of dollars in private donations to assist developing countries. In 1994, NGOs raised $284 million for a wide range of projects, including agricultural projects, medical facilities, and training programs. There are over 240 NGOs in Canada, among them World Vision, Oxfam, and the Red Cross. They employ thousands of people in Canada and overseas.

15 Refer to Figure 21.5.

a) On an outline map of the world, draw a bar 5 mm wide in each country that received humanitarian aid from CIDA; the base of the bar should be in the centre of the country. Calculate the length of the bar using the following scale: less than $1 000 000—1 cm; $1 000 000 – $2 000 000—2 cm; $2 000 000 – $3 000 000—3 cm; more than $4 000 000—4 cm.

b) Colour code each bar by type of aid: green for general aid, red for war-related aid, and blue for aid for natural disasters or disease.

c) What was the total amount of aid distributed by CIDA in 1994? Which region received the greatest share of this aid?

16 "Give people fish and you feed them for a day. Teach them to fish and you feed them for life."

In your own words, explain the meaning of this ancient proverb as it applies to international aid projects.

COUNTRY	PURPOSE	AMOUNT
Afghanistan	Postwar aid	$6 300 000
Angola	Postwar aid	$4 864 000
Armenia	General aid	$500 000
Azerbaijan	General aid	$680 000
Bangladesh	Refugee repatriation	$3 469 000
Burundi	General aid	$3 172 000
Cambodia	Postwar aid	$1 000 000
Colombia	General aid	$425 000
Cuba	Optical neuritis	$250 000
Djibouti	Cholera epidemic	$100 000
Ecuador	Landslide	$63 000
Eritrea	Storms	$100 000
Ethiopia	Refugee repatriation	$500 000
Georgia	General aid	$2 000 000
Haiti	Emergency health care	$5 000 000
Honduras	Tropical storm	$500 000
India	Earthquake	$500 000
Iraq	General aid	$999 000
Jordan	Peace implementation	$895 000
Lebanon	Health care	$350 000
Liberia	Food and medical	$2 987 000
Madagascar	Cyclones	$50 000
Mauritania	Locust infestation	$500 000
Mozambique	Postwar aid	$4 250 000
Nepal	Refugee repatriation	$700 000
Nicaragua	Tropical storm	$50 000
Peru	General aid	$750 000
Rwanda	Emergency medical/ water	$1 144 000
Somalia	Postwar aid	$4 271 000
Sri Lanka	General aid	$1 500 000
Sudan	Postwar aid	$8 468 000
Swaziland	Cholera outbreak	$31 000
Syria	Peace implementation	$695 000
Togo	Refugee repatriation	$250 000
Vietnam	General aid	$1 500 000
Zaïre	General aid	$2 075 000
Ex-Yugoslavia	War-related aid	$13 525 000

Figure 21.5
Humanitarian aid through CIDA, 1994

Source: CIDA estimates, 1995.

17 Refer to Figure 12.6.
  a) Which country contributes the greatest amount of international aid?
  b) Where does Canada rank in total aid contributions? Where does Canada rank in aid on a per capita basis?
  c) Why is it important to know both total aid and aid per capita? Why might aid as a percentage of the donor's Gross National Product be the most revealing information of all?

18 Some Canadians do not support contributing foreign aid to developing countries. Others believe that Canada does not contribute enough aid.
  a) Working with a group, brainstorm a list of arguments both for and against foreign aid.
  b) Decide whether you think Canada contributes too much aid, not enough aid, or just the right amount of aid. Give reasons for your answer. (You might want to refer to Figure 21.6.)

Figure 21.6
Aid to developing countries by major donors, 1994

DONOR	TOTAL AID (millions $US)	AID PER CAPITA	AID AS % OF GNP
Australia	$953	$53	.35
Austria	$544	$69	.30
Belgium	$808	$81	.39
Canada	$2 373	$87	.45
Denmark	$1 340	$256	1.03
Finland	$356	$71	.45
France	$7 915	$139	.63
Germany	$6 954	$86	.37
Ireland	$81	$23	.20
Italy	$3 034	$21	.31
Japan	$11 259	$91	.26
Luxembourg	$50	$125	.35
Netherlands	$2 525	$166	.82
New Zealand	$98	$29	.25
Norway	$1 014	$236	1.01
Spain	$1 213	$31	.25
Sweden	$1 769	$203	.98
Switzerland	$793	$256	.33
United Kingdom	$2 908	$50	.31
United States	$9 721	$38	.15

Source: CIDA, 1995.

Environmental links

One of the most important links Canada shares with the rest of the world is the environment. The actions we take within our own country can affect the environment in other parts of the world. One of the best examples of this is the earth's atmosphere. It is in constant motion as wind systems move air around the globe. Pollutants that Canadians emit into the atmosphere over Canada today may affect the atmosphere in Britain next week. Similarly, actions taken in Mexico yesterday may have an impact on the air over Canada tomorrow.

The greenhouse effect

One of the most dramatic and rapid changes to the environment is the **greenhouse effect**. This produces a gradual warming of global temperatures. Much of the greenhouse effect is the result of increased levels of carbon dioxide (CO_2) in the atmosphere. The sun's energy enters the atmosphere as light. Once it strikes the earth's surface, it is reflected back into the atmosphere as heat. Much of this energy is absorbed by carbon dioxide, which acts like the glass in a greenhouse. It lets the sun's rays through, but traps some of the heat that would otherwise be radiated back into space.

Natural levels of carbon dioxide make life on earth possible. Without CO_2, average temperatures on earth would be 30°C cooler! Each year, however, we add more carbon dioxide to the atmosphere. About 80 per cent of this is the result of the burning of fossil fuels, which have high carbon levels. The rest is from deforestation. Trees absorb carbon dioxide when they are alive. Once they are cut and burned, however, the gas is released. The higher levels of CO_2 absorb more heat. The result is global warming. The amount of carbon dioxide in the atmosphere has increased by 26 per cent in the last 100 years. During this same period, temperatures have increased, too. (See Figure 21.7.) It is predicted that average global temperatures may rise by as much as 5°C over the next century. What will this mean?

As the polar icecaps slowly begin to melt from the warmer temperatures, sea levels will rise. Low-lying deltas and coastal cities will be flooded. Island atolls will disappear. Hundreds of millions of people will be threatened by floods or will be forced to relocate. Rainfall patterns will change. Some places will experience heavy rains and widespread flooding. In other places, rainfall may decline, leading to drought. Changes in rainfall patterns will in turn affect agricultural patterns. In some places, farmers will be able to plant crops they were unable to grow under cooler conditions. Other agricultural regions, however, will be lost because climatic change will make them unproductive. Many plant and animal species will become extinct as they are unable to adapt to these rapid changes. Diseases like malaria and cholera, which thrive in tropical climates, will spread as regions become warmer. Figure 7.19 on page 122 shows some of the predicted effects a warmer climate might have on Canada.

Scientists believe it is impossible to eliminate global warming because of the high carbon levels that already exist. It is possible, however, to slow down the rate of warming. The best way to do this is to conserve energy, reduce deforestation, and plant more trees. At the Earth Summit in Rio de Janeiro in 1992, the industrialized countries agreed to reduce their carbon emissions to 1990 levels by the year 2000. However, in Canada in 1996, carbon emissions were actually rising.

Those countries that are in the process of industrializing are not bound by the agreement to reduce carbon emissions. Countries like China, India, Brazil, and Indonesia rely on traditional carbon-based resources to fuel their industries. Alternative power sources that are less harmful to the environment are costly for everyone. In Canada, experts believe that reducing our use of fossil fuels will cost Canadian industry $35 billion over the next twenty years.

Figure 21.7
The increase in carbon levels and temperatures since 1900

19 Describe the main causes of global warming.

20 Refer to Figure 21.7.
   a) Describe the increase in both carbon emissions and global temperatures.
   b) How may developing countries contribute to this problem in the next fifty years?

21 Refer to Figure 7.19 on page 122. Under the headings "Good effects" and "Bad effects," list the changes that are predicted for Canada as a result of global warming.

22 a) Assume you are a member of the Canadian delegation to an environmental summit. In a strategy planning session, create a proposal for solving the problem of global warming. Be specific. Be sure

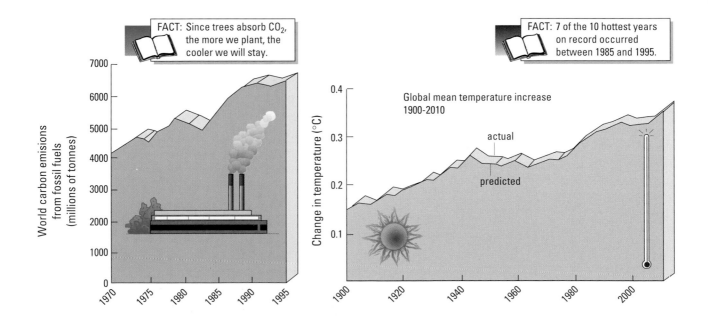

FACT: Since trees absorb CO_2, the more we plant, the cooler we will stay.

FACT: 7 of the 10 hottest years on record occurred between 1985 and 1995.

World carbon emissions from fossil fuels (millions of tonnes)

Change in temperature (°C)

Global mean temperature increase 1900-2010

actual

predicted

to consider the needs of both developed and developing countries. Decide how to enforce any resolutions the summit passes.

b) Share your strategy with other groups. To what extent are they similar and different? Are there any ideas you could add to your strategy?

Simulation: designing Canada's foreign policy

While we belong to international organizations like the United Nations, ultimately Canada must decide on its own about the nature and substance of its relations with the rest of the world. The decisions Canada makes about its global relationships are called **foreign policy**.

In 1995, the Canadian government issued a statement outlining the direction of foreign policy in the twenty-first century. The statement acknowledged:

- that as one of the world's leading economic nations, Canada has a responsibility to exert its influence in the global interest
- that Canada's geographic location offers it an advantageous position in the emerging economies of the Pacific Rim and Latin America
- that Canada has strong cultural ties to both English- and French-speaking countries as well as to the homelands of our immigrant population
- that Canada has a history of internal peace and multiculturalism and plays an important role as an international peacekeeper.

23 As a member of the federal cabinet, you must discuss and formulate a foreign policy for Canada.

a) Form groups of six. Select one student to act as the prime minister. Each of the remaining five students will take on the role of one of the cabinet ministers. (See the briefing notes on page 464.) Each minister, including the prime minister, should review the list of policy topics and select four for discussion at the cabinet meeting. Ministers should submit their choices to the prime minister. The prime minister should then count the number of "votes" for each topic. The four topics with the most votes will be discussed at the cabinet meeting. The prime minister will then create an agenda.

b) Review these four topics in the text and your notebook before beginning the cabinet meeting. Make notes of important information that will help you form your policy statements.

c) Hold your cabinet meeting. The prime minister will chair the discussion. Each topic on the agenda must be discussed in order. Ministers may raise their hands to speak or they may be asked to speak in turn. The prime minister will set a time limit.

d) As a group, form foreign policy statements for each topic. Begin each with the statement *"The Government of Canada believes that...."* Be prepared to defend your reasons for the policies you have established.

e) Share your policy statements with those of other cabinet groups. Discuss any similarities and differences.

Foreign policy topics

(1) Immigration: Determine the number of immigrants that will be allowed to enter the country over the next five years and decide whether Canada should accept more refugees. (Review pages 259–264.)

(2) Culture: Formulate a policy to help Canada maintain its cultural independence in a world of global communications and the information superhighway. (Review pages 452–455.)

(3) Trade alliances: Decide whether Canada should increase its trade links with a greater number of countries, and if so, where these trade relationships should be forged. This should include whether or not to extend the North American Free Trade Agreement to countries in Central and South America. (Review pages 449–451.)

(4) The United Nations: Decide the future of Canadian forces as international peacekeepers on behalf of the United Nations. (Review pages 455–457.)

(5) Military alliances: Determine the future of Canada's participation in the North Atlantic Treaty Organization and how NATO and Canada's role in it should change as a result of the end of the Cold War. (Review page 457.)

(6) Humanitarian aid: Determine Canada's level of commitment to developmental and humanitarian projects in developing countries. (Review pages 457–460.)

(7) The environment: Establish Canada's international role in environmental protection, particularly in resolving the problem of global warming. (Review pages 461–463.)

Briefing notes

Minister of Defence: Canada's most important military alliance is with NATO. The end of the Cold War, however, means that NATO must redefine its role and purpose. As neighbours and allies, Canada's defence relationship with the United States is the ultimate key to our international security. You are also proud of Canada's excellent reputation for international peacekeeping on behalf of the United Nations.

Minister of International Trade: The United States is Canada's largest trading partner, receiving 80 per cent of our exports. The European Union is becoming an increasingly powerful trading bloc and Canada has strong ties with EU countries. The Pacific Rim is the fastest-growing economic region in the world. Among the new leading trade exporters are Korea, Taiwan, China, and Mexico. Brazil is also emerging as a strong exporting country. You support the global trend towards free trade with many countries.

Minister of Multiculturalism: You believe that Canada has a unique culture that should be promoted around the world. Instead of Canadian culture being threatened by global communications, you believe the information superhighway should be used to enhance our cultural profile. You support increased immigration as a means of further developing the potential of this great country. Our multicultural heritage is also reinforced through our formal and humanitarian links with other countries.

Minister of Foreign Affairs: Canada is highly regarded as a diplomatic leader at the United Nations and around the world. We have always contributed troops to peacekeeping operations in the world's trouble spots. But the United Nations has faced criticism that its peacekeeping efforts in places like Bosnia have been ineffective. Canada has also been a leading supporter of aid programs in developing countries. Foreign aid is one way to help countries develop the skills and resources needed for sustainable development.

Minister of the Environment: The problem of global warming and other environmental concerns can only be resolved through international co-operation. Canada is one of the world's largest consumers of fossil fuels. It is also responsible for 20 per cent of world trade in forest products and has a responsibility to practice effective forest management and to protect the natural environment. Industrialized countries like Canada must act to reduce the damage their pollution causes to the environment. They must also act to help developing countries improve their quality of life without causing further environmental harm.

24 Assume the role of a political columnist in a national newspaper. Write an editorial about one aspect of Canada's foreign policy in which you support or reject the government's position.

Canada: is there any place you would rather live?

In 1995, the United Nations named Canada the best country in the world in which to live.

25 a) Brainstorm a list of factors that you think are important in determining the quality of life.

b) Consider how each of these factors relates to Canada. Make point-form notes beside each factor based on the knowledge you have gained in this course and using other sources, such as atlases and almanacs.

c) Write a personal essay expressing your view about life in Canada. Explain why you think Canada is, or is not, the best country in the world in which to live.

APPENDIX: SELECTED STATISTICS

	GNP/CAPITA	LIFE EXPECTANCY (years)	VALUE OF MANUFACTURING ($ millions)	ENERGY CONSUMPTION (kg oil/capita)	% EMPLOYED IN AGRICULTURE	% OF FOOD CONSUMED IN RELATION TO NEED	POPULATION/PHYSICIAN	ROAD DENSITY (km/1000 pop.)	POPULATION/TELEVISION	TOTAL TRADE — EXPORTS PLUS IMPORTS ($ billions)	LITERACY RATE	INFANT MORTALITY RATE (under 1 year/1000)
HIGH-INCOME COUNTRIES												
Australia	17 500	78	43 679	5 316	5	117	454	471	2	85	99	7
Canada	19 970	78	122 972	7 821	3	127	510	592	2	276	99	7
France	22 490	77	271 133	4 031	8	135	319	525	2	408	99	7
Italy	18 840	78	250 345	2 697	9	138	234	410	3	315	99	8
Japan	31 490	80	1 023 048	3 642	7	111	662	464	2	603	99	4
Netherlands	20 950	78	58 476	4 533	4	127	450	487	2	265	99	7
Sweden	24 740	78	43 603	5 385	3	109	387	682	2	92	99	5
United Kingdom	18 060	76	201 859	3 781	1	128	609	473	2	386	99	7
United States	24 740	76	1 570 135	7 918	3	136	512	565	1	1068	99	9
Germany	23 560	76	565 603	4 170	3	124	438	457	2	728	99	6
MIDDLE-INCOME COUNTRIES												
Jamaica	1 440	74	620	1 096	25	109	2 040	70	140	3	98	14
Mexico	3 610	71	67 157	1 439	25	127	1 492	80	8	80	87	35
Congo	950	67	228	165	62	85	7 692	498	222	1	57	84
Thailand	2 110	69	31 185	678	60	106	6 250	31	9	82	93	36
Russia	2 340	65	200 237	2 390	25	117	213	154	3	77	98	21
Hungary	3 350	69	7 381	2 385	21	124	306	125	3	21	98	15
LOW-INCOME COUNTRIES												
Burkina	300	47	184	16	87	88	50 034	2	196	0.2	12	129
Ethiopia	100	48	210	23	80	97	97 678	3	476	0.9	19	117
Ghana	430	56	598	96	59	116	20 000	3	69	2.8	60	79
Zimbabwe	520	53	1 379	471	65	96	7 142	12	38	2.6	67	67
India	300	61	41 558	242	63	98	2 500	8	37	44.2	48	80
Kenya	270	58	764	99	81	94	10 000	8	116	2.7	69	61
Mali	270	46	234	20	86	74	25 000	1	2500	0.8	32	157
Pakistan	430	62	7 538	209	50	95	2 941	10	63	16.3	35	88
China	490	69	147 302	66	74	103	1 010	10	37	195.0	73	30

Glossary

Aboriginal: a descendant of Canada's first inhabitants

Absolute location: the exact location of a place or feature

Accessibility index: a calculation used to determine how accessible a community is in relation to all others

Acid precipitation: toxic rainwater that contains more than 0.2 parts per million of sulphur dioxide

Active layer: the upper layer of permanently frozen soil that thaws briefly during the summer

Active solar energy: the use of the sun to create heat or generate electricity

Actual reserves: known reserves of oil, gas, or other minerals that can be mined profitably under current conditions

Air mass: a large body of air with a uniform moisture and temperature content

Albedo: the reflection of heat energy from the earth back into the atmosphere

Alienation: a feeling of being apart or separate from most other people in a society

Altitude: the height above sea level

Anthracite coal: a carbon-rich coal once used extensively for home heating

Apartheid: a system of segregation or discrimination based on race

Appalachians: a mountain system running along the east coat of North America

Aquaculture: the raising of marine life in a controlled environment

Arctic Lowlands: the low-lying areas of the islands of the far North

Area code: the system of regional codes used by telephone companies

Area symbol: a coloured pattern representing a feature on a topographic map

Artificial boundary: a political boundary that does not follow a natural feature

Assimilation: when all ethnic groups are encouraged to blend into a single dominant culture

Atmosphere: the layer of gases surrounding the earth

Baby boom: a sharp increase in the number of births

Bar graph: a bar, or bars, on a graph that compare data

Bar map: a map on which bars of different heights are drawn to represent data

Bench: a spiralling terrace built into the side of an open-pit mine to allow trucks to move in and out

Birth rate: the number of births per 1000 population

Bituminous coal: a soft coal used mainly in iron and steel mills and thermal electric plants

Block: an area between major streets in a town or city

Boom-and-bust cycle: the fluctuations in the economy that are typical of natural resource industries

Boom-and-bust economy: a resource-based economy that fluctuates according to market price and demand

Brine: a super-heated mixture of salt and water within magma that solidifies after cooling to form veins of metallic minerals

Canadian International Development Agency: the federal agency responsible for distributing aid to foreign countries

Canadian Shield: a land mass of hard granite rock that covers 50 per cent of the country

Cap rock: an impervious layer of rock overlaying porous rock under which oil and gas are trapped

Capillary action: the movement of moisture upwards in soil that carries minerals closer to the surface

Cardinal points: the four main directions—north, south, east, west

Carrying capacity: in agriculture, the number of hectares of land needed to support one grazing animal

Census: the means by which governments count and collect population data

Census Metropolitan Area: an urban centre that exceeds 100 000 population

Census subdivision: a geographic region established for the purpose of conducting a census

Census tract: in urban areas, the further division of a census subdivision into smaller units

Chinook: a warm wind that flows from the Rocky Mountains across the foothills of Alberta

Clear-cut: a method of forest harvesting in which all trees in a given area are cut

Climagraph: a combined line and bar graph showing average monthly temperature and precipitation

Climate: the long-term pattern of weather conditions

Co-generation: the process in which heated water remaining after the production of thermal or nuclear electricity is used as a source of heat

Comfort temperature: the temperature at which people feel most comfortable

Commonwealth: an association of countries that works towards understanding and economic co-operation

Comparative bar graph: a graph that presents several bars of information for complex comparisons

Condensation: the changing of a vapour or gas into a liquid

Consortium: a group of companies that joins together to carry out large, complex, and expensive projects

Continental climate: a climate with a large range between the maximum and minimum monthly temperatures, usually found in the centre of large land masses

Continental shelf: the gently sloping submarine fringe of a continent, usually less than 200 m deep

Continuous line graph: a graph that joins plotted points with a smooth line

Contour interval: the difference in elevation between contour lines

Contour line: a line on a map connecting places of the same elevation

Convection: the process by which heat is transferred from one part of a liquid or gas to another

Convectional precipitation: precipitation that occurs as a result of warm, moist air rising, then cooling and creating condensation

Conventional oilfield: a field that produces oil in liquid form that is capable of flowing naturally or being pumped without processing

Co-ordinate: a reference number and letter assigned to a grid on a map

Core: the area of a country with the greatest concentration of major towns and cities

Cost-benefit analysis: considering the social and financial advantages and disadvantages before making a decision

Crime rate: the overall number of crimes committed in an area

Cultural imprint: the effects of culture, either physical or social, on the environment

Cultural mosaic: a society in which ethnic groups retain their cultural heritage

Culture: a learned social behaviour transmitted through such things as customs, beliefs, values, technology, and art

Culture clash: a feeling of isolation that people experience when they move to a different environment

Cyclonic precipitation: precipitation created when a warm, moist body of air is forced to rise by a cooler body of air

Death rate: the number of deaths per 1000 population

Degree days: the number of days in a year when the average daily temperature rises above 5.6°C

Demography: the study of population numbers, distribution, trends, and issues

Dependency load: the portion of the population under sixteen and over sixty-five

Direct employment: jobs that are involved in the production of a product or raw material

Direction: movement, or the location of a place or object, in relation to the North Pole

Directional symbol: a map symbol that shows the direction of north

Divergence bar graph: a graph showing plus and minus values for a particular period

Divided bar graph: a graph in which each bar is subdivided to show its component parts

Divided circle graph: a circular, or pie, graph that shows comparisons using percentages

Downlink: the transmission of a signal from a satellite to a ground-receiving station

Drainage basin: the area that is drained by a major river and its tributaries

Drift-net: a kilometre-long net used in the open seas to catch tuna and other large fish

Drumlin: an oval-shaped hummock or small hill left behind by a melting ice sheet

Easting: a reference line on a map, drawn vertically from north to south, identified by the numbers displayed from west to east across the map

Economy of scale: the lower cost per unit that results from mass production of a product

Elevation: see *Altitude*

Emigration: when people leave one country to live in another

Environmental impact assessment: a study to investigate the possible effects of a construction project on the environment

Equalization payment: federal government financial support to a province needing assistance in providing public services

Equator: the 0° line of latitude that circles the earth from west to east

Erosion: the gradual wearing away of land or rock by natural forces

Esker: a long ridge of material deposited by a meltwater stream flowing beneath it

Ethnic neighbourhood: an area with a unique cultural flavour

Export: a product or service that leaves a country as a result of trade

Extensive farm: a large farm in which land values, inputs and outputs, and yields per hectare are low and the crops produced are less perishable and of lower value

Fertility rate: the average number of live births per year for each woman of child-bearing age

Fibre optics: thin glass fibres that allow light to be transmitted within a cable

Fiord: a deep river valley shaped by glacial ice flowing into an ocean

First-generation Canadian: an immigrant who becomes a citizen of Canada

First language: the language a person learns to speak first

Fishing bank: a shallow area on the continental shelf that provides a feeding and spawning ground for fish

Fissure: a long, narrow crack that develops in a rock near the surface of the earth

Floodplain: the level valley floor on either side of a river that is flooded during periods of high runoff

Flow line: a line on a map or plan showing the movement of people or things

Focal point: a place from which people view their surroundings

Fold mountains: mountains that have been squeezed into folds by pressure from within the earth's crust

Footloose industry: a company free to locate anywhere without being restricted by specific location factors

Foreign policy: a government's plan for international relations

Fossil fuel: a combustible material formed from the remains of living organisms transformed over time by heat and pressure

Four-figure grid reference: a map location identified using eastings and northings

Francophonie: an association of countries with the purpose of protecting French heritage through cultural exchanges and economic assistance

Free trade: a reduction or elimination of tariffs and quotas on exports and imports

Frictional blight: the co-existence of two or more disagreeable types of land use

Front: the leading edge of an air mass

Frontal precipitation: see *Cyclonic precipitation*

Functional blight: the negative effect that results when an area is no longer used for its original purpose

Gazetteer: an index of places and physical features that indicates their location in an atlas

Genetic engineering: the science of altering the genes of plants or animals to increase their desirable characteristics

Geographic centre: the centre point of a country measured from north to south and east to west

Geographic information system: computer software application of spacial or digital information

Geographic location: the map co-ordinates or spacial description of a place

Geostationary orbit: a satellite orbiting the earth at a speed that keeps it exactly above a certain ground position

Gill net: a curtain-line net suspended from floats and held down by lead weights that catches fish by the gills

Glacier: a massive ice sheet formed during the Ice Age

Global economy: the growing trend towards lower trade barriers and increasing economic links between countries

Global warming: the warming of world temperatures as a result of rising levels of carbon dioxide and other greenhouse gases in the atmosphere

Graded shading: a method of illustrating data using shades of the same colour, with the lightest shade representing the lowest value and the darkest shade representing the highest value

Gradient: the measurement of how much a slope drops over a certain distance

Great circle route: a line drawn on the surface of a globe showing the shortest distance between two points

Great Lakes-St. Lawrence Lowlands: the area that surrounds the Great Lakes and the St. Lawrence River

Greater Toronto Area: an area comprising Metropolitan Toronto and the surrounding municipalities of York, Durham, Halton, and Peel

Greenhouse effect: the absorption of heat energy by greenhouse gases and reradiation into the atmosphere

Greenwich Mean Time: the time at Greenwich, England, through which the Prime Meridian (0°) passes

Greying of the population: the growing trend towards an older average population

Grid: reference lines on maps, usually at right angles, used to locate places

Gross Domestic Product: the total value of all goods and services produced in a country in a single year

Groundwater: water that sinks into the earth and is absorbed into the soil and bedrock

Growing season: the number of days in the year when the average temperature is above 5.6°C, the temperature at which plants grow

Habitant: an early French peasant settler in Quebec

Habitat: the natural environment in which an organism lives successfully

Hailstone: an ice pellet formed when a frozen raindrop is caught in violent updrafts in the atmosphere

Hardwood: a dense, strong wood typical of most deciduous and tropical evergreen trees

Hemisphere: the division of the world into four spheres (Northern, Southern, Eastern, Western)

Herbicide: a chemical used to kill weeds

High-order product: a high-priced product or service that is purchased infrequently

Hinterland: an area beyond the highly urbanized core of a region or country

Historical imprint: a cultural imprint left by people in the past

Horizon: a distinctive layer of soil, divided into A, B, and C horizons

Hudson Bay Lowlands: the land area found to the south of Hudson Bay

Human resources: the abilities and skills possessed by people

Humus: the soil substance that forms from decomposed animal and plant life

Hurricane: a massive storm that produces heavy rain and winds exceediing 120 km/h

Hydrologic cycle: the constant movement and evaporation of water from the oceans, lakes, and other bodies of water

Hypothesis: a theory formed as the basis for an inquiry but not regarded as true until supported by evidence

Ice Age: the period of time, ending approximately 10 000 years ago, when freezing temperatures created ice sheets across continents

Igneous rock: very hard, impervious rock formed from molten magma beneath the earth's surface

Immigration: the movement of a person into a foreign country as a permanent resident

Impervious: a substance that does not allow water to pass through it

Import: a product or service brought into a country as a result of trade

Indirect employment: jobs that are created to supply, service, or further process the products of a primary industry

Industrial inertia: the attraction of businesses to move next to an area of existing business

Infant mortality rate: the number of infants per 1000 births who die before the age of one

In-filling: the development of less desirable areas of land in an area of urban sprawl

Information superhighway: the vast network of computers and other information technology that allows global communication

Innuitian Mountains: a mountain range in the far North

Input: the cost factors or expenses involved in producing a product

Insecticide: a substance used to kill insects

Inshore fishing: daily fishing using small boats close to the shore

Instream water use: the use of water without removing it from its source for activities such as fishing and hydroelectric power

Intensive farm: a small farm in which the land values, inputs and outputs, and yields per hectare are high and the crops produced are perishable and of high value

Interbasin transfer: the diversion of water from one drainage basin to another

Intermittent: a stream or lake that is occasionally dry

Intermodal transportion: the movement of goods between places using more than one type of transportation

International Date Line: the division line at 180° longitude as one days ends and the next begins

Jet stream: a west to east movement of air flowing at speeds of up to 400 km/h at an altitude between 8000 m and 15 000 m

Just-in-time delivery and assembly system: the ordering and receiving of parts as they are needed

Large-scale map: a map that shows a small area in detail

Latitude: imaginary horizontal lines showing positions, measured in degrees, north and south of the Equator

Leaching: when rain and groundwater cause soil and its minerals to move deeper into the ground

Leap-frogging: the development of land well away from an existing community

Life expectancy: the average lifespan of a population

Lignite coal: a soft, low-value coal used in thermal electric plants

Line graph: straight or curved lines joining plotted points on a graph to show variables in data over time

Line symbol: a linear symbol used to represent features on topographic maps

Linear scale: a line on a map that gives equivalent actual distance

Linear sprawl: urban growth along important transportation routes away from a community

Linkage: the movement of people, goods, and information among cities, regions, and countries

Longitude: imaginary vertical lines drawn between the poles showing positions, measured in degrees, minutes, and seconds, east and west from the Prime Meridian

Low-order product: a product or service that is purchased frequently

Magma: molten rock found beneath the earth's crust from which igneous rock is formed

Mainstreet: usually the busiest and most central road in a community

Maritime climate: a climate with a small range between the maximum and minimum monthly temperatures, usually found in coastal locations

Market gardening: intensive farming that concentrates on vegetables, fruits, flowers, and other high-value crops destined for nearby urban centres

Mass production: large-scale manufacturing of a product to lower the cost per item

Melting pot: see *Assimilation*

Metamorphic rock: rock that has been transformed by heat or pressure beneath the earth's surface

Métis: people of mixed Native Indian and European descent

Microwave transmission: the sending of short-wave radio signals using a series of towers and dishes

Middle-order product: a necessary good or service that people buy occasionally

Migration: the movement of people from one place to another

Mineral: a naturally formed substance obtained from the ground

Minute: one-sixtieth of a degree of latitude or longitude

Moderated temperature: a climate created by the proximity of water that makes land temperatures milder in winter and cooler in summer

Moraine: a glacial hill formed along the edge of a glacier

Multiculturalism: a social system in which people of different ethnic backgrounds are encouraged to maintain their traditions and customs

Multi-factor region: a region that is based on many different characteristics, such as climate, language, and industry

Multi-line graph: a line graph in which two or more factors are present using a common scale

Multiplier effect: the total impact on the economy that results from the expansion of one of its parts

Native peoples: see *Aboriginals*

Natural boundary: a political boundary that follows physical features

Natural increase: the difference between the birth rate and the death rate

Natural resource: a substance found in nature that is useful or valuable to people

Natural vegetation: plant life that grows without human interference

Net exporter: a country that exports more goods than it imports

Net migration: the number of people immigrating to a country compared to the number of people emigrating from it

Network: a multiple number of pathways joined together

Nomadic: the movement of people from place to place to be near the food or water supply or to find pasture

Nongovernmental organization: a private organization that provides humanitarian aid

Nonrenewable resource: a resource that cannot be replaced by natural processes

Non-status Indian: a Native Indian not covered under the Indian Act

Nordic: a climate in the northern latitudes in which summers are short and mild and winters are long and cold

Normal sprawl: development that takes place at the outer edges of an urban community

North American Free Trade Agreement: an agreement to eliminate trade restrictions between Canada, the US, and Mexico

North American Indian: the term by which Native Indians are recognized in the Canadian Constitution

North Atlantic Treaty Organization: an alliance of nations committed to helping one another in the event of armed attack

Northing: a series of reference lines on a map running east-west and identified by numbers increasing from south to north

Nuclear fission: the process of generating heat energy by splitting the atoms of radioactive materials

Nunavut: a new Native territory in Canada as of 1 April 1999

Nutrient: any substance providing essential nourishment for life

Offshore fishing: fishing carried out over several weeks using large trawlers on fishing banks at sea

Old-growth forest: an area of mature forest that has not been disturbed by human activity

Open-pit mine: a method of mining to recover deposits near the earth's surface by means of excavating a large hole

Ore: a mineral deposit that is large enough to be mined profitably

Orographic precipitation: precipitation that occurs when relatively warm, humid air is forced to rise over an elevated landform

Output: the products of a farm, industry, or other business

Overburden: the waste soil and rock lying on top of a mineral deposit

Oxbow lake: a lake formed in the old-age stage of river development when meanders become curved and are cut off

Parent material: soil from the C horizon containing minerals from the bedrock and glacial deposits

Passive solar energy: heat obtained from the sun through the careful placement of windows and methods of reducing heat loss

Pathway: a route between places once a link has been established

Peak value intersection: the place at which the two most important streets in a community meet and the land value is highest

Periphery: a less densely populated area surrounding a densely populated core

Permafrost: permanently frozen soil that does not thaw during the summer

Photovoltaic energy: the electricity produced directly from sunlight through the use of electromagnetic radiation

Physical blight: the physical decay of buildings and neighbourhoods

Physical imprint: the way in which people leave distinct cultural signs on their environment

Physiographic region: a region defined by its natural features

Phytoplankton: microscopic, single-celled plant organisms in the top layer of ocean waters

Plate: a rigid segment of the earth's crust that floats atop the heavier, semi-molten rock below

Point symbol: a symbol representing constructed features, such as bridges and buildings, on a topographic map

Point-of-use delivery: the practice of having parts delivered directly to the site where they are needed rather than being stored in a warehouse

Points system: the method used by the Canadian government to assess potential immigrants

Population density: the number of people living in a measured land area

Population distribution: the pattern of population in an area

Population pyramid: a graph that depicts population by age group

Port: a place through which people and products enter and leave a country

Postal code: a combination of letters and numbers identifying specific regions of Canada for the purpose of directing the mail

Potential reserves: reserves of oil, gas, or other minerals that are known to exist but cannot be mined profitably under current conditions

Primary industry: an industry involved in obtaining raw materials

Primary language: the most common language spoken in a community

Primary manufacturing: the first level of secondary industry in which raw materials are processed

Prime Meridian: the 0° line of longitude that circles the earth from north to south

Principle of least effort: a journey between two places following the shortest possible route

Productive forest: a forest stand that can be logged profitably and is accessible to transportation

Protectionism: the placement of high tariffs and quotas on imported goods in order to protect domestic industries from foreign competition

Pull factors: the economic and political considerations that influence an immigrant's choice of destination

Purse seine: a net designed to encircle and trap a school of fish

Push factors: the economic and political considerations that influence a person's decision to emigrate

Quaternary industry: an industry involved in processing information

Quota: a limit placed on the number or value of products being imported into a country; in immigration, a figure set annually as a target number of immigrants

Radial land pattern: a French pattern of land use radiating from a central point

Radiation: the amount of heat energy received as light from the sun

Rain shadow: a dry area on the leeward side of a land mass

Rang: a row of long, narrow land lots given to early French settlers

Ratio scale: a means of indicating that the distance on the ground is a number of times greater than the same distance on a map

Region: an area sharing similar characteristics, such as landscape, climate, or human activity

Relative location: the general location of a place relative to another place

Relief: the shape, slope and altitude of the earth's surface

Relief precipitation: see *Orographic precipitation*

Renewable resource: a resource that can be replaced by natural processes in a relatively short period of time

Research and development: the human and financial resources invested by businesses, governments, and academic institutions in new technologies

Reserve: a residential area allocated for Status Indians

Reservoir rock: a porous sandstone or limestone reef rock where oil and gas accumulate underground

Rise: the vertical distance in the gradient of a mountain slope

Risk capital: money available to invest in projects that have a high risk of failure

Rock cycle: the change in composition, structure, and texture of rock resulting from heat and pressure

Roture: a land grant offered to early French settlers in Quebec

Run: the horizontal distance in the gradient of a mountain slope

Runoff: water that flows over the ground during heavy rains or spring thaw

Runoff pattern: the different times of the year when runoff reaches it maximum or minimum levels

Runoff rate: the amount of water that flows over the ground during runoff

Rural: an area that is well removed from large urban centres

Second-generation Canadian: a person born to parents who immigrated to Canada

Secondary industry: an industry involved in processing raw materials at the first stage of manufacturing

Secondary manufacturing: the level of secondary industry in which a product of primary manufacturing is used to produce another product

Sediment: eroded rock debris carried by rivers, winds, waves, and glaciers

Sedimentary rock: rock composed of sediments, usually formed in layers

Seed tree retention: a method of forest harvesting in which all of the forest is removed except for a few seed-bearing trees

Seigneuries: long, narrow land lots given to early French settlers; see *Rang*

Seigneurs: French landlords responsible for establishing early settlements in Quebec

Selective cutting: a method of forest harvesting in which only the mature trees of a certain species are cut singly or in small groups

Service centre: a community in which the main function is to provide goods and services to a surrounding area

Service hierarchy: the ranking of communities based on population and services provided

Shelterwood logging: a method of forest harvesting in which up to 70 per cent of the trees are cut, leaving small patches of old-growth forest standing to provide seeds for regeneration

Silviculture: the science of breeding, developing, and cultivating trees

Single-factor region: a region based on a single characteristic, such as climate

Single-industry town: a town that is dependent on one industry

Site: the specific physical location of a community

Six-figure grid reference: a detailed map reference using eastings and northings to locate a small feature

Small-patch clear-cutting: a method of forest harvesting in which 1 or 2 ha of old-growth forest are cut, leaving a border of trees to provide seeds for regeneration

Small-scale map: a map that shows a large area

Social imprint: a pattern of behaviour, such as customs, language, and religion, of a social group

Softwood: a fibrous, less dense wood typical of most coniferous trees

Soil profile: a vertical series of soil horizons from the ground to the parent rock

Statement scale: a map scale expressed in numbers and letters

Status Indian: a person registered under the Indian Act

Strip mine: a method of mining that recovers layered mineral deposits by removing and discarding overlying waste rock

Subsistence economy: a society with little or no cash in which people use only those natural resources they need

Subsistence farming: the growing of food to be used primarily within one's own family

Suburbs: low-density housing usually found on the outskirts of a community

Sunrise industry: an industry that is relatively new and expanding in number

Sunset industry: an industry that is outdated owing to new technology or decreased demand

Sustainable development: the harvesting of natural resources so that they can recover at a rate equalling or exceeding the rate of harvesting

System: a collection of things that forms a whole

Tariff: a duty or tax placed on goods

Telecommunication: information transmitted by wire and cable or through the air

Teleport: satellite earth stations

Temperature range: a calculation made by subtracting the coldest temperature from the warmest temperature

Tertiary industry: industry that provides services rather than products

Threshold population: the number of customers needed to make a business profitable

Tidal range: the difference in water height between highest and lowest ocean tides

Till: fine glacial rock particles that produce good quality topsoil

Time distance: the time it takes to travel between two locations

Time zone: a division of the earth's surface, usually extending across 15° longitude, that establishes a uniform time

Topographic map: a map that uses grids and symbols to provide detailed information about human and physical features

Topsoil: the surface layer of soil

Tornado: a destructive, rotating storm under a funnel-shaped cloud that advances across land at speeds of 50 to 100 km/h

Town-forming: an activity or business that attracts money and employment to a community

Town-serving: an activity or business that provides services for people in a community

Toxins: a natural or manufactured chemical substance that is harmful to living organisms

Trading bloc: a group of countries that share lower tariffs and special trading privileges

Trading economy: an economy in which certain goods and services are exchanged for other goods and services

Transect: an analysis of land use along a designated line through a community

Transpiration: the process in which plants give off water, mainly through pores in their leaves

Transportation hub: the main gateway for people and products entering and leaving a region

Transportation node: a community that is the centre of a network of transportation pathways

Trap: an elevated portion of porous sedimentary rock lying beneath an impervious rock layer where oil and gas accumulate

Treeline: the line at high latitudes and altitudes beyond which trees will not grow

Troll line: a long stainless-steel line, let out into a school of fish in deep water and retrieved by power-driven reels

Truck farming: see *Market gardening*

Unconventional oilfields: fields where some form of processing or heating is required to recover the oil

Underground mine: a method of mining used to recover deep mineral deposits

Unproductive forest: a small, less valuable forest stand that is not profitable and is not accessible to markets

Uplink: the transmission of a ground signal to a satellite

Urban: a community of 1000 or more people, or where there is a density of at least 1000 persons per 1.6 km^2

Urban fringe: the outer edge of a community where there is a mixture of urban and rural land use

Urban sprawl: the spread of urban communities into the surrounding rural area

Urbanization: the process in which an area is transformed from rural to urban

Vertical drop: the amount of elevation between the top and bottom of a slope

Vertically integrated company: a company that controls all aspects of production, from raw materials to finished goods

Vicious circle: the cycle of poverty created by the migration of skilled workers

from a region, thereby discouraging new investment

Videotext: a system of transmitting information from a central databank to a television at home or work

Wage economy: an economy in which people work for money

Water wealth: a measure of the amount of water available in rivers for human use

Watershed: an imaginary line that marks the boundary between two drainage basins

Weather: the combination of temperatures, precipitation, cloud cover, and winds experienced daily

Weathering: the means by which rocks and other matter are broken down over time

Westerlies: winds in the Northern Hemisphere that blow from west to east

Windsor-Quebec City Axis: a heavily populated and industrialized area between Windsor, ON, and Quebec City, PQ

Withdrawal water use: water that is permanently removed from a river for consumption in homes, industries, agriculture, or business

Zero growth: no annual increase in population size

Zone of influence: the area surrounding a community that is influenced by services provided by that community

Zooplankton: microscopic, single-celled animal organisms that live in the top layer of ocean waters